Geostationary Satellites Collocation

Hengnian Li

Geostationary Satellites Collocation

Hengnian Li
State Key Laboratory of Astronautic Dynamics
Xi'an, China

ISBN 978-3-642-40798-7 ISBN 978-3-642-40799-4 (eBook)
DOI 10.1007/978-3-642-40799-4
Springer Heidelberg New York Dordrecht London

Jointly published with National Defense Industry Press, Beijing
ISBN: 978-7-118-09492-3 National Defense Industry Press, Beijing

Library of Congress Control Number: 2014942926

Printed on acid-free paper

Springer is part of Springer Science+Business Media (www.springer.com)

Preface

The geostationary satellite should fly along a special orbit occupying a very limited region which is confined by the satellite longitude above the equator of the Earth. In order to utilize the limited orbit resources efficiently, the satellite is required to be maintained in a dedicated position, and what is more, sometimes it is collocated with two or more satellites sharing the same location. As a result, a safety collocation strategy needs to be deployed to diminish collision risks of the collocated satellites.

The main strength of this work is targeted at the latest scientific questions and engineering requirements arising from the maintenance for geostationary satellites resided in narrow allocative positions, and collocated geostationary satellites operated by the same or different organizations. There are some publications related to those topics in recent years, some of those investigations are referenced in this book.

Peter Berlin (2004) The Geostationary Application Satellite is a comprehensive investigation about the satellites in geostationary orbit, which covers the space environment and mechanisms of orbit and attitude of geostationary satellite, the structure including thermal, power, propulsion, and application payload, as well as telemetry, tracking and command system.

Donald Jansky (1987) Communication Satellite in the Geostationary Orbit is a monograph about geostationary satellite application, which focuses on signal processing and payload designation as a key spot in space communication.

Hephaestus Book (2009) Artificial Satellites in Geosynchronous Orbit represents a new publishing paradigm, which collects disparate materials about geosynchronous orbit into a cohesive informative book; some contents come from Wikipedia articles and related comments.

E. M. Soop (1994) Handbook of Geostationary Orbits is a masterpiece by honored Professor Soop, who had got good relationship with the organization the author backed. This book covers the orbit perturbation and practical maneuver related resources for geosynchronous satellite, and details of orbit correction techniques for maintaining of ESA's satellites.

Li H. N. (2010) Geostationary Satellite Orbit Analysis and Collocation Strategies was published in Chinese by the National Defense Industry Press in 2010. The contents focus on the orbit perturbation analysis for the geostationary orbit, and the mathematical and physical principle of orbit maneuver and collocation strategies for multi-geostationary satellites. After receiving some professional reviews and readers's comments for this work, I always think I'd had a chance to respond those constructive advises and to reflect the latest engineering requirements. A chance's coming, the China News Press Association has announced this work was nominated to publish internationally funded by China Classical International Publish project (2014).

The book targets at the latest scientific questions and engineering requirements arising from the maintenance of geostationary satellites resided in narrow allocative positions, and collocated geostationary satellites operated by the same or different organizations. It aims to find solutions for deploying a safe and reliable collocation control. It focuses on the dynamic foundations of geostationary orbit, the orbit perturbation analysis on geostationary satellites, as well as the physical principles of orbit maneuvers explained in mathematics, which are available to engineers of different backgrounds to have the initiative to penetrate with knowledge that encourages the insight for engineering solutions. Moreover, the book presents some practical techniques and mathematical models to help readers master the corrective method for planning maneuvers of geostationary satellite station keeping. Engineers and scientists in the fields of aerospace technology and space science can benefit from this work.

The author is grateful in particular to China Xi'an Satellite Control Center (XSCC), which made this book possible by giving permission for the publication of the development results, and the State Key Laboratory of Astronautic Dynamics (ADL) for providing financial and administrative support, with which the author is affiliated. XSCC has operated four pairs of satellites sharing the same longitude slot respectively for each pair, and in addition, a satellite of XSCC is collocated with a Russian and a Japanese satellite, the three sharing the same longitude slot, which serves as an engineering background to fully ascertain the solutions mentioned in this book.

Special thanks are given to Xin Lei, Dong WeiHua and Wang RongHui for their effort in performing some translation and word processing for the manuscript. The book has also greatly benefited from the assistance of many colleagues, who have provided the book with invigorating discussions during the time that the book was being prepared, as well as helpful suggestions and constructive reviews when the book is finished. In addition, the author wishes to express his sincere gratitude to Yuan Jing for being such a supportive and understanding wife during a long time, without which the book could not have been written. Last but not least, the final acknowledgement is to the publisher's reviewer, who has provided encouragement and useful comments to the book.

Xi'an, China Hengnian Li
September 12, 2012

Contents

Chapter 1
Introduction

Abstract The inherent characteristics of the geostationary orbit are introduced in the context of a very simple dynamic problem, and the current status of geostationary satellites is presented simply to arouse two topics, on which this book will focus.

1.1 General

It was Sir C. Clarke, the author of *2001, a Space Odyssey*, who published an article entitled "Extra-terrestrial Relays" [1] in October 1945, in which he proposed that three satellites, placed 120° apart, on a specific orbit that over the Earth's equator would be able to provide reliable worldwide radio communications. He argued that because of such a specific orbit on which the satellite orbits the Earth in exactly the same time as the Earth rotates on its axis, the satellite could be kept over the dedicated locations on the Earth at all times. It is worth noting that his article had been published almost 20 years, until 1963, when America launched the first geostationary SynCom2 and successfully broadcasted the Tokyo Olympic Games. From then on, about several hundred satellites, which belong to different organizations, have been located above the Earth's equator to serve different missions for communication, navigation, and data relay functions.

Three connective segments are required to insert the geostationary satellite into orbit position. There are the powered segment, the transfer orbit segment, and the geostationary capture segment. The launcher puts the satellite at about 200 km height above the Earth and leaves the satellite into a transfer orbit with its perigee altitude as 200 km and its apogee altitude as 36,000 km or a bit higher than 36,000 km and its inclination equals the latitude of the launch pad, which is called the geosynchronous transfer orbit (GTO) or super geosynchronous transfer orbit (SGTO), respectively. For example, the orbit inclination of the satellite launched

H. Li, *Geostationary Satellites Collocation*, DOI 10.1007/978-3-642-40799-4_1,

Fig. 1.1 A snapshot of geostationary satellites population

from China Xichang Satellite Launch Center by the Long March rocket should be near 28.6°, while the orbit inclination of the satellite launched from Kourou by Ariane rocket should be around 7°. After some orbit controlling maneuvers, the satellite will be transited to the geostationary capture segment, where the orbit is almost a circle and the inclination is almost zero. After some orbit modification, the satellite will be put into working position, where the satellite is fixed relative to the rotation of the Earth. Figure 1.1 illustrates that geostationary satellites populated the geostationary ring above the Earth's equator.

In general, there are two types of orbit maneuvers required to inject the spacecraft from the GTO orbit into the geostationary orbit. The apogee motor is scheduled to fire about 4–10 times to put the satellite into the near geostationary orbit, which is called the orbit transfer maneuver as illustrated in Fig. 1.2. After that, several miniature velocity changes are scheduled to compensate for the errors induced by the uncertainties of apogee motor burns. The consumed fuel that makes up almost the half weight of the satellite increases the flight velocity at apogee from 1.6 to 3 km/s. The greater the inclination of the GTO orbit, the more fuel consumed for the satellite to transfer into the geostationary orbit. For example, for transferring into the geostationary orbit, the GTO orbit with an inclination of 28.6° requires a velocity increment of about 1.8 km/s, while the one with an inclination of 7° requires a velocity increment of about 1.5 km/s. If the apogee

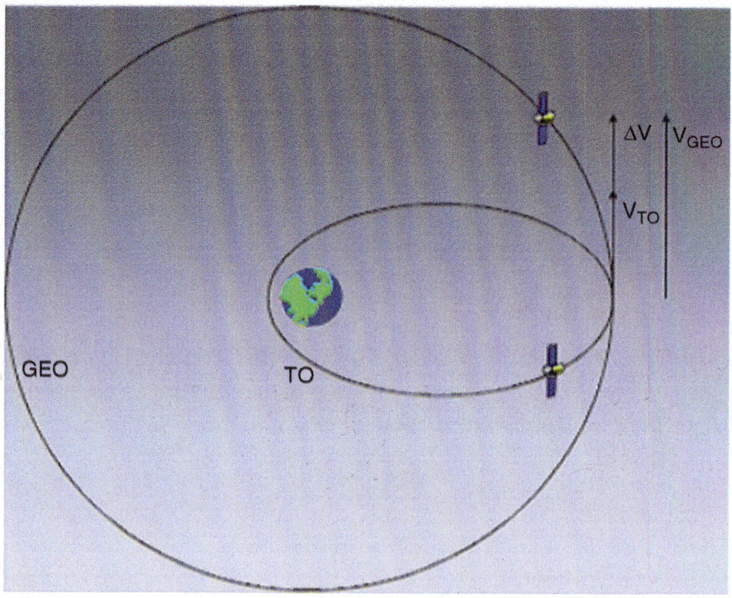

Fig. 1.2 Orbit transferred by firing apogee motor

motor's impulse specific propellant (Isp) is 300 s, the consumed fuel will be 40–46 % of the weight of the satellite, which means that the mass of the satellite will remain the half after the satellite is put into the geostationary orbit.

1.2 The Geostationary Orbit in Math

A perfect geostationary orbit is a mathematical conception that can be realized only based on that the Earth is a spherical symmetric body, the satellite is not influenced by other forces except the central gravity attraction from the Earth, and the central body rotates around its spin axis with a constant angular velocity. According to Newton's law of gravity, the perfect geostationary orbit is of the characteristics below:

1. The period is equal to one sidereal day.

The time it takes the Earth to complete one rotation is one sidereal day, which equals the time it takes any one primary plane to pass the same direction in inertial space. There is a minor difference between it and one solar day. The Earth's rotation rate is known with a very high accuracy, and the value adopted by International Earth Rotation Service (IERS) [2] is

$$\omega_e = \frac{360.98654°}{86400.0^s} \cdot \frac{\pi}{180°} = 7.292115 \times 10^{-5} (\text{rad/s})$$

One sidereal day is

$$\text{One sidereal day} = \frac{2\pi}{\omega_e} = 23^h 56^m 04^s = 86164.0^s$$

2. The orbit is a circular orbit.

It is known from Newton's law of gravity that the attractive force between two bodies is proportional to the masses of the two bodies and inversely proportional to the square of the distance between each other

$$F = \frac{gM_e \cdot m}{r^2} = \frac{\mu \cdot m}{r^2}$$

where the gravity constant is

$\mu = gM_e = 398600.4415(\text{km}^2/\text{s}^3)$ (in JGM-3 [3]).

The centrifugal force of the spacecraft's motion in the orbit must balance the attractive force. Suppose the geostationary orbit with radius r, and rotation rate w_e,

$$F_r = m\omega_e^2 \cdot r = \frac{\mu.m}{r^2} = F$$

So the radius of a perfect geostationary orbit should be

$$r = \sqrt[3]{\mu/\omega_e^2} = 42164.2\,(\text{km})$$

3. The plane is identical to the equator plane of the Earth.

When the line from the center of the Earth to the center of the spacecraft rotates with the orbit motion, there will form a plane, which is called the orbit plane. If there is an inclination between the orbit plane and the equator plane, the spacecraft will trespass the equator twice a day, and it will result in a relative motion to the observer from the Earth. So being geostationary, the spacecraft should orbit on the equatorial plane, flying in the same direction as the rotation of the Earth.

4. The nominal longitude is the only free parameter.

The size of the geostationary orbit is determined by balancing the force of the Earth's gravitation, the orbit plane is decided by the equatorial plane to finish the relative motion, and the constant angular rate is required to accommodate the even

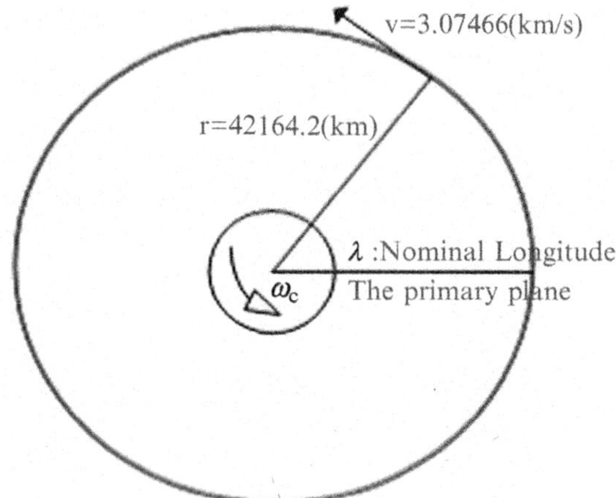

Fig. 1.3 The geostationary orbit seen from the north pole of the Earth

rotation of the Earth. But the nominal longitude, which is the projection of the spacecraft on the Earth's surface, can be selected arbitrarily as illustrated in Fig. 1.3.

In practice, the geostationary orbit only exists instantaneously; the spacecraft will not stay absolutely in the same position relative to the Earth because additional forces acting on it will change the shape of the orbit, the orientation of the orbit plane, and the spacecraft longitude. Nevertheless, the perfect geostationary orbit is useful as an approximate description of the real case, since all the other forces from the Moon, the Sun, and the non-spherical part of the Earth's gravity are small in comparison to the central attractive force. It is very important to discuss the relative motion which is caused by the additional forces [4].

1.3 The Status of Geostationary Satellites

The geostationary satellite should fly along a special orbit constituting a very limited region in space. The region is confined by the radius distance and the orbit plane. The former should be close to the geostationary radius, and the latter should be approximately overlapped with the equatorial plane. The only free parameter is the satellite's nominal longitude above the equator of the Earth. In 1971, the World Administrative Radio Conference (WARC [5]) recognized the geostationary orbit as limited natural resources like the frequencies for terrestrial radio communications, and in 1973, the allocation of the geostationary longitude position on an "equitable access" basis, which was administered by the International Telecommunication Union (ITU) later, was added to the responsibilities of WARC. Many nations, although without technology to access space, requested the geostationary positions for possible future use just because of the fear of losing the opportunities to access to this limited resources. Until 2006, there were 2,350 pieces of geostationary satellite application registered in WARC. In 1976, a claim by a group of equatorial nations for sovereignty over the geostationary longitudes above their territory did not obtain a positive response by the space accessible states [6].

In order to utilize the limited resources efficiently, it is required to maintain the satellite residing in the dedicated position allocated by WARC, and sometimes two or more satellites are collocated, sharing the same location. For example, ESA's Olympus communication satellite was operated from 1989 to 1990 in the longitude slot $19.0° \pm 0.07°$ in collocation with one German and two French satellites [7]. Xi'an Satellite Control Center (XSCC) has operated four pairs of satellites sharing the longitude slot $\pm 0.1°$, and another satellite is collocated with one Russian satellite and one Japanese satellite. They are sharing the same longitude slot with a dead band of $\pm 0.1°$ [8].

In consideration of that, the typical shared dead band is 100 km wide in longitude as well as in latitude and 50 km wide in the radial direction. The satellite operators have realized that the potential risk of physical collision between collocated satellites is not negligible. A safe collocation strategy should be deployed to alleviate any collision risk of collocated satellites.

1.4 The Framework of the Book

The main strength of this work targets the new scientific questions and engineering requirements which arise from maintaining the satellite residing in a very narrow position allocation and collocating multi-geostationary satellites which are governed by same or different organizations. The work covers dynamic foundations of orbit converged to the geostationary orbit, orbit perturbation analysis especially for geostationary satellites, as well as physical principles of orbit maneuvers explained in mathematics, which are available to engineers in different backgrounds to have the initiative to penetrate with knowledge that encourages the insight for engineering solution, as well as the practical techniques, and application cases presented to assert the algorithms and mathematical models for specific engineering requirements.

Chapter 1: *Introduction*. The inherent characteristics of the geostationary orbit are introduced in the context of a very simple dynamic problem, and the current status of geostationary satellites is presented simply to arouse two topics, on that this book will focus.

Chapter 2: *Orbit Motion Foundations*. An attempt is made in this chapter to figure out the main ideas concerning the motion of the Earth, time systems, space reference systems, as well as the non-perturbation Kepler orbit. The problems dealt within this chapter make use of definitions used in a wide variety of scientific fields, such as astronomy, geodesy, celestial mechanics, timekeeping, and satellite tracking and controlling.

Chapter 3: *Geostationary Satellite Motion*. There is no absolute stationary orbit for the geostationary orbit to reside in. Special attention we pay in this chapter to the geostationary satellite's relative motion to the Earth's rotation motion. We will illustrate the orbit motion of real geostationary satellite with the rotational Earth in inertial space.

Chapter 4: *Geostationary Orbit Perturbation*. The perturbation motion equations of geostationary orbit are established via Lagrange equation and are discussed due to the non-spherical part of the Earth's gravitational attraction, the gravitational attraction of the Sun and Moon, and the Solar radiation pressure, respectively.

Chapter 5: *Harmonic Analysis Geostationary Orbit*. The characteristics of the perturbation period of the geostationary satellite are analyzed. The spectral decomposing algorithm is established to identify periodical motions from the high-precise osculating ephemeris, and an identification algorithm of periodical motions based on singular value decomposition is presented.

Chapter 6: *Correction Geostationary Orbit*. The relation between the relative motion of geostationary satellite and station keeping elements is proposed. The orbit correction equations of radial/tangential/normal impulse thrust and continuous thrust are put forward and the common property of in-plane correction and normal correction is analyzed.

Chapter 7: *Maintenance Geostationary Orbit*. The principles, strategies, and algorithms of the station keeping of geostationary satellite are discussed. For north/south station keeping, the design of inclination confined ring and the calculation of inclination control target for single satellite and collocated satellites are discussed. The relation between control moment and local satellite time is also discussed, and a specific case simulation of the control process is given. For east/west station keeping, the complicated situation of coupling control of the drift rate and eccentricity is analyzed, including the distribution strategy and the pulse execution algorithm of single pulse, dual pulses with the same direction, dual pulses with opposite direction, and three pulses. This chapter covers the principles, strategies, and algorithms of the station keeping of the geostationary satellite which should be well grasped by satellite engineers.

Chapter 8: *Collocation Prototypes and Strategies*. A detailed assessment of the strategies used for efficient management of collocated satellites is provided. The relation between the separation distance with uncertainty of OD and the orbit element offset is built for each pair of collocated satellites. And some new strategies are addressed to meet the current needs of sharing a slot by four GEO satellites. The theory and algorithms for each satellite to locate the eccentricity and inclination are put forward, and the simulation is carried out to ascertain that if there are orbit offset with those strategies, the minimal distance could ensure not only the physical separation but also the radio frequency (RF) separation.

References

1. Clarke AC (1945) Extra-terrestrial relays – can Rocket Stations give world-wide radio coverage? Wirel World, Oct 1945, pp 305–308
2. International Earth Rotation Service (IERS). Earth orientation data. http://www.iers.org. Accessed 20 Feb 2012

3. ERS Precise Orbit Determination: JGM-3 Gravitation Model. http://www.deos.tudelft.nl/ers/precorbs/details.shtml. Accessed 20 Feb 2013
4. Chao CC (2005) Applied orbit perturbation and maintenance. The Aerospace Press, El Segundo. California 90245–4691
5. World Administrative Radio Conference (WARC) (1992) Issues for U.S. International Spectrum Policy, Washington DC: U.S. Government Printing
6. Soop EM (1988) Handbook of geostationary orbits. Kluwer Academic Publishers, Dordrecht, Netherlands
7. Colocation at 19°W, web site: http://www.dlr.de/rb/en/desktopdefault.aspx. Accessed 20 Sept 2012
8. Li HN, Gao ZZ, Li JS et al (2013) Mathematical prototypes for collocating geostationary satellites. Sci China Tech Sci 56:1086–1092. doi:10.1007/s11431-013-5157-x

Chapter 2
Orbit Motion Foundations

Abstract An attempt is made in this chapter to figure out the main ideas concerning the motion of the Earth, time systems, space reference systems, as well as the non-perturbation Kepler orbit. The problems dealt with in this chapter make use of definitions used in a wide variety of scientific fields, such as astronomy, geodesy, celestial mechanics, timekeeping, and satellite tracking and control. Some certain considerations are taken into account to measure the geostationary orbit.

2.1 Introduction

In order to model the orbit motion in inertial space centered at the Earth's center and the time system associated with the Earth's motion, a thorough understanding of the Earth's motion and rotation remains essential for a rigorous description of satellite orbit and the accurate modeling of ground-based measurements.

The Earth's motion associated with the depiction of the orbit round the Earth is discussed in this chapter, including the rotation with respect to the inertial space and the rotation with respect to its spin axis. Detailed information of methodology is described precisely. The time system induced by the Earth's motion is also introduced here. Despite the apparent familiarity with time, time system has remained an issue that requires careful attention in the description of astronomical, physical, and geodetic phenomena. In accordance with the advancement of physical theories, observational measures, and devices, the concepts and definitions of time have undergone continued revisions and refinements up to the present date. In this chapter, we just introduce the time systems that are highly associated with the precise depiction of the orbit motion of the Earth's satellite.

The motion of satellite relative to inertial space or to the rotational Earth should be modeled in convenient reference systems. The systems and the transformation relationship are discussed in this chapter. The reference frames centered on the Earth with or without considering the spin motion of the Earth depict the motion

H. Li, *Geostationary Satellites Collocation*, DOI 10.1007/978-3-642-40799-4_2,

of spacecraft relative to inertial space and to the Earth, respectively. Satellite observations are commonly obtained from an observation coordination frame which originates at the ground-based measurements. The spacecraft's motions relative to its center are generally defined on the spacecraft-fixed frame.

The motion of a satellite in the spherically symmetric force field of a central mass is usually referred as Kepler problem, or two-body problem, which follows the Kepler three basis laws, and the six-element parameters which define the shape, size, orientation, and location in the orbit at a particular epoch and on the orbit plane in space are called the Kepler classical orbit elements. They identify the position and velocity vectors in the three-dimensional reference frame. Some relation formulas about the classical elements will be very useful for learning the geostationary orbit. We present some cases that the same orbit element can be depicted in different coordinates in this chapter, the so-called station keeping elements are introduced in the case of the geostationary orbit with nearly zero inclination and eccentricity, and the relationship between the classical and station keeping elements is also discussed in this chapter.

The problems dealt with in this chapter are complex, concerning definitions used in a wide variety of scientific fields, such as astronomy, geodesy, celestial mechanics, timekeeping, and also satellite tracking and control. Thus, for each type of applications, considering the precision specified, certain consideration must be taken into account to achieve the special concern.

2.2 The Motion of the Earth

A brief review of the Earth motion is as follows: the Earth spins around an axis, and it takes a bit more than one day for the Earth to go around once. The spin axis is pointing off somewhere in space, which almost doesn't move. At the same time, the Earth is orbiting the Sun. It takes (a bit more than) 1 year for the Earth to go around once. The plane of the Earth's orbit (almost) doesn't move. The spin axis of the Earth's daily rotation is not perpendicular to the plane of the Earth's orbit. It is tilted (approximately) 23.4°. The angle of the tilt (mostly) doesn't change. That is the big picture. In this section, the expressions such as "a bit more" and "mostly" used in the rough depiction of the orbit will be examined precisely, though usually the above expressions are of minuscule effects. All of the "mostly" issues change by less than one degree during your entire lifetime. The "bit more than" effects are somewhat noticeable, which means that the precise timing and positioning of spacecraft require the consideration of the exact nature and magnitude of these miniscule effects.

2.2.1 A Solar Day

The solar day measures the motion which the Earth rotates along its orbit around the Sun. One solar day means the concept of "one day" in common sense, which is

Fig. 2.1 The Earth's orbit around the Sun on the ecliptic plane

equal to 24 h or 86,400 s. Precisely, the period of the Earth rotating with the Sun is 365.2425 days. A good way to think of this is to draw a circle around the Sun and divide it into 365 full-size pieces and one spare piece that is one quarter the size of the others, as illustrated in Fig. 2.1. The size of the full-size piece defines what we exactly mean by "one day" in civil life. For the convenience of counting down the years, a mean year is defined as 365 days. In order to compensate the real orbit motion of the Earth, one additional day should be inserted into the selected year, which is called the leap follows, which the general rules: there should be an insertion of 1 day for every 4 years and a reduction of 3 days for every 400 years, which means that there are 146,097 days in every 400 years. Hence, in the calendar, a leap year is the year which is divisible by 4 and indivisible by 100, plus the year which is divisible by 400. For example, the year 2008 which is divisible by 4 and indivisible by 100 is a leap year, while the year 2000 which is divisible both by 4, 100, and 400 is also a leap year.

2.2.2 *A Sidereal Day*

The size of the above piece defines what we exactly mean by "one day." Surprisingly, the above "one day" is not the same as the time it takes the Earth to rotate one 360° turn around its axis. Because of the Earth's orbit motion, the direction of the Sun has advanced a hair, so that the Earth has to revolve a hair more than 360° to get the same spot directly under the Sun again. The day is actually 360.985647° of the Earth revolution. This is illustrated in Fig. 2.2. The Earth protestation angle during one solar day is

$$360.0^\circ + \frac{360.0^\circ}{365.2425} = 360.985647^\circ$$

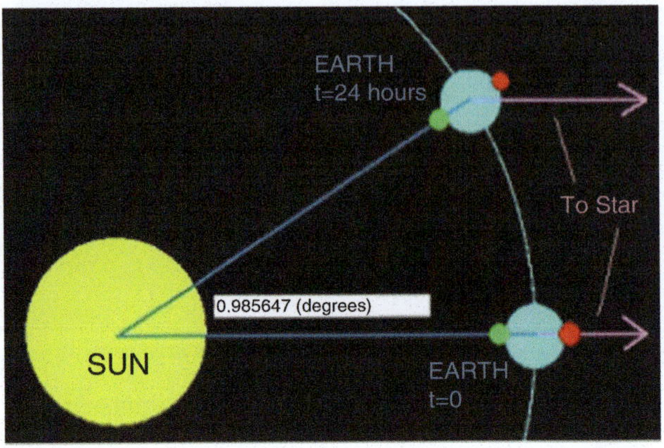

Fig. 2.2 Geometry of a sidereal day

One sidereal day measures the time it takes the Earth to rotate one perfect round along its spin axis, and the size is

$$\text{One sidereal day} = \frac{360.0}{360.985647} \times 86400.0 = 86164.091 \text{ (SI)}$$

And the angular rate of the Earth is

$$\text{The angular rate}\, \omega_e = \frac{2\pi}{86164.091} = 7.2921158479 \text{ (rad/s)}$$

Therefore, a perfect geostationary orbit should accommodate to the Earth's rotation motion. The orbit period is one sidereal day, and the orbit angular rate is identical to the rotation angular rate of the Earth.

2.2.3 *Equinox Direction*

The plane that the Earth rotates around the Sun is the ecliptic plane. It is tilted away from the Earth's equatorial plane by an angle of approximately 23.44°, which is called the obliquity of the ecliptic. As illustrated in Fig. 2.3, the line of the intersection of the equator and the ecliptic is called the equinox. There are two directions that point outward from the center of the Earth along the equinox. The one that points to the direction of the Sun when the Earth is in the position of its orbit that corresponds to March is the vernal equinox, and the other one that points to the direction of the Sun when the Earth is in the position of September is the autumnal equinox.

The exact angle of the tilt varies from time to time. Figure 2.4 illustrates the tilt angle variation from 2000 to 2008. It changes a few hundredths of a degree per year

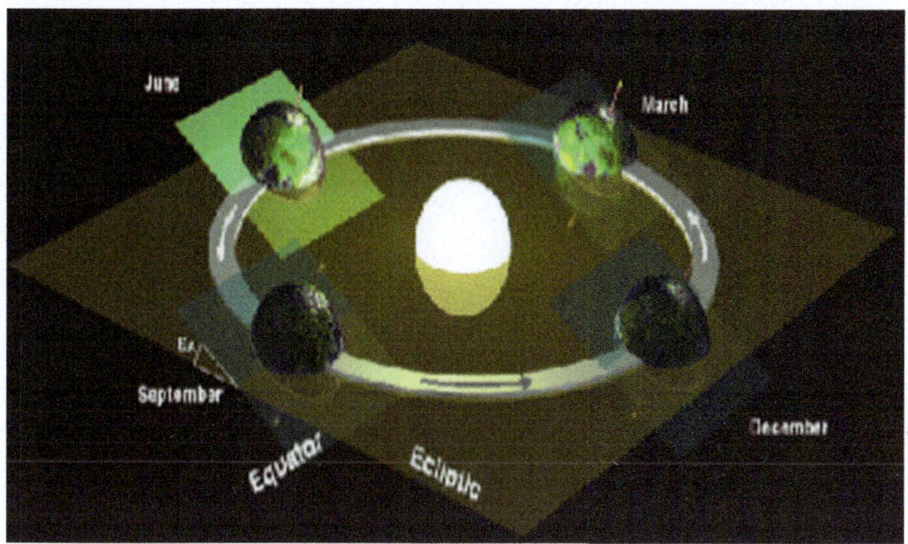

Fig. 2.3 Tilt of equator to Earth's orbit plane

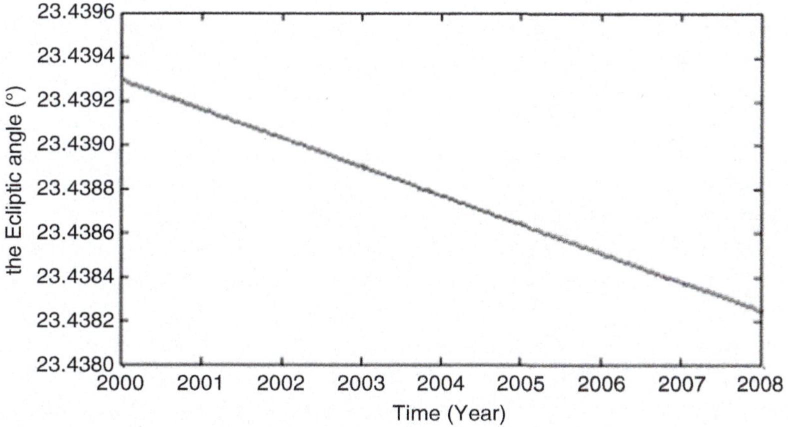

Fig. 2.4 Ecliptic angle variation from 2000 to 2008

for two reasons: firstly, the equatorial plane undulates constantly because of the nutation and precession; secondly, the ecliptic plane itself undulates constantly due to additional attractions from the Sun and Moon. The equinoxes are more or less fixed in space; their intersection is also more or less fixed in space. That's why the Earth's north pole direction is used for defining the Earth-centered Cartesian coordinate system.

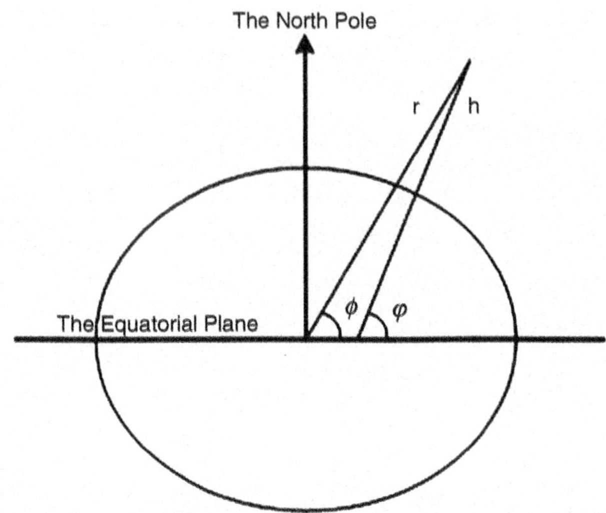

Fig. 2.5 Geocentric and geodetic latitude

2.2.4 *Primary Longitude*

The locations on or near the Earth's surface are usually expressed in terms of their latitude and longitude on the surface and their altitude above the surface. Ordinarily, the latitude and altitude are with respect to the surface of an oblate sphere and are measured with the geodetic coordinate reference. Latitude is measured with respect to the equator, and longitude is measured with respect to the prime meridian, which is a line that travels from the north pole to the south pole and passes through Greenwich, England.

When the Earth is considered to be an oblate sphere, there will be a little difference between the geodetic latitude and the centric latitude as illustrated in Fig. 2.5.

Suppose a satellite with the altitude (h) from the surface of the Earth, the radius (r) from the center of the Earth, and the centric latitude (ϕ), the formulas to define the relationship between the geocentric parameters (r, ϕ) and the geodetic parameters (h, φ), are listed below:

The Excursion of Geocentric to Geodetic Latitude. The excursion of the geocentric latitude to the geodetic latitude satisfies the relation

$$\sin(\varphi - \phi) = \frac{e_E^2 \sin\varphi \cos\varphi}{r\sqrt{1 - e_E^2 \sin^2\varphi}} \tag{2.1}$$

The maximum excursion occurs when the geodetic latitude is approximately $\phi = 45°$, and the maximum value is approximately $0.1°$. Then the geodetic latitude follows the recursive equation listed below:

$$\varphi = \phi + \arcsin\left(\frac{e_E^2 \sin\varphi \cos\varphi}{r\sqrt{1 - e_E^2 \sin^2\varphi}}\right) \tag{2.2}$$

A recursive refinement method is listed to calculate the geodetic latitude from the geocentric latitude.

$$\begin{aligned} &\phi_i = \varphi \\ &\phi_{i+1} = \varphi + \arcsin\left(\frac{e_E^2 \sin\phi_i \cos\phi_i}{r\sqrt{1 - e_E^2 \sin^2\phi_i}}\right) \\ &i = 1, 2, \ldots, n \end{aligned} \tag{2.3}$$

Convergence until $|\phi_{i+1} - \phi_i| \leq 10^{-8}$

The Geodetic Altitude. The geodetic altitude of the satellite, which defines the altitude from the surface of the Earth along the normal direction of the local horizon plane, can be calculated from the formula listed below.

$$h = \begin{cases} R_e\left(\dfrac{r\cos\phi}{\cos\varphi} - \dfrac{1}{\sqrt{1 - e_E^2 \sin^2\varphi}}\right), |\varphi| \leq \dfrac{\pi}{4} \\ R_e\left(\dfrac{r\sin\phi}{\sin\varphi} - \dfrac{1 - e_E^2}{\sqrt{1 - e_E^2 \sin^2\varphi}}\right), |\varphi| > \dfrac{\pi}{4} \end{cases} \tag{2.4}$$

Here, R_e is the equatorial radius of the Earth, and e_E^2 is the square of oblate coefficient of the Earth.

2.2.5 Local Solar Time

The people who stand on the surface of the Earth experience the local time, which just reflect the angle excursion between the solar direction and the longitude where people stand just now. Suppose the longitude λ_p and λ_S represent the projection of the people and the Sun along the equation plane, respectively, and then the local solar time (LST) is defined as

$$\text{LST} = (\lambda_P - \lambda_S) \cdot \frac{24^h}{360°} + 12^h \tag{2.5}$$

Because the LST is only related to the excursion of the local spot from the solar direction, the projection of the spot and the Sun can be measured in any coordinate frame as illustrated in Fig. 2.6.

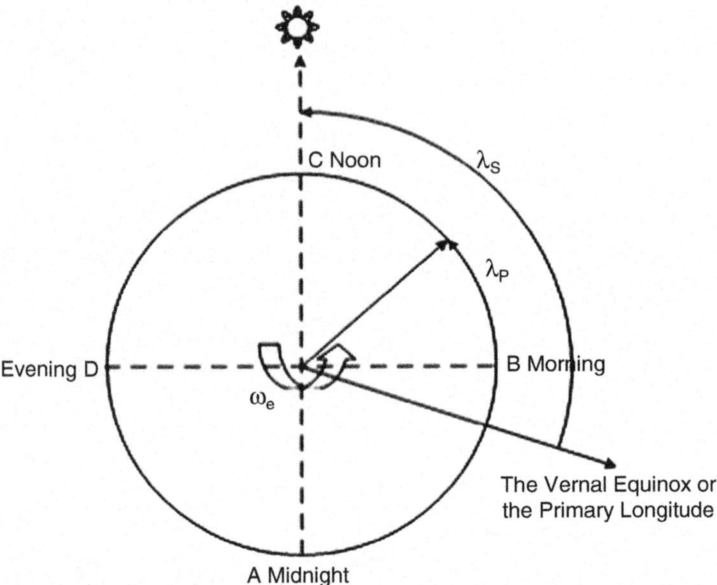

Fig. 2.6 The solar day and solar time

The people who are fixed in the Earth rotating with the spin of the Earth will experience midnight (A), morning (B), noon (C), and evening (D) during one solar day, and the local solar time is

$$
\begin{aligned}
\mathrm{LST}|_A(\lambda_P - \lambda_S = 180^\circ) &= 12^h + 12^h = 0^h \\
\mathrm{LST}|_B(\lambda_P - \lambda_S = -90^\circ) &= -6^h + 12^h = 6^h \\
\mathrm{LST}|_C(\lambda_P - \lambda_S = 0^\circ) &= 0^h + 12^h = 12^h \\
\mathrm{LST}|_D(\lambda_P - \lambda_S = 90^\circ) &= 6^h + 12^h = 18^h
\end{aligned}
$$

The local time people experienced can be extended to the satellite hanging in space, and it is very important for analyzing the motion of geostationary satellite and scheduling the plan for geostationary orbit maneuver.

2.2.6 *Polar Motion*

The Earth spins around an axis. One might think that the Earth spins about the poles. This is not too far from the truth. The actual place that it is spinning around is about 10 m away from the pole. During a single week, the spot doesn't move very much. The Earth just keeps spinning about this spot. Over a long period, this spot is drifting. Figure 2.7 illustrates the motion of the spin axis with respect to the physics pole of the Earth from 2000 to 2007.

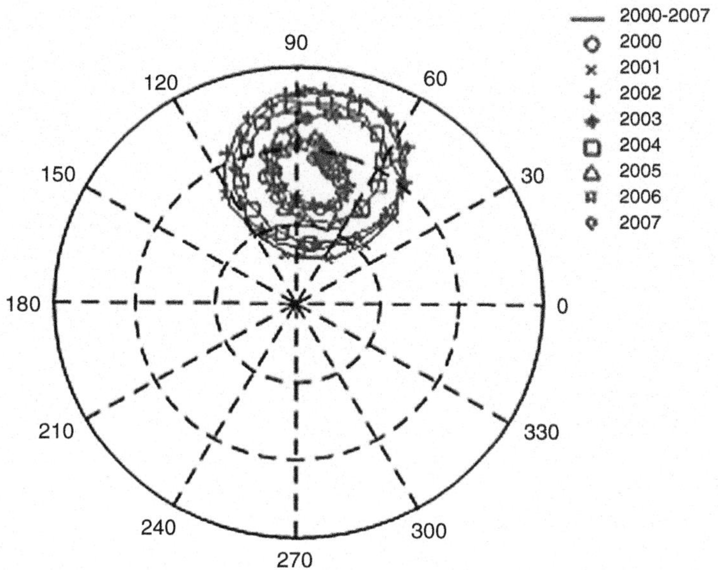

Fig. 2.7 The motion of the spin axis from 2000 to 2007

The true point is managed and broadcasted by the International Earth Rotation Service (IERS)[1]. For example, the parameters in bulletin C are listed below.

International Earth Rotation Service
Earth Rotation Parameters
EOP (IERS) C 04
FORMAT(2X,I4,2X,A4,I3,2X,I5,2F9.6,F10.7,2X,F10.7,2X,2F9.6)
****

Date	MJD	x (″) y (″)	UT1-UTC (s)	LOD (s)	dPsi (″)	dEpsilon (″)
1962 JAN 1	37665–0.012700	0.213000	0.0326338	0.0017230	0.065037	0.000436
1962 JAN 2	37666–0.015900	0.214100	0.0320547	0.0016690	0.065045	0.000300
1962 JAN 3	37667–0.019000	0.215200	0.0315526	0.0015820	0.065217	0.000174
1962 JAN 4	37668–0.021999	0.216301	0.0311435	0.0014960	0.065526	0.000085
1962 JAN 5	37669–0.024799	0.217301	0.0308154	0.0014160	0.065912	0.000054
1962 JAN 6	37670–0.027599	0.218301	0.0305353	0.0013820	0.066302	0.000088
...	......			......		......

where

Date (mjd) = Modified Julian Date = Julian date – 24000000.5 (days)
X-pole = deviation in arc seconds of polar motion (arc seconds)
Y-pole = deviation in arc seconds of polar motion (arc seconds)
UT1-UTC = difference between UT1 and UTC (seconds)
LOD = error of the length of day (seconds)
dPsi = mutation longitude
DEpsilon = mutation obliquity

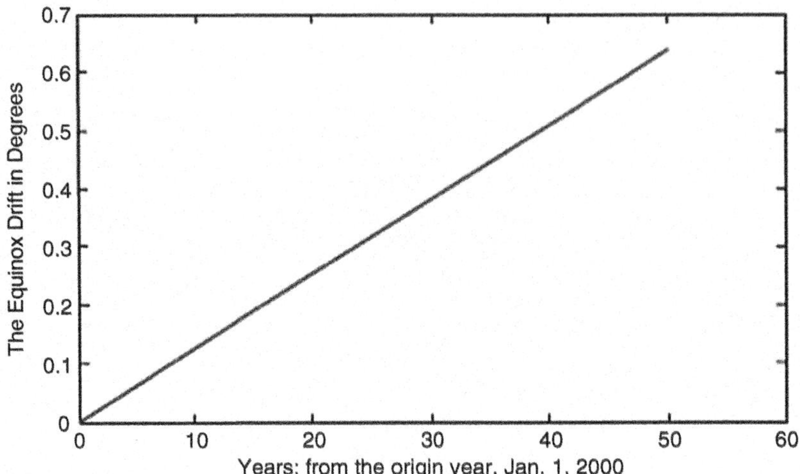

Fig. 2.8 The precession axis over 50 years

The International Earth Rotation Service (IERS) publishes the measurements on the web in several different bulletins, depending on the accuracy required. It shows that the pole motion is nearly a perfect spiral, and the maximum excursion is 0.6 arc sec, approximately 2.91×10^{-6} radian, and the distance in the surface of the Earth is about 18.5 m. Although it is a miniature value relative to the radius of the equator plane of the Earth, there still exists navigable error to measure the motion of the satellite accurately.

2.2.7 Precession Motion

The Earth is a spin-stabilized body; its rotation motion is perturbated by additional torques caused by large attractive bodies, such as the Sun and Moon, which cause the nutation and precession motion of the spin axis of the Earth, and force the equinox direction move westward. The average period of procession motion is 26,000 years, which means that the equinox turns around every 26,000 years. The equinox drifts westward of 0.014° every year; the equinox is not fixed in inertial space as shown in Fig. 2.8.

The equinox on Jan. 1, 2000 (12 UTC) can be taken as a fixed direction relative to inertial space, serving as the origin axis which ties to the equatorial plane on the same epoch. It is defined as a basic inertial coordination frame, shortly as the J2000.0, by which the motion of the satellite in inertial space can be pictured. The connection between the equinox and equatorial plane on any epoch to the basic

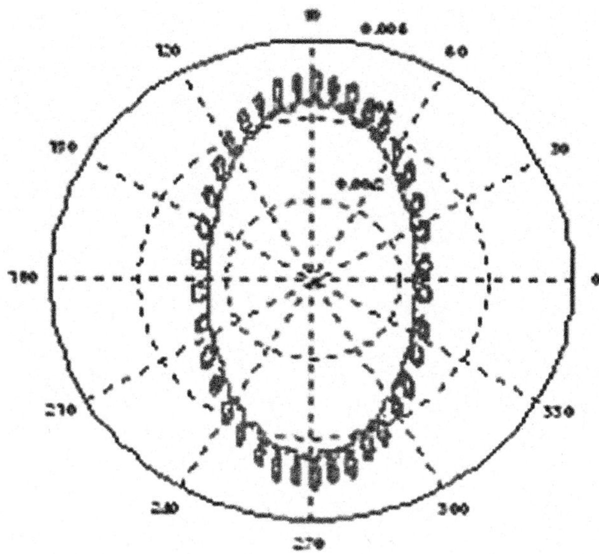

Fig. 2.9 The displacement of the earth pole

J2000.0 can be depicted by the three Euler angles, whose relation is induced by Lieske et al. [2, 3] and Newcomb's [4] equations:

$$\begin{aligned} \varsigma &= 2306''.2181 \cdot T + 0''.30188 \cdot T^2 + 0''.017998 \cdot T^3 \\ \vartheta &= 2004''.3109 \cdot T - 0''.42665 \cdot T^2 - 0''.041833 \cdot T^3 \\ \xi &= 2306''.2181 \cdot T + 1''.09468 \cdot T^2 + 0''.018203 \cdot T^3 \end{aligned} \tag{2.6}$$

Here, T is the centuries from the epoch J2000 measured in Julian date.

$$T = \frac{(\mathrm{Jd}(T) - 2451545.0)}{36525.0}$$

x'' represents the arc seconds, and it satisfies the conversion of $1^\circ = 3600.0''$.

2.2.8 Nutation Motion

Due to the equatorial bulge and uneven mass distribution of the Earth, the angular moment axis does not coincide with the spin axis of the Earth. The phenomenon that the spin axis rotates around the moment axis of the Earth is called the nutation motion of the Earth. As compared with the procession motion, the nutation motion shows the short period displacement of the Earth's pole with a period of about 18.6 years. From the moment axis vision point, the nutation motion shows that the nutation of the Earth does follow an almost perfect circle as illustrated in Fig. 2.9. The maximum radius is 0.006 in degrees, and the period is about 18.6 years.

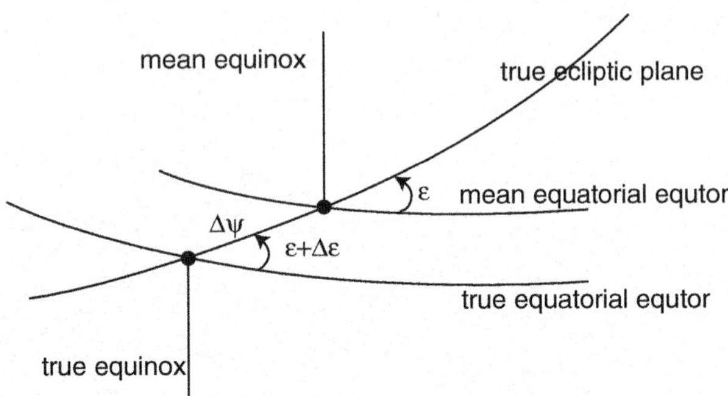

Fig. 2.10 The nutation longitude and obliquity

Obviously, the Earth's nutation is related to the motion of the Moon, whose orbit plane is tilted away the ecliptic plane by about 5.14°. With an 18.6-year-period procession motion, the lunar orbit plane is tilted away the Earth's equatorial plane by an angle from 18.3 to 28.6°. Therefore, the Earth's nutation motion is mainly caused by the grads of the gravity of the Moon.

The Earth's nutation motion results in that the true time equatorial plane is not identical with the true time mean equatorial plane. As Fig. 2.10 shows, the nutation motion of the Earth results in that the true time equatorial plane is tilted away the true time mean equatorial, and the true time equinox shows a few excursions from the true time mean equinox. Two Euler angles are used to describe the nutation with respect to the true time mean pole motion. The nutation longitude $\Delta\psi$ is along the longitude direction, and the nutation obliquity $\Delta\varepsilon$ is along the latitude direction.

The main contribution to the nutation that arises from the varying orientation of the lunar orbit with respect to the Earth's equator can be expressed by the longitude of the lunar ascending node Ω_L, such as

$$\Delta\psi \approx -17''.200 \cdot \sin(\Omega_L)$$
$$\Delta\varepsilon = +9''.203 \cdot \cos(\Omega_L)$$

With the longitude of the lunar ascending nodes Ω_L with the true time is

$$\Omega_L = 125°.044522 - 1934°.136261 \cdot T + 0°.116793 \cdot T^2 + 2.2° \times 10^{-6} \cdot T^3$$

Here, T is the Julian century numbers relative to the J2000.0. From the above simplified expression, the true celestial pole performs an elliptic motion around the mean position as affected by the lunisolar precession. The maximum excursion of the true pole from the mean one is about

$$\sqrt{\Delta\psi^2 + \Delta\varepsilon^2} = 0.0054187°,$$

and the period is about

$$\frac{360.0}{1934.136261} \cdot 100 = 18.61296\ (\text{Years})$$

The currently adopted IAU 1980 nutation series is based on the theories of Kinoshita[5] (1977) and Wahr[6] (1981), and the vernal equinox and obliquity are described by the expression below:

$$\Delta\psi = \sum_{i=1}^{106} (\Delta\psi)_i \cdot \sin(\phi_i) \tag{2.7}$$

$$\Delta\varepsilon = \sum_{i=1}^{106} (\Delta\varepsilon)_i \cdot \cos(\phi_i) \tag{2.8}$$

The period series is correlated with the motion of the lunisolar motion. According to Seidelmann [7] (1982), the formulas are summarized here:

$$\phi_i = p_l^i \cdot l + p_{l'}^i \cdot l' + p_F^i \cdot F + p_D^i \cdot D + p_\Omega^i \cdot \Omega$$

$$(\Delta\psi)_i = (\Delta\psi)_0^i + (\Delta\psi)_1^i \cdot T$$

$$(\Delta\varepsilon)_i = (\Delta\varepsilon)_0^i + (\Delta\varepsilon)_1^i \cdot T$$

where the coefficients $p_l^i, p_{l'}^i, p_F^i, p_D^i, p_\Omega^i$ of period items, as well as the coefficients of magnitudes corresponding to each period item of the series, are summarized in Table 2.1. The phase angles including l, l', F, D, Ω are the orbit parameters of lunisolar with respect to the Earth. l' is the mean anomaly of the Moon, and l' is the mean anomaly of the Sun. F is the mean angular distance of the moon from the ascension node, D is the difference between the mean longitudes of the Sun and Moon, and Ω is the longitude of the ascension node.

$$l = 134.962982^\circ + 477198.8674^\circ T + 0.516753^\circ T^2 + 0.0000178^\circ T^3$$

$$l' = 357.527723^\circ + 35999.05034^\circ T - 0.00016028^\circ T^2 - 3^\circ.333333 \times 10^{-6} T^3$$

$$F = 93.27191028^\circ + 483202.017538^\circ T - 0.0036825^\circ T^2 + 3^\circ.055556 \times 10^{-6} T^3$$

$$D = 297.850363^\circ + 445267.11148^\circ T - 0.001914^\circ T^2 + 5^\circ.277778 \times 10^{-6} T^3$$

$$\Omega = 125^\circ.044522 - 1934^\circ.136261 T + 0^\circ.116793 T^2 + 2.2^\circ \times 10^{-6} T^3$$

Nevertheless, the IAU 1980 series is retained as the official standard in the IERS conventions, and the existing deficiencies are compensated by observed values of the celestial pole offsets dPsi and dEpsilon, which are broadcasted by the IERS bulletin B. So the improved nutation angles are obtained by adding these corrections to the IAU 1980 values:

$$\Delta\psi = (\Delta\psi)_{\mathrm{IAU}} + \mathrm{dPsi} \tag{2.9}$$

$$\Delta\varepsilon = (\Delta\varepsilon)_{\mathrm{IAU}} + \mathrm{dEpsilon} \tag{2.10}$$

Table 2.1 1980 IAU nutation theory

p_l^i	$p_{l'}^i$	p_F^i	p_D^i	p_Ω^i	$(\Delta\psi)_0^i$ (0.0001″)	$(\Delta\psi)_1^i$ (0.0001″)	$(\Delta\varepsilon)_0^i$ (0.0001″)	$(\Delta\varepsilon)_1^i$ (0.0001″)	Items
0	0	0	0	1	−1719960	−1742	920250	89	1
0	0	0	0	2	20620	2	−8950	5	2
−2	0	2	0	1	460	0	−240	0	3
2	0	−2	0	0	110	0	0	0	4
−2	0	2	0	2	−30	0	10	0	5
1	−1	0	−1	0	−30	0	0	0	6
0	−2	2	−2	1	−20	0	10	0	7
2	0	−2	0	1	10	0	0	0	8
0	0	2	−2	2	−131870	−16	57360	−31	9
0	1	0	0	0	14260	−34	540	−1	10
0	1	2	−2	2	−5170	12	2240	−6	11
0	−1	2	−2	2	2170	−5	−950	3	12
0	0	2	−2	1	1290	1	−700	0	13
2	0	0	−2	0	480	0	10	0	14
0	0	2	−2	0	−220	0	0	0	15
0	2	0	0	0	170	−1	0	0	16
0	1	0	0	1	−150	0	90	0	17
0	2	2	−2	2	−160	1	70	0	18
0	−1	0	0	1	−120	0	60	0	19
−2	0	0	2	1	−60	0	30	0	20
0	−1	2	−2	1	−50	0	30	0	21
2	0	0	−2	1	40	0	−20	0	22
0	1	2	−2	1	40	0	−20	0	23
1	0	0	−1	0	−40	0	0	0	24
2	1	0	−2	0	10	0	0	0	25
0	0	−2	2	1	10	0	0	0	26
0	1	−2	2	0	−10	0	0	0	27
0	1	0	0	2	10	0	0	0	28
−1	0	0	1	1	10	0	0	0	29
0	1	2	−2	0	−10	0	0	0	30
0	0	2	0	2	−22740	−2	9770	−5	31
1	0	0	0	0	7120	1	−70	0	32
0	0	2	0	1	−3860	−4	2000	0	33
1	0	2	0	2	−3010	0	1290	−1	34
1	0	0	−2	0	−1580	0	−10	0	35
−1	0	2	0	2	1230	0	−530	0	36
0	0	0	2	0	630	0	−20	0	37
1	0	0	0	1	630	1	−330	0	38
−1	0	0	0	1	−580	−1	320	0	39
−1	0	2	2	2	−590	0	260	0	40
1	0	2	0	1	−510	0	270	0	41
0	0	2	2	2	−380	0	160	0	42
2	0	0	0	0	290	0	−10	0	43

(continued)

Table 2.1 (continued)

p_l^i	$p_{l'}^i$	p_F^i	p_D^i	p_Ω^i	$(\Delta\psi)_0^i$ (0.0001″)	$(\Delta\psi)_1^i$ (0.0001″)	$(\Delta\varepsilon)_0^i$ (0.0001″)	$(\Delta\varepsilon)_1^i$ (0.0001″)	Items
1	0	2	−2	2	290	0	−120	0	44
2	0	2	0	2	−310	0	130	0	45
0	0	2	0	0	260	0	−10	0	46
−1	0	2	0	1	210	0	−100	0	47
−1	0	0	2	1	160	0	−80	0	48
1	0	0	−2	1	−130	0	70	0	49
−1	0	2	2	1	−100	0	50	0	50
1	1	0	−2	0	−70	0	0	0	51
0	1	2	0	2	70	0	−30	0	52
0	−1	2	0	2	−70	0	30	0	53
1	0	2	2	2	−80	0	30	0	54
1	0	0	2	0	60	0	0	0	55
2	0	2	−2	2	60	0	−30	0	56
0	0	0	2	1	−60	0	30	0	57
0	0	2	2	1	−70	0	30	0	58
1	0	2	−2	1	60	0	−30	0	59
0	0	0	−2	1	−50	0	30	0	60
1	−1	0	0	0	50	0	0	0	61
2	0	2	0	1	−50	0	30	0	62
0	1	0	−2	0	−40	0	0	0	63
1	0	−2	0	0	40	0	0	0	64
0	0	0	1	0	−40	0	0	0	65
1	1	0	0	0	−30	0	0	0	66
1	0	2	0	0	30	0	0	0	67
1	−1	2	0	2	−30	0	10	0	68
−1	−1	2	2	2	−30	0	10	0	69
−2	0	0	0	1	−20	0	10	0	70
3	0	2	0	2	−30	0	10	0	71
0	−1	2	2	2	−30	0	10	0	72
1	1	2	0	2	20	0	−10	0	73
−1	0	2	−2	1	−20	0	10	0	74
2	0	0	0	1	20	0	−10	0	75
1	0	0	0	2	−20	0	10	0	76
3	0	0	0	0	20	0	0	0	77
0	0	2	1	2	20	0	−10	0	78
−1	0	0	0	2	10	0	−10	0	79
1	0	0	−4	0	−10	0	0	0	80
−2	0	2	2	2	10	0	−10	0	81
−1	0	2	4	2	−20	0	10	0	82
2	0	0	−4	0	−10	0	0	0	83
1	1	2	−2	2	10	0	−10	0	84
1	0	2	2	1	−10	0	10	0	85
−2	0	2	4	2	−10	0	10	0	86

(continued)

Table 2.1 (continued)

p_l^i	$p_{l'}^i$	p_F^i	p_D^i	p_Ω^i	$(\Delta\psi)_0^i$ (0.0001″)	$(\Delta\psi)_1^i$ (0.0001″)	$(\Delta\varepsilon)_0^i$ (0.0001″)	$(\Delta\varepsilon)_1^i$ (0.0001″)	Items
−1	0	4	0	2	10	0	0	0	87
1	−1	0	−2	0	10	0	0	0	88
2	0	2	−2	1	10	0	−10	0	89
2	0	2	2	2	−10	0	0	0	90
1	0	0	2	1	−10	0	0	0	91
0	0	4	−2	2	10	0	0	0	92
3	0	2	−2	2	10	0	0	0	93
1	0	2	−2	0	−10	0	0	0	94
0	1	2	0	1	10	0	0	0	95
−1	−1	0	2	1	10	0	0	0	96
0	0	−2	0	1	−10	0	0	0	97
0	0	2	−1	2	−10	0	0	0	98
0	1	0	2	0	−10	0	0	0	99
1	0	−2	−2	0	−10	0	0	0	100
0	−1	2	0	1	−10	0	0	0	101
1	1	0	−2	1	−10	0	0	0	102
1	0	−2	2	0	−10	0	0	0	103
2	0	0	2	0	10	0	0	0	104
0	0	2	4	2	−10	0	0	0	105
0	1	0	1	0	10	0	0	0	106

2.3 Time System

Time is traditionally measured in days of 86,400 s, where the length of the solar day is determined by the subsequent meridian transits of the Sun. The time we measure the rotation of the Earth, which is known as a sidereal day, is about 4 min shorter than a solar day and is equal to the time between the successive meridian passages of the vernal equinox. Based on a conventional expression for the right ascension of the mean Sun that is derived from Newcomb's tables of the motion of the Earth, the Greenwich Mean Time (GMT) or Universal Time (UT) was established in 1925 as an international time scale for astronomical and civil purposes. Due to irregularities and secular variations in the Earth's rotation, the Ephemeris Time (ET) was established based on the orbit motion of solar system bodies. With the advent of atomic clocks, International Atomic Time (TAI) was introduced as a new time system that is free from the deficiencies of dynamic models.

Despite the apparent familiarity and usage of time every day, time has remained an issue that requires careful attention in the description of astronomical, physical theories, observational methods, and measuring devices. The underlying concepts and definitions have undergone continued revisions and refinements up to the present date.

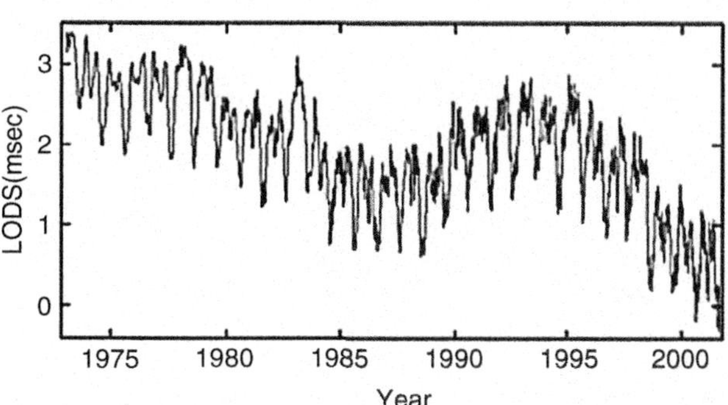

Fig. 2.11 The variation in the length of one solar day

2.3.1 *Seconds in a Day*

The time system which is used in civil life by people is the mean solar time. During one solar day, the Earth trespasses 0.985647° along the ecliptic plane and rotates 360.985647° with its true time pole. One solar day lasts 24 h, in 86,400 s (SI). Due to minor variation of the angular rate of the rotation motion of the Earth, the actual amount of time it takes for the Earth to rotate 360.985647° is a few milliseconds longer than 86,400 s. Figure 2.11 shows the variation in the length of 1 day since 1973. It shows, for example, that in 1975, it was about 3 ms longer than 86,400 s of one day, while in 1999, it was 1 ms longer than 86,400 s of one day.

The timepiece used by people is not aware of these minute variations of the length of day, and thus when your watch says that 24 h have elapsed, the Earth has not made its full turn yet. For any single day, this difference seems insignificant, but such differences accumulate. Today, your watch disagrees with the Sun by 1 ms by the moment when it completes one full turn. Tomorrow, the time when two full turns are done, the disagreement becomes 2 ms. The day after tomorrow, it becomes 3 ms. In 1 or 2 years, the accumulated errors will raise to 0.5 s. When the accumulated error becomes larger, an extra second will be inserted into our timepiece. Ordinarily, the second pointer of your watch counts 55, 56, 57, 58, 59, and then back to zero. When an extra second is inserted, it will count 55, 56, 57, 58, 59, and 60 and then go back to zero. After the insertion of the extra second which is called the leap second, your watch will be more coordinated with the rotation of the Earth. Table 2.2 lists the accumulated leap seconds from 1972 to 2012.

2.3.2 *Sidereal Time and Universal Time*

The sidereal time is also called the Greenwich hour angle, which defines the angle between the vernal equinox of date and the Greenwich meridian. It is a direct measure of the Earth's rotation and may be expressed in angular units corresponding to 86,400 s. The Universal Time (UT) is adopted to realize a mean solar

Table 2.2 The extra second inserted into the timing system from 1972 to 2012

Year-month-date	Modified Julian Day(MJD)	Accumulated leap seconds
1972-01-01	41317.0	−11.0
1972-07-01	42048.0	−12.0
1973-01-01	42048.0	−13.0
1974-01-01	42413.0	−14.0
1975-01-01	42778.0	−15.0
1976-01-01	43144.0	−16.0
1977-01-01	43448.0	−17.0
1978-01-01	43874.0	−18.0
1979-01-01	44239.0	−19.0
1980-01-01	44786.0	−20.0
1981-07-01	45151.0	−21.0
1982-07-01	45516.0	−22.0
1983-07-01	46247.0	−23.0
1985-07-01	47161.0	−24.0
1990-01-01	47892.0	−25.0
1991-01-01	48257.0	−26.0
1992-07-01	48804.0	−27.0
1993-07-01	49169.0	−28.0
1994-07-01	49534.0	−29.0
1996-01-01	50083.0	−30.0
1997-07-01	50630.0	−31.0
1999-01-01	51179.0	−32.0
2006-01-01	53736.0	−33.0
2008-12-31	54832.0	−34.0
2012-07-01	56109.0	−35.0

time scale with the purpose of achieving a constant average length of the solar day of 24 h. As a result, the length of one second of the Universal Time is not constant because the actual mean length of a day depends on the rotation of the Earth and the apparent motion of the Sun. It is not possible to determine the Universal Time by a direct conversion from constant Atomic Time because the rotation of the Earth cannot be predicted accurately. Every change in the Earth's rotation alters the length of a day, and must be taken into account in the Universal Time (UT). Therefore, the Universal Time is defined as a function of sidereal time, which directly reflects the rotation of the Earth, and it is also a continuous and nonuniform time system.

2.3.3 *Julian Days and Modified Julian Days*

The Julian day is often confused with another time numbering system, the cardinal date of the year. Instead of using calendar months and dates, the cardinal date is the count of days since the beginning of the year. For example, Jan 1 is Day 001,

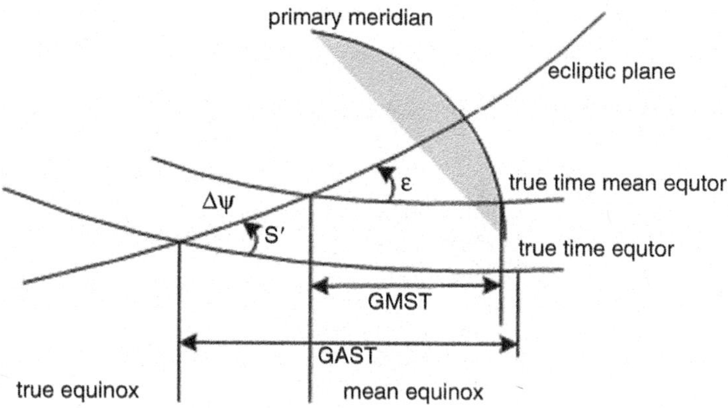

Fig. 2.12 The Greenwich mean and true sidereal time

Feb 1 is Day 032, and March 1 is either Day 059 in ordinary years or Day 060 in the leap years. The confusion of names arises because another name in common usage for the cardinal day is the "Julian day," or even sometimes "Julian date." The Julian date counts the number of times that the Earth has made a full turn since the noon on January 1, 4173 BC. For example, the cardinal day of July 1, 1997, the day when Hong Kong reunited, corresponds to the day in Julian day:

$$\mathrm{Jd}\left(2000^Y 7^M 1^D 0^H 0^m 0^s.0\,\mathrm{UTC}\right) = 2454282.5$$

and J2000.0

$$\mathrm{Jd}\left(2000^Y 1^M 1^D 12^H 0^m 0^s.0\,\mathrm{UTC}\right) = 2451545.0$$

In view of convenience, the Julian day is usually modified relative to the determinate day. For example, the Modified Julian Day adopted by the bulletin B published by the IERS is relative to the day 2400000.5, and it is

$$\mathrm{MJd} = \mathrm{Jd} - 2400000.5$$

2.3.4 Greenwich Sidereal Time

The Greenwich Sidereal Time measures the angle between the primary meridian and the vernal equinox. The Greenwich Mean Sidereal Time (GMST) measures the angle from the prime meridian to where the X-axis would be if the axis of nutation were the same as the axis of precession. The Greenwich Apparent Sidereal Time (GAST) measures the angle from the prime meridian to the true equinox, in consideration of both the precession and nutation motion of the Earth as illustrated in Fig. 2.12.

For any particular day, 0^hUT1 is defined as the instant when the Greenwich Mean Sidereal Time (GMST) has the value according to Aoki [8] (1982)

$$\begin{aligned}\mathrm{GMST}\left(0^h\mathrm{UT1}\right) &= 24110^s.54841 + 8640184^s.812866 \cdot T_0 \\ &\quad + 0^s.093104 \cdot T_0^2 - 0^s.0000062 \cdot T_0^3\end{aligned} \tag{2.11}$$

In this expression, the time increments denote the numbers of Julian centuries of the Universal Time that have elapsed since the 2000 Jan. 1.5 UT1 at the beginning of the day.

$$T_0 = \frac{\mathrm{JD}\left(0^h\mathrm{UT1}\right) - 2451545}{36525} \tag{2.12}$$

And taking into account the rotation of the Earth, the angle with the elapsed time is given by

$$\mathrm{GMST}\left(0^h\mathrm{UT1}\right) = \mathrm{GMST}\left(0^h\mathrm{UT1}\right) \cdot \frac{2\pi}{86400^s.0} \tag{2.13}$$

Similar to the GMST, the Greenwich Apparent Sidereal Time (GAST) measures the hour angle of the true equinox. Both values differ by the nutation in the right ascension:

$$\mathrm{GAST} - \mathrm{GMST} = \Delta\psi \cos\left(\varepsilon\right) \tag{2.14}$$

where ε is the obliquity of the ecliptic over the equatorial plane (Table 2.3).

2.3.5 *International Atomic Time*

The International Atomic Time (TAI) provides the practical realization of a uniform time scale based on atomic clocks, which ticks with 1 s (SI) defined by the duration of exactly 9192631770 periods of the radiation corresponding to the transition between the two hyperfine levels of the ground state of the cesium-133 atom. It begins from 0 h, Jan. 1, 1958. That is,

$$(\mathrm{TAI} - \mathrm{UT1})_{1958.0} \approx 0.0^s$$

With the advent of atomic clocks, TAI is introduced as a time system that is more easily accessible by laboratory standards and free from deficiencies of dynamic models.

Table 2.3 Julian date, Modified Julian Date, and the Greenwich hour angle

year	Julian Day	Modified Julian Day	MJd_{J2000}	MJd_{B1950}	GMST (J2000.0) (°)	GMST (true time) (°)	GAST (true time) (°)
1963	2438031.00	38030.50	−13514.00	4748.5766	280.89623	280.4220	280.4184
1964	2438396.00	38395.50	−13149.00	5113.5766	280.64451	280.1831	280.1790
1965	2438762.00	38761.50	−12783.00	5479.5766	281.37887	280.9303	280.9261
1966	2439127.00	39126.50	−12418.00	5844.5766	281.12723	280.6915	280.6877
1967	2439492.00	39491.50	−12053.00	6209.5766	280.87595	280.4530	280.4502
1968	2439857.00	39856.50	−11688.00	6574.5766	280.62478	280.2146	280.2131
1969	2440223.00	40222.50	−11322.00	6940.5766	281.35861	280.9613	280.9611
1970	2440588.00	40587.50	−10957.00	7305.5766	281.10697	280.7225	280.7236
1971	2440953.00	40952.50	−10592.00	7670.5766	280.85527	280.4836	280.4862
1972	2441318.00	41317.50	−10227.00	8035.5766	280.60372	280.2448	280.2485
1973	2441684.00	41683.50	−9861.00	8401.5766	281.34139	280.9954	280.9996
1974	2442049.00	42048.50	−9496.00	8766.5766	281.08941	280.7562	280.7606
1975	2442414.00	42413.50	−9131.00	9131.5766	280.83792	280.5175	280.5218
1976	2442779.00	42778.50	−8766.00	9496.5766	280.58648	280.2789	280.2824
1977	2443145.00	43144.50	−8400.00	9862.5766	281.32031	281.0255	281.0278
1978	2443510.00	43509.50	−8035.00	10227.5766	281.06873	280.7868	280.7877
1979	2443875.00	43874.50	−7670.00	10592.5766	280.81700	280.5478	280.5473
1980	2444240.00	44239.50	−7305.00	10957.5766	280.56567	280.3093	280.3073
1981	2444606.00	44605.50	−6939.00	11323.5766	281.29625	281.0527	281.0495
1982	2444971.00	44970.50	−6574.00	11688.5766	281.04562	280.8149	280.8110
1983	2445336.00	45335.50	−6209.00	12053.5766	280.79498	280.5771	280.5729
1984	2445701.00	45700.50	−5844.00	12418.5766	280.54416	280.3391	280.3350
1985	2446067.00	46066.50	−5478.00	12784.5766	281.27594	281.0837	281.0802
1986	2446432.00	46431.50	−5113.00	13149.5766	281.02639	280.8469	280.8446
1987	2446797.00	46796.50	−4748.00	13514.5766	280.77298	280.6064	280.6053
1988	2447162.00	47161.50	−4383.00	13879.5766	280.52356	280.3697	280.3700
1989	2447528.00	47527.50	−4017.00	14245.5766	281.25565	281.1147	281.1164
1990	2447893.00	47892.50	−3652.00	14610.5766	281.00598	280.8778	280.8808
1991	2448258.00	48257.50	−3287.00	14975.5766	280.75568	280.6403	280.6443
1992	2448623.00	48622.50	−2922.00	15340.5766	280.50105	280.3985	280.4029
1993	2448989.00	48988.50	−2556.00	15706.5766	281.23592	281.1462	281.1506
1994	2449354.00	49353.50	−2191.00	16071.5766	280.98498	280.9081	280.9121
1995	2449719.00	49718.50	−1826.00	16436.5766	280.73429	280.6702	280.6733
1996	2450084.00	50083.50	−1461.00	16801.5766	280.48342	280.4321	280.4339
1997	2450450.00	50449.50	−1095.00	17167.5766	281.21473	281.1763	281.1766
1998	2450815.00	50814.50	−730.00	17532.5766	280.96458	280.9390	280.9379
1999	2451180.00	51179.50	−365.00	17897.5766	280.71515	280.7023	280.6999
2000	2451545.00	51544.50	0.00	18262.5766	280.46212	280.4621	280.4586
2001	2451911.00	51910.50	366.00	18628.5766	281.19511	281.2079	281.2038
2002	2452276.00	52275.50	731.00	18993.5766	280.94272	280.9684	280.9642
2003	2452641.00	52640.50	1096.00	19358.5766	280.69047	280.7289	280.7250
2004	2453006.00	53005.50	1461.00	19723.5766	280.43854	280.4898	280.4867
2005	2453372.00	53371.50	1827.00	20089.5766	281.17215	281.2363	281.2344
2006	2453737.00	53736.50	2192.00	20454.5766	280.92415	281.0011	281.0006

(continued)

Table 2.3 (continued)

year	Julian Day	Modified Julian Day	MJd_{J2000}	MJd_{B1950}	GMST (J2000.0) (°)	GMST (true time) (°)	GAST (true time) (°)
2007	2454102.00	54101.50	2557.00	20819.5766	280.67137	280.7611	280.7620
2008	2454467.00	54466.50	2922.00	21184.5766	280.41922	280.5217	280.5240
2009	2454833.00	54832.50	3288.00	21550.5766	281.15331	281.2687	281.2721
2010	2455198.00	55197.50	3653.00	21915.5766	280.90179	281.0300	281.0342
2011	2455563.00	55562.50	4018.00	22280.5766	280.65027	280.7913	280.7957
2012	2455928.00	55927.50	4383.00	22645.5766	280.39875	280.5526	280.5569
2013	2456294.00	56293.50	4749.00	23011.5766	281.13284	281.2995	281.3032
2014	2456659.00	56658.50	5114.00	23376.5766	280.88132	281.0608	281.0634
2015	2457024.00	57023.50	5479.00	23741.5766	280.62980	280.8221	280.8233
2016	2457389.00	57388.50	5844.00	24106.5766	280.37828	280.5834	280.5831
2017	2457755.00	57754.50	6210.00	24472.5766	281.11237	281.3303	281.3287
2018	2458120.00	58119.50	6575.00	24837.5766	280.86085	281.0916	281.0887
2019	2458485.00	58484.50	6940.00	25202.5766	280.60933	280.8529	280.8490
2020	2458850.00	58849.50	7305.00	25567.5766	280.35781	280.6142	280.6100
2021	2459216.00	59215.50	7671.00	25933.5766	281.09190	281.3611	281.3570
2022	2459581.00	59580.50	8036.00	26298.5766	280.84038	281.1224	281.1188

Note: The epoch listed above corresponds to Jan. 1 (12 h UT1) of the particular year and J2000.0 stands for Jan. 1, 2000 (12 h UTC). The B1950 corresponds to the beginning of the Bessel year, when the solar ascension is equal to 280°

2.3.6 Coordinated Universal Time

On one hand, the duration of a day is dictated by the ticks of a watch. On the other hand, the duration of a day is dictated by the geometry of the Earth's passage around the Sun. A time system has been adopted to reconcile the two conditions.

The Coordinated Universal Time (UTC) is tied to the International Atomic Time (TAI) by an offset of integer seconds that is regularly updated to keep close agreement with the Universal Time (UT1) and is coordinated to the dynamic Universal Time. That is why we call it a coordinated time system. Being adopted to coordinate TAI with UT1, UTC is a discontinuous uniform time system. When the accumulated error between the TAI and UT1 becomes larger, as shown in Fig. 2.13, an extra second will be inserted into UT1 timing system.

Ordinarily, the second pointer of your watch counts 55, 56, 57, 58, and 59 and then goes back to zero. When an extra second is inserted, it will count 55, 56, 57, 58, 59, and 60, and then go back to zero. After the insertion of the extra second, your watch will be more coordinated with the rotation of the Earth. The leap second cannot be predicted accurately, so an international organization maintains the UTC time system. There is a way of knowing when the timepiece needs to speed up or slow down to accommodate the changing spin rate of the Earth. The International Earth Rotation Service (IERS) publishes the measurements on the web in several different bulletins, depending on the accuracy required.

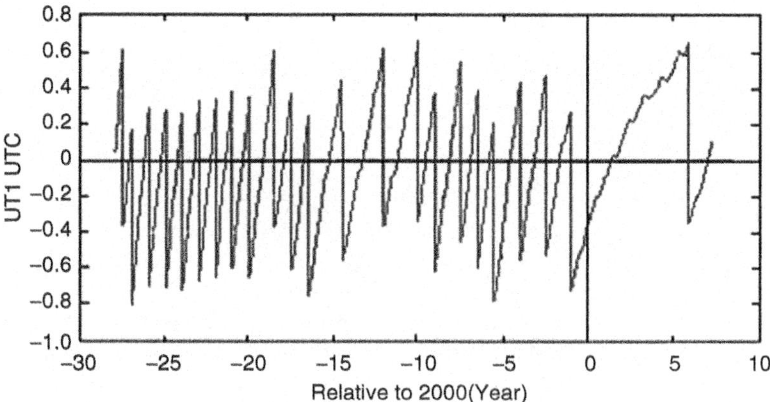

Fig. 2.13 The difference between UT1 and UTC

2.3.7 Local Time

The time on your watch is a few time zones away from UTC. It is called the local time (LT) system which is important for engineers to track the geostationary satellites. There is only a time zone difference between UTC and local time. The time zone indicates where you are on or above of the Earth. Time zones are centered at the Greenwich primary plane, each zone being 15° wide of longitude. Counting from 7.5°E eastwardly, there are Zone + 1, Zone + 2,. . ., Zone + 12 of every 15° wide; counting from 7.5°W eastwardly, there are Zone-1, Zone-2, . . ., Zone-12 of every 15° wide. So the relation between the two time systems is

$$LT = UTC + \text{Time Zone}$$

The geostationary satellite local sunrise and sunset depends upon only the nominal longitude relative to the primary meridian, which is similar to the sunrise and sunset that we see from on the Earth surface. The only difference is that the geostationary satellite can see the Sun at middle night, except the eclipse season. See Fig. 2.14.

For example, China is situated at Zone + 8, and its standard time is Beijing Time (BJT). The relation between BJT and UTC is (Table 2.4)

$$BJT = UTC + 8$$

2.3.8 Ephemeris Time

The Ephemeris Time was adopted in 1960 to cope with irregularities in the Earth's rotation that affects the flow of the mean solar time. The definition of Ephemeris Time is based on Newcomb's analytical theory of the Earth's motion around

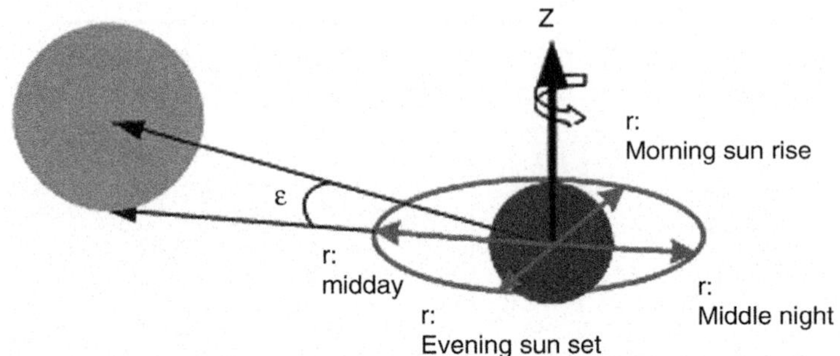

Fig. 2.14 Local time illustration

Table 2.4 Local time and time zone

Time zone (E)	Longitude coverage (°)	LT	Time zone (W)	Longitude coverage (°)	LT
0	0.0 ~ 7.5E	UTC + 0	0	0.0 ~ 7.5 W	UTC-0
+1	7.5E ~ 22.5E	UTC + 1	−1	7.5 W ~ 22.5 W	UTC-1
+2	22.5E ~ 37.5E	UTC + 2	−2	22.5 W ~ 37.5 W	UTC-2
+3	37.5E ~ 52.5E	UTC + 3	−3	37.5 W ~ 52.5 W	UTC-3
+4	52.5E ~ 67.5E	UTC + 4	−4	52.5E ~ 67.5E	UTC-4
+5	67.5E ~ 82.5E	UTC + 5	−5	67.5 W ~ 82.5 W	UTC-5
+6	82.5E ~ 97.5E	UTC + 6	−6	82.5 W ~ 97.5 W	UTC-6
+7	97.5E ~ 112.5E	UTC + 7	−7	97.5 W ~ 112.5 W	UTC-7
+8	112.5E ~ 127.5E	UTC + 8	−8	112.5 W ~ 127.5 W	UTC-8
+9	127.5E ~ 142.5E	UTC + 9	−9	127.5 W ~ 142.5 W	UTC-9
+10	142.5E ~ 157.5E	UTC + 10	−10	142.5 W ~ 157.5 W	UTC-10
+11	157.5E ~ 172.5E	UTC + 11	−11	157.5 W ~ 172.5 W	UTC-11
+12	172.5E ~ 180.0E	UTC + 12	−12	172.5 W ~ 180.0 W	UTC-12

the Sun. In his analytical solution, the motion of the Earth-Moon barycenter relative to the Sun can be expressed with ecliptic longitude:

$$L_{\odot} = 279°41'48''.04 + 129602768''.12 \cdot T + 1''.089 \cdot T^2 \tag{2.15}$$

Here, $L_{\odot}$ refers to the mean ecliptic longitude of the date, while T measures the time from the noon 1900 January 0^{h} in Julian centuries of 36,525 days.

$$T = \frac{\mathrm{Jd}(T) - \mathrm{Jd}\left(1900^Y 1^M 0^D 12^h\right)}{36525.0} = \frac{\mathrm{Jd}(T) - 2415020.0}{36525.0}$$

The formula (2.15) is later adopted as a conventional expression in the definition of Ephemeris Time. The instant at which the geometric mean longitude of the Sun has a value of $279°41'48''.04$ near the beginning of the calendar year AD 1900 is defined as 1900 January 0,12^h Ephemeris Time (ET). The ephemeris time unit is defined as the fraction (1/31556925.9747) of the tropical year at 1900 January 0.5 ET, where a tropical year specifies the time during which the Sun's mean longitude, as referred to the mean equinox of date. When the uniform seconds (SI) of TAI was proposed, the Ephemeris Time became superseded by the use of atomic time scales, which provided a much better short-term availability together with an excellent long-term stability. The time unit of TAI is defined as SI second, and the origin has arbitrarily been chosen that the TAI closely matches Universal Time on January 1, 1958 yielding the relation:

$$\text{ET} - \text{TAI} = 32.184(\text{SI}) \tag{2.16}$$

By this time scale, time is defined as the independent argument of planetary and lunar ephemeris. Based on this definition, the Earth's Moon with tabulated data is predicted from analytical or numerical theories of motion. The Ephemeris Time is thus a prototype of dynamic time scale, which considers time as a continuously and uniformly passing physical quantity in the dynamic theories of motion.

2.3.9 GPS Time

In addition to TAI, the atomic time scale established by the Global Positioning Satellite (GPS) system has become very significant in the past decades due to the common availability of GPS receivers. Besides serving the direct needs of geodetic and navigational measurements, GPS provides high-precision timing signals with a near-instantaneous and worldwide availability. It is realized by an independent set of atomic clocks and is maintained to follow the United States Naval Observatory (USNO) atomic clock time with an accuracy of 1 μs, which differs from TAI by less than 5 μs. The origin of GPS time was arbitrarily chosen to coincide with UTC on January 6.0 UTC, so GPS time differs from TAI by a constant offset, aside from the aforementioned clock offsets on microsecond level.

$$\text{GPS} - \text{TAI} = 19(\text{SI}) \tag{2.17}$$

2.3.10 Time System Summaries

Universal Time (*UT1*) is the time system tied to the rotation of the Earth. With uncertainty of spin rate of the Earth, every change in the Earth's rotation alters the length of a day, and therefore it must be taken into account in the Universal Time. The UT1 is therefore defined as a function of the sidereal time, which directly reflects the rotation of the Earth, and the Universal Time is also a continuous and nonuniform time system.

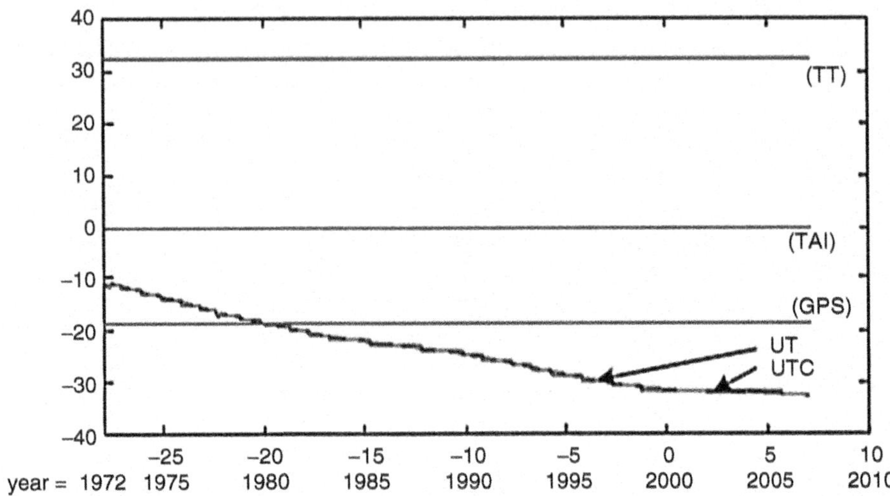

Fig. 2.15 The time systems and their relationship

The International Atomic Time (*TAI*) provides the practical realization of a uniform time scale based on atomic clocks, which ticks with one second (SI). The TAI is introduced as a time system that is more easily accessible by laboratory standards and free from deficiencies of dynamic models.

The GPS Time is realized by an independent set of on-board atomic clocks and is maintained to follow the United States Naval Observatory (USNO) atomic clock time with an accuracy of 1 μs, which differs from TAI by less than 5 μs.

The Coordinated Universal Time (UTC) which is tied to the International Atomic Time (TAI) by an offset of integer seconds is regularly updated to keep close agreement with the Universal Time (UT1). It ticks with perfect one second (SI) and is coordinated to the dynamic Universal Time, and that's why we call it a coordinated time system. Being adopted to coordinate the TAI with UT1, the UTC is a discontinuous but uniform time system. There is only time zone difference between UTC and the local Time (LT). The time zone indicates where you are on or above of the Earth.

The Ephemeris Time (ET) defines the time as the independent argument of planetary and lunar ephemeris. Based on this definition, the Earth's Moon with tabulated data is predicted from analytical or numerical theories of motion. The Ephemeris Time is thus a prototype of a dynamic time scale, which considers time as a continuously and uniformly passing physical quantity in the dynamic theories of motion.

The time systems show some dissonances between them; the mutual relations of the time systems are illustrated in Fig. 2.15.

UTC and TAI. The Coordinated Universal Time (UTC), which differs with the International Atomic Time (TAI) by an offset of integer seconds, is regularly updated to keep close agreement with the Universal Time (UT1). It ticks with perfect one second (SI) and is coordinated to the dynamic Universal Time on 0^h, January 1, 1958. From then on, there have been 35 leap seconds. So if the epoch locates between July 1, 2006, and January 1, 2009, then UTC−TAI = −33 (seconds). If it is between January 1, 2009, and July 1, 2012, then UTC−TAI = −34 (seconds). If it is between July 1, 2012, and Autumn 10th, 2012, when I finished the manuscript of this book, then UTC−TAI = −35 (seconds).

TAI and ET. From 1967, when the uniform seconds (SI) of TAI was proposed, the Ephemeris Time became superseded by the use of atomic time scales, which provided a much better short-term availability together with an excellent long-term stability. The time unit of TAI is defined as SI second, and the origin has arbitrarily been chosen that TAI closely matches the Universal Time on January 1, 1958, yielding the relation

$$\mathrm{ET} - \mathrm{TAI} = 32.184(\mathrm{SI}) \tag{2.18}$$

UTC and UT1. UTC is adopted to coordinate TAI with UT1. When the accumulated error between TAI and UT1 becomes larger, a leap second is inserted into UTC. The leap second cannot be predicted accurately, so an international organization maintains the UTC time system. There is a way of knowing when the timepiece needs to speed up or slow down to accommodate the changing spin rate of the Earth. The International Earth Rotation Service publishes the measurements on the web in several different bulletins.

2.4 Reference System

This section presents several fundamental concepts concerning the reference frames used in the space dynamics for positioning space object at a given timing. Being a wide range of possible choices, the choices are justified in terms of the nature of the problems to be studied.

The J2000.0 Earth-centered inertial system (ECI) is used to depict the perturbation motion of satellite.

The mean equator and equinox of the epoch reference system are used to measure the precession of the Earth's motion.

The nutation of the Earth's motion is depicted by the true equator and equinox of the epoch reference system.

The Greenwich Earth-fixed reference system (ECF) is used to describe the relative motion to the Earth.

Other reference systems are also deployed naturally when dealing with satellite tracking and observations issues. For example, for orbit measurement and observation, the observation stations are measured in the Earth-fixed coordination system. For perturbation analysis of orbit motion of the geostationary satellite, the additional forces are projected into satellite-fixed radial/tangential/normal coordinate system. For three-axis-stabilized satellite, the attitude is fixed and evaluated with the satellite-fixed East/South/Down reference frame. For planning station keeping maneuver of the geostationary satellite, the drift motion relative to the nominal point is depicted in the satellite-fixed orbit coordinate system. For portraying the propellant configuration of the satellite, the installation cosine vector is projected into the satellite body coordinate system, etc.

2.4.1 Background and General Definitions

A reference system in space is mathematically represented by a reference frame (O, ε), where O is a point in space serving as the origin of the frame, and ε is an orthogonal basis. Theoretically, the problem is relatively simple, but the reference frames used in the space dynamics are subjected to the additional perturbations from the planet and the oblateness of the Earth, all of which make the problem quite complex, and the transformation between them is also relatively difficult depending on the precision desired. There are three terms from the element of a reference system, the origin, reference plane, and reference direction definition.

The Origin of the Frame. The terms used in space frames are topocentric system, whose origin is a point on the Earth's surface; geocentric system, whose origin is the mass center of the Earth; barycentric system, whose origin is the mass center of the system of bodies; and satellite system, whose origin is the satellite's center of gravity. The meanings of the terms selenocentric, planet centric, heliocentric, Earth-Moon barycentric, and solar system barycentric follow the definition terms above.

The Reference Plane. The reference plane serves as the basic plane to form the orthogonal basis. Among all the reference planes, the following ones are frequently used. The equatorial plane, which is perpendicular to the pole axis of the celestial sphere, is used to form a celestial spherical coordinate frame. The ecliptic plane, in which the Earth revolves around the Sun, is used to form an ecliptic coordinate frame. The orbit plane, which is defined interims of the angular momentum of orbit motion and intersects the equator along the line of orbit nodes, is used to form the orbit-related coordinate frame. The meridian plane, which contains the Earth's rotation axis and the vertical of a point on the Earth, defines the local meridian plane; the Greenwich meridian was chosen to be the origin meridian used to determine all points on the Earth. The local horizontal plane, which is perpendicular to the zenith of local position on the Earth, is used to be the primary plane to realize the local tangential coordinate system.

The Reference Direction. Among all the reference directions, the following ones are frequently used to form a space frame. The vernal equinox is the intersection of the celestial equator and the ecliptic plane; the orientation of intersection line is given by the direction of the ascending node of the Sun, where the Sun crosses from the southern hemisphere to the northern hemisphere. This privileged direction is the spring equinox and always defines the point; the inclination of the ecliptic over the equator is called the obliquity. The vertical of a plane, which is provided by the

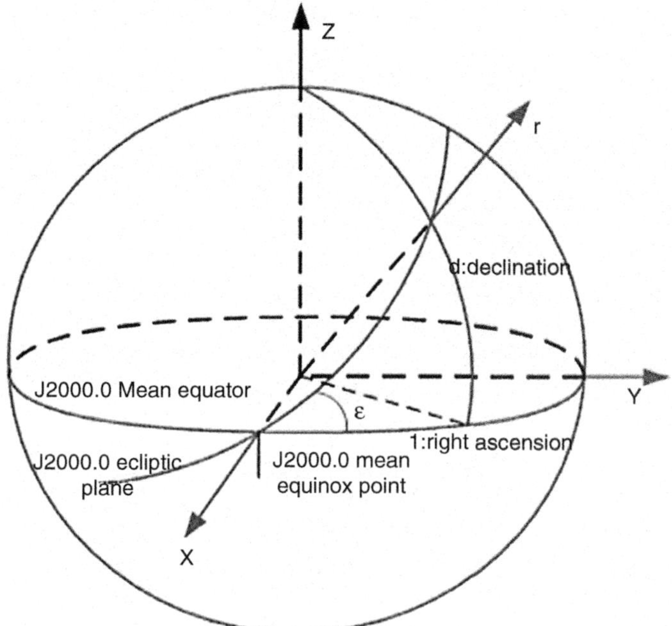

Fig. 2.16 The J2000.0 geocentric inertial coordinate

plumb line and is the normal to the surface of the celestial, is also called the geoids. The Earth's rotation axis plays a fundamental role in conversion between the terrestrial reference and the celestial reference system.

These mathematical concepts will be used to provide some classical definitions which are widely encountered in forming space frames. The practical methods of realizing these systems will be examined carefully in this section.

2.4.2 J2000.0 Earth-Centered Inertial System

In view of the fact that the orientation of the equator and ecliptic is time dependent, so a standard reference frame is usually based on the mean equator, the mean ecliptic, and the equinox of some dedicated epoch, which is currently selected as the beginning of the year 2000. So the J2000.0 Earth-centered inertial system ($O-\mathbf{XYZ}$) is also called the Earth mean equator and equinox of epoch 2000 (EME2000). Its origin is located at the mass center of the Earth; its primary plane lies on the mean equatorial plane of the Earth; its reference direction points from the origin to the intersection point where the equator and ecliptic plane intersected at the epoch 12 h in UTC, January 1, 2000. As illustrated in Fig. 2.16, the X-axis points to the J2000.0 mean equinox point, the Z-axis is along the normal direction of J2000.0 mean equatorial plane, and the Y-axis is perpendicular to the primary orientation to form a right orthogonal frame, upon which the motion dynamics of the satellite is established. Being a quasi-inertial celestial reference frame, the position of a space object can be measured by the spherical coordinate (r, l, d), which are the radius, the right ascension, and the declination, respectively.

The ephemeris of a satellite at a given epoch is composed of the position vector $\mathbf{r}_{\text{ECI}}$ and the velocity vector $\dot{\mathbf{r}}_{\text{ECI}}$. For example, the ephemeris of a satellite at epoch 12 h, May 1, 2006, in UTC can be expressed as

$$\mathbf{r}_{\text{ECI}} = \begin{pmatrix} 40602699.018938 \\ 11370550.587838 \\ 34665.479136 \end{pmatrix} (\text{m}), \quad \dot{\mathbf{r}}_{\text{ECI}} = \begin{pmatrix} -829.050151 \\ 2960.841057 \\ 0.031711 \end{pmatrix} (\text{m/s})$$

2.4.3 The Mean Equator and Equinox

Both the fundamental planes and the principal directions are moving with time. A reference system defined in terms of these planes and directions will be well defined when it is associated with a given epoch. The epoch mean equator and mean ecliptic system $(O - \mathbf{X}_M\mathbf{Y}_M\mathbf{Z}_M)$ which is also called Mean Of Date (MOD) is defined with the primary plane and principal orientation associated with the epoch and takes the mass center of the Earth as the origin. $\mathbf{X}_M$-axis points to the equinox point at the epoch, $\mathbf{Z}_M$-axis is perpendicular to the normal direction of the mean equator plane, and $\mathbf{Y}_M$-axis lies on primary plane and forms a right orthogonal frame. In realization of the transformation between the J2000.0 $(O - \mathbf{XYZ})$ and the epoch MOD $(O - \mathbf{X}_M\mathbf{Y}_M\mathbf{Z}_M)$, according to Newcomb, the orientation of the mean equator and equinox of epoch T with respect to the equator and equinox of J2000.0 is defined by the three Euler angles (2.6). The transformation matrix may now be written as

$$\mathbf{P}(T) = \mathbf{R}_z(-90^\circ - \xi)\mathbf{R}_x(\vartheta)\mathbf{R}_z(90^\circ - \varsigma) = \mathbf{R}_z(-\xi)\mathbf{R}_x(\vartheta)\mathbf{R}_z(-\varsigma) \tag{2.19}$$

The Greenwich Mean Sidereal Time (GMST) is measurable in this reference frame. Figure 2.17 illustrates the right ascension, the Greenwich Mean Sidereal Time (GMST), and the Greenwich longitude, as well as the relation of the longitude and the right ascension of a satellite, which may now be described as

$$\lambda = S - \text{GMST} \tag{2.20}$$

Suppose there is a satellite with the position vector $\mathbf{r}_{\text{ECI}}$ and the velocity vector $\dot{\mathbf{r}}_{\text{ECI}}$ in the J2000.0 reference frame and their projections in the MOD reference frame are $\mathbf{r}_{\text{MOD}}$ and $\dot{\mathbf{r}}_{\text{MOD}}$, respectively, and then the coordinate transformation expressions satisfy

$$\mathbf{r}_{\text{MOD}} = \mathbf{P}(T) \cdot \mathbf{r}_{\text{ECI}} \tag{2.21}$$

$$\dot{\mathbf{r}}_{\text{MOD}} = \mathbf{P}(T) \cdot \dot{\mathbf{r}}_{\text{ECI}} + \frac{\mathrm{d}\mathbf{P}(T)}{\mathrm{d}t} \cdot \mathbf{r}_{\text{ECI}} \approx \mathbf{P}(T) \cdot \dot{\mathbf{r}}_{\text{ECI}} \tag{2.22}$$

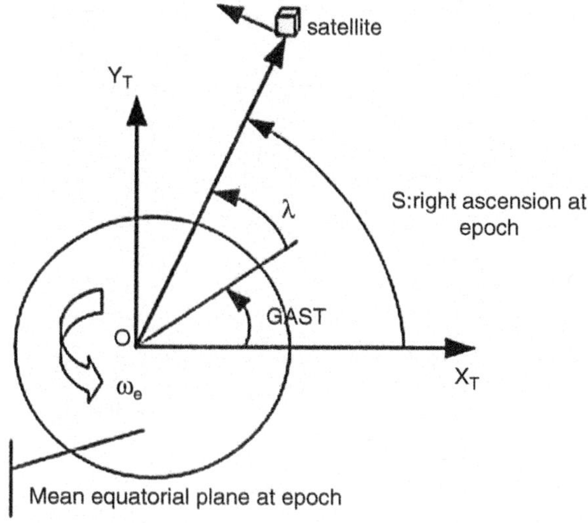

Fig. 2.17 Right ascension and the Greenwich Longitude

The expression transformation between arbitrary mean equinox reference frame at the given epoch T_1 and T_2 is thus obtained from

$$\mathbf{P}(T_1, T_2) = \mathbf{P}(T_2)\mathbf{P}^T(T_1) \tag{2.23}$$

For example, the ephemerides of a satellite at epoch 12 h, May 1, 2006, in UTC are the position vector $\mathbf{r}_{\text{ECI}}$ and the velocity vector $\dot{\mathbf{r}}_{\text{ECI}}$. According to IERS bulletin C-04, the Ephemeris Time has an offset satisfying

$$(\text{ET} - \text{UTC})_{2005^Y 5^M 1^D 12^h (UTC)} = 64.184(\text{SI}) \tag{2.24}$$

Taking ET as an independent argument, the precession transformation matrix from the mean equator and equinox of J2000 to the mean equator and equinox at the given epoch 12 h, May 1, 2006 (UTC) is determined as

$$\mathbf{P}(T) = \begin{bmatrix} 0.99999881 & -0.00141550 & -0.0006150799 \\ 0.00141550 & 0.999998998 & -4.3532892 \times 10^{-7} \\ 0.00061508 & -4.35319447 \times 10^{-7} & 0.99999998 \end{bmatrix}$$

The satellite with the position vector $\mathbf{r}_{\text{ECI}}$ and the velocity vector $\dot{\mathbf{r}}_{\text{ECI}}$ in the J2000.0 reference frame can be projected as $\mathbf{r}_{\text{MOD}}$, $\dot{\mathbf{r}}_{\text{MOD}}$ in the MOD reference frame at the given epoch 12 h in UTC, May 1, 2006.

$$\mathbf{r}_{\text{MOD}} = \begin{pmatrix} 40586534.283672 \\ 11428012.450287 \\ 59634.426859 \end{pmatrix} (\text{m}), \quad \dot{\mathbf{r}}_{\text{MOD}} = \begin{pmatrix} -833.240265 \\ 2959.664568 \\ -0.4795096 \end{pmatrix} (\text{m/s})$$

2.4.4 The True Equator and Equinox

Aside from the secular precession motion, the orientation of the Earth's rotation axis is also affected by small periodic perturbations that are known as nutation motion. The effect will cause an observable movement of the fundamental planes and the principal directions with time and have a slight of excursion with the mean equator and equinox at a given epoch. So true equator and equinox is referred to form the true equator and equinox system, which is also referred as the True of Date coordinates (TOD) $(O - \mathbf{X}_T\mathbf{Y}_T\mathbf{Z}_T)$. It takes the mass center of the Earth as the origin O. The $\mathbf{X}_T$-axis points to intersection of the true equator and true ecliptic at given epoch, the $\mathbf{Z}_T$-axis is perpendicular to the true equatorial plane of given epoch, and the $\mathbf{Y}_T$-axis forms a right orthogonal frame. The transformation from Mean of Date coordinate which refers to the mean equator and equinox to True of Date coordinate which refers to the true equator and equinox may be written as

$$\mathbf{r}_{\text{TOD}} = \mathbf{N}(T)\mathbf{r}_{\text{MOD}} \tag{2.25}$$

With the nutation matrix expressions recommended by the IERS discussed in Sect. 2.2.8,

$$\mathbf{N}(T) = \mathbf{R}_{\mathbf{x}}(-(\varepsilon + \Delta\varepsilon)) \cdot \mathbf{R}_{\mathbf{z}}(-\Delta\psi) \cdot \mathbf{R}_{\mathbf{x}}(\varepsilon) \tag{2.26}$$

where c ε is the true obliquity of the ecliptic at a given epoch T.

$$\varepsilon = 23°26'21''.448 - 46''.8150T - 0''.00059T^2 + 0''.001813T^3$$

and the Julian century is

$$T = (\text{JD(TT)} - 2451545.0)/36525.$$

Greenwich Apparent Sidereal Time (GAST) is measurable in this reference frame. Figure 2.18 illustrates the right ascension, the GAST, and the Greenwich Longitude, as well as the relation of longitude and right ascension of a satellite, which may now be described as

$$\lambda = S_T - \text{GAST} \tag{2.27}$$

Suppose there is a satellite with the position vector $\mathbf{r}_{\text{ECI}}$ and the velocity vector $\dot{\mathbf{r}}_{\text{ECI}}$ in the J2000.0 reference frame, and their projections in the TOD reference frame are $\mathbf{r}_{\text{TOD}}$ and $\dot{\mathbf{r}}_{\text{TOD}}$, respectively, and then the coordinate transformation expressions satisfy

$$\mathbf{r}_{\text{TOD}} = \mathbf{N}(T) \cdot \mathbf{P}(T) \cdot \mathbf{r}_{\text{ECI}} \tag{2.28}$$

$$\begin{aligned} \dot{\mathbf{r}}_{\text{TOD}} &= \mathbf{N}(T) \cdot \mathbf{P}(T) \cdot \dot{\mathbf{r}}_{\text{ECI}} + \frac{\mathrm{d}(\mathbf{N}(T)\mathbf{P}(T))}{dt} \cdot \mathbf{r}_{\text{ECI}} \\ &\approx \mathbf{N}(T) \cdot \mathbf{P}(T) \cdot \dot{\mathbf{r}}_{\text{ECI}} \end{aligned} \tag{2.29}$$

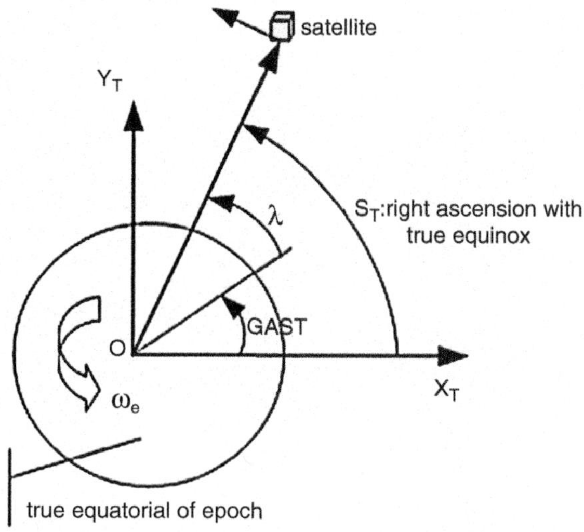

Fig. 2.18 Greenwich apparent sidereal time

The expression transformation between arbitrary true equinox reference frame at the epoch T_1 and T_2 is thus obtained from

$$\mathbf{N}(T_1, T_2) = \mathbf{N}(T_2)\mathbf{P}(T_2)\mathbf{P}^T(T_1)\mathbf{N}^T(T_1)$$

The nutation longitude $\Delta\psi$ along longitude direction and the nutation obliquity $\Delta\varepsilon$ along the latitude direction (see 2.2.8) can be calculated by formulas (2.7 and 2.8), which are expressed as the function of incremental variable epoch. According to the IERS bulletin C-04[11], the accuracy modification of nutation at epoch 12 h in UTC, May 1, 2006, may be queried in terms of Modified Julian Days (Mjd= 53856.5) as

$$\delta(\Delta\psi) = -0''.053991$$
$$\delta(\Delta\varepsilon) = -0''.006356$$

Then nutation transformation matrix may be calculated by the above argument at the epoch

$$\mathbf{N}(T) = \begin{bmatrix} 1.0 & 8.298138 \times 10^{-6} & 3.597542 \times 10^{-6} \\ -8.29798 \times 10^{-6} & 1.0 & -4.395197 \times 10^{-5} \\ -3.59791 \times 10^{-6} & 4.395194 \times 10^{-5} & 1.0 \end{bmatrix}$$

The satellite with the position vector $\mathbf{r}_{\mathrm{ECI}}$ and the velocity vector $\dot{\mathbf{r}}_{\mathrm{ECI}}$ in the J2000.0 reference frame can be projected as $\mathbf{r}_{\mathrm{TOD}}, \dot{\mathbf{r}}_{\mathrm{TOD}}$ in the TOD reference frame at the given epoch 12 h in UTC, May 1, 2006.

$$\mathbf{r}_{\mathrm{TOD}} = \begin{pmatrix} 40586629.327781 \\ 11427673.031534 \\ 59990.683512 \end{pmatrix} (\mathrm{m}), \quad \dot{\mathbf{r}}_{\mathrm{TOD}} = \begin{pmatrix} -833.215706 \\ 2959.671499 \\ -0.3464286 \end{pmatrix} (\mathrm{m/s})$$

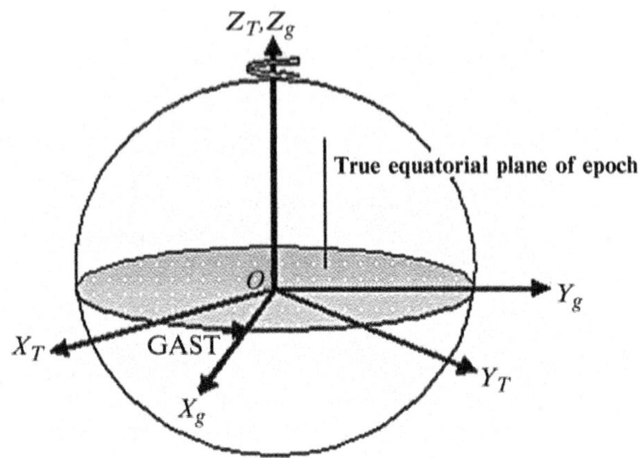

Fig. 2.19 Epoch true equatorial frame

2.4.5 The Greenwich Meridian-Fixed System

The precession and nutation theories built the instantaneous orientation of the Earth's rotation axis, that is, the orientation of the Celestial Ephemeris Pole (CEP) with respect to the International Celestial Reference System (ICRS). The rotation about the CEP axis itself is described by the Greenwich Mean Sidereal Time (GMST) and the Greenwich Apparent Sidereal Time (GAST), respectively. The former measures the angle between the mean vernal equinox and the Greenwich meridian, while the latter measures the angle between the true vernal equinox and the Greenwich meridian. Both of the values differ by the nutation in right ascension, which is also known as the equation of the equinoxes.

$$\mathrm{GAST} - \mathrm{GMST} = \Delta\psi \cos \varepsilon$$

The Greenwich meridian-fixed system $(O - \mathbf{X}_g\mathbf{Y}_g\mathbf{Z}_g)$ takes the mass center of the Earth as the origin. The primary direction $\mathbf{X}_g$-axis points to the intersection of the Greenwich meridian and the true equator of the epoch. The $\mathbf{Z}_g$-axis points from the origin to the CEP instantaneous pole of the epoch. $\mathbf{Y}_g$-axis lies on the true equatorial plane of the epoch and forms the right orthogonal frame. Figure 2.19 illustrates the relation between the Epoch True Equatorial Frame and the Earth-Fixed Frame. The transformation matrix between the True of Date coordinate and the Greenwich meridian-fixed system is known as the sidereal matrix.

$$\mathbf{\Theta}(T) = \mathbf{R}_z(\mathrm{GAST}) \tag{2.30}$$

Suppose there is a satellite with the position vector $\mathbf{r}_{\mathrm{ECI}}$ and the velocity vector $\dot{\mathbf{r}}_{\mathrm{ECI}}$ in the J2000.0 reference frame and their projection in the CEP reference frame are $\mathbf{r}_{\mathrm{CEP}}$ and $\dot{\mathbf{r}}_{\mathrm{CEP}}$, respectively, and then the coordinate transformation expressions satisfy

$$\mathbf{r}_{\mathrm{CEP}} = \mathbf{\Theta}(T) \cdot \mathbf{N}(T) \cdot \mathbf{P}(T) \cdot \mathbf{r}_{\mathrm{ECI}} \tag{2.31}$$

$$\begin{aligned}\dot{\mathbf{r}}_{\mathrm{CEP}} &= \mathbf{\Theta}(T) \cdot \mathbf{N}(T) \cdot \mathbf{P}(T) \cdot \dot{\mathbf{r}}_{\mathrm{ECI}} + \frac{\mathrm{d}(\mathbf{\Theta}(T)\mathbf{N}(T)\mathbf{P}(T))}{\mathrm{d}t} \cdot \mathbf{r}_{\mathrm{ECI}} \\ &\approx \mathbf{\Theta}(T) \cdot \mathbf{N}(T) \cdot \mathbf{P}(T) \cdot \dot{\mathbf{r}}_{\mathrm{ECI}} + \frac{\mathrm{d}(\mathbf{\Theta}(T))}{\mathrm{d}t}\mathbf{N}(T)\mathbf{P}(T) \cdot \mathbf{r}_{\mathrm{ECI}}\end{aligned} \tag{2.32}$$

Here,

$$\frac{\mathrm{d}(\mathbf{\Theta}(T))}{\mathrm{d}t} = \begin{bmatrix} 0 & \omega_e & 0 \\ -\omega_e & 0 & 0 \\ 0 & 0 & 0 \end{bmatrix} \cdot \mathbf{\Theta}(T) \tag{2.33}$$

$$\omega_e = 7.29211585 \times 10^{-5}(\mathrm{Rad/s})$$

Given the UT1-UTC or UT1-TAI time difference published by the IERS[11], the Greenwich Apparent Sidereal Time (GAST) at any instant can be computed by the conventional relations (2.11, 2.12, 2.13, and 2.14). For example, from the IERS bulletin C-04, at epoch 12 h in UTC, May 1, 2006 (Modified Julian Day is equal to 53856.5), the UT1-UTC time difference has the value

$$(\mathrm{UT1} - \mathrm{UTC})_{2006^Y 5^M 1^D 12^h \mathrm{UTC}} = 0^s.2359553$$

From the conventional relation, the GAST at this instant is

$$\mathrm{GAST} = 39^\circ.277841$$

then the sidereal matrix satisfies

$$\Theta(T) = R_z(\mathrm{GAST}) = \begin{bmatrix} 0.774085 & 0.633082 & 0.0 \\ 0.633082 & 0.774085 & 0.0 \\ 0.0 & 0.0 & 1.0 \end{bmatrix}$$

The satellite with the position vector $\mathbf{r}_{\mathrm{ECI}}$ and the velocity vector $\dot{\mathbf{r}}_{\mathrm{ECI}}$ in the J2000.0 reference frame can be projected as $\mathbf{r}_{\mathrm{CEP}}$, $\dot{\mathbf{r}}_{\mathrm{CEP}}$ in the CEP reference frame at the given epoch 12 h in UTC, May 1, 2006.

$$\mathbf{r}_{\mathrm{CEP}} = \begin{pmatrix} 38652154.296443 \\ -16848654.526410 \\ 59990.683512 \end{pmatrix} (\mathrm{m}), \quad \dot{\mathbf{r}}_{\mathrm{CEP}} = \begin{pmatrix} 0.1101302 \\ -0.028749 \\ -0.3464287 \end{pmatrix} (\mathrm{m/s})$$

2.4.6 International Terrestrial Reference System

The common z-axis of both systems points to the Celestial Ephemeris Pole, which is not, however, fixed with respect to the surface of the Earth, but performs a periodic motion around its mean position from which it differs by 10 m at most. This motion is known as polar motion, and the motion data have been consistently referred to as the IERS Reference Pole (IRP). This can be understood by considering a rotationally symmetric gyroscope, in which the rotation axis moves around the axis of figure in the absence of external torques. So a pole motion fixed coordinate is known as the International Terrestrial Reference System (ITRS), which was introduced in 1984, by following the introduction of the International Terrestrial Reference System (ITRS), which provides the conceptual definition of an Earth-centered-fixed reference system (ECF). Its origin is located at the mass center of the Earth, and its orientation is consistent with the IERS Reference Pole (IRP) and IERS Reference Meridian (IRM), respectively, which are maintained by the International Earth Rotation Service (IERS) [1].

The transformation from the Greenwich meridian-fixed coordinate to the International Terrestrial Reference System may be expressed as

$$\begin{aligned}\mathbf{\Pi}(T) &= \mathbf{R_y}\left(-x_p\right)\cdot\mathbf{R_x}\left(-y_p\right)\\ &= \begin{bmatrix}\cos\left(x_p\right) & \sin\left(x_p\right)\cdot\sin\left(y_p\right) & \sin\left(x_p\right)\cdot\cos\left(y_p\right)\\ 0 & \cos\left(y_p\right) & -\sin\left(y_p\right)\\ -\sin\left(x_p\right) & \cos\left(x_p\right)\cdot\sin\left(y_p\right) & \cos\left(x_p\right)\cdot\cos\left(y_p\right)\end{bmatrix}\end{aligned} \tag{2.34}$$

Here, the coordinates x_p and y_p of the Celestial Ephemeris Pole (CEP) with respect to the IERS Reference Pole (IRP) are a function of time. The current values of the pole coordinates are published on a monthly basis in bulletin C of the international Earth Rotation Service [1] with a resolution of one and five days, respectively. From these data, intermediate values for any time may be obtained by quadratic interpolation with sufficient accuracy.

In view of the small angles involved in pole rotation matrix, second-order terms can be safely neglected in the expansion of the trigonometric functions, and the linearization form of it is fully adequate for all applications.

$$\mathbf{\Pi}(T) = \begin{bmatrix}1 & 0 & x_p\\ 0 & 1 & -y_p\\ -x_p & y_p & 1\end{bmatrix} \tag{2.35}$$

Suppose there is a satellite with the position vector $\mathbf{r}_{\mathrm{ECI}}$ and the velocity vector $\dot{\mathbf{r}}_{\mathrm{ECI}}$ in the J2000.0 reference frame and their projection in the ECF reference frame are $\mathbf{r}_{\mathrm{ECF}}$ and $\dot{\mathbf{r}}_{\mathrm{ECF}}$, respectively, and then the coordinate transformation expressions satisfy

$$\mathbf{r}_{\mathrm{ECF}} = \mathbf{\Pi}(T)\cdot\mathbf{\Theta}(T)\cdot\mathbf{N}(T)\cdot\mathbf{P}(T)\cdot\mathbf{r}_{\mathrm{ECI}} \tag{2.36}$$

$$\begin{aligned}\dot{\mathbf{r}}_{\mathrm{ECF}} &= \mathbf{\Pi}(T)\cdot\mathbf{\Theta}(T)\cdot\mathbf{N}(T)\cdot\mathbf{P}(T)\cdot\dot{\mathbf{r}}_{\mathrm{ECI}} \\ &\quad+\frac{\mathrm{d}(\mathbf{\Pi}(T)\mathbf{\Theta}(T)\mathbf{N}(T)\mathbf{P}(T))}{\mathrm{d}t}\cdot\mathbf{r}_{\mathrm{ECI}} \\ &\approx \mathbf{\Pi}(T)\cdot\mathbf{\Theta}(T)\cdot\mathbf{N}(T)\cdot\mathbf{P}(T)\cdot\dot{\mathbf{r}}_{\mathrm{ECI}} \\ &\quad+\mathbf{\Pi}(T)\cdot\frac{\mathrm{d}(\mathbf{\Theta}(T))}{\mathrm{d}t}\cdot\mathbf{N}(T)\cdot\mathbf{P}(T)\cdot\mathbf{r}_{\mathrm{ECI}}\end{aligned} \tag{2.37}$$

Here,

$$\frac{\mathrm{d}(\mathbf{\Theta}(T))}{\mathrm{d}t} = \begin{bmatrix} 0 & \omega_e & 0 \\ -\omega_e & 0 & 0 \\ 0 & 0 & 0 \end{bmatrix}\cdot\mathbf{\Theta}(T) \tag{2.38}$$

$$\omega_e = 7.29211585\times10^{-5}(\mathrm{Rad/s})$$

For example, according to the IERS bulletin C-04 [1], at epoch 12 h in UTC, May 1, 2006 (Modified Julian Day is equal to 53856.5), the coordinates of CEP with respect to the IRP are

$$x_p = 0''.109801$$

$$y_p = 0''.360164$$

Hence, the pole rotation matrix from the Greenwich meridian-fixed coordinate to the International Terrestrial Reference System may be evaluated by

$$\mathbf{\Pi}(T) = \begin{bmatrix} 1.0 & 0.0 & 5.323303\times10^{-7} \\ 0.0 & 1.0 & -1.746124\times10^{-6} \\ -5.323303\times10^{-7} & 1.746124\times10^{-6} & 1.0 \end{bmatrix}$$

The satellite with the position vector $\mathbf{r}_{\mathrm{ECI}}$ and the velocity vector $\dot{\mathbf{r}}_{\mathrm{ECI}}$ in the J2000.0 reference frame can be projected as $\mathbf{r}_{\mathrm{ECF}}$, $\dot{\mathbf{r}}_{\mathrm{ECF}}$ in the CEP reference frame at the given epoch 12 h in UTC, May 1, 2006.

$$\mathbf{r}_{\mathrm{ECF}} = \begin{pmatrix} 38652154.328357 \\ -16848654.631135 \\ 59940.687954 \end{pmatrix}(\mathrm{m}),\quad \dot{\mathbf{r}}_{\mathrm{ECF}} = \begin{pmatrix} 0.110130 \\ -0.028748 \\ -0.3464288 \end{pmatrix}(\mathrm{m/s})$$

In general, the transformation between the J2000.0 inertial coordinate (ECI) and the conceptual Earth-centered-fixed reference system (ECF) is accomplished by conventional models for:

1. The precession transformation, describing the secular change in the orientation of the Earth's rotation axis and the equinox
2. The nutation transformation, describing the periodic and short-term variation of the Earth's equator and the vernal equinox
3. The sidereal time transformation, describing the Earth's rotation about itself
4. The pole transformation, describing the motion of the Celestial Ephemeris Pole (CEP) with respect to the IERS Reference Pole (IRP)

The transformation at a particular epoch, from J2000.0 inertial coordinate (ECI) to the conceptual Earth-centered-fixed reference system (ECF), may be expressed as

$$\mathbf{M}_{\mathrm{ECF}}^{\mathrm{ECI}}(T) = \mathbf{\Pi}(T) \cdot \mathbf{\Theta}(T) \cdot \mathbf{N}(T) \cdot \mathbf{P}(T) \tag{2.39}$$

For example, at epoch 12 h in UTC, May 1, 2006, the transformation matrix is

$$\begin{aligned}\mathbf{M}_{\mathrm{ECF}}^{\mathrm{ECI}}(T) &= \mathbf{\Pi}(T) \cdot \mathbf{\Theta}(T) \cdot \mathbf{N}(T) \cdot \mathbf{P}(T) \\ &= \begin{bmatrix} 0.77497506 & 0.63199162 & -0.0005009 \\ -0.63199153 & 0.77497522 & 0.00035102 \\ 0.00061003 & 0.00004454 & 0.99999981 \end{bmatrix}\end{aligned}$$

Until now, we have built the mutual relation between the J2000.0 inertial coordinate (ECI) and the conceptual Earth-centered-fixed reference system (ECF), meaning that we have understood the motion of the Earth with time at inertial space more precisely.

2.4.7 Global Geodetic System

Besides the International Terrestrial Reference System (ITRS) and its annually updated realizations, a variety of other global geodetic systems are in widespread usage in establishing global coordinate systems that originate at the Earth's mass center and are closely aligned with the Greenwich meridian and the IERS adopted pole.

The world Geodetic System 1972 (WGS72) and 1984 (WGS84) have been established by the US Department of Defense (DOD) and the Defense Mapping Agency (DMA) for the usage of GPS satellite navigation system. WGS84, in its initial realization, was itself based on reference station coordinates obtained by TRANSIT Doppler measurements and achieved a global accuracy of 1–2 m. To improve its precision, two new realizations named WGS84 (G730) and WGS84 (G873) were established based on precise GPS positioning techniques. The revised systems are considered to agree with the ITRF on the decimeter and centimeter level. Similar to the use of WGS84 in GPS applications, the Russian GLONASS system employs a special datum known as PZ-90 reference frame.

Table 2.5 The earth parameters

Global geodetic frame	$R_{\oplus}$ (m)	$1/f$
GEM-10B	6378138.0	298.257
GEM-T3	6378137.0	298.257
WGS72	6378135.0	298.26
WGS84	6378137.0	298.257223563
ITRF(GRS-80)	6378137.0	298.257222101
PZ-90	6378136.0	298.257839303
CGCS2000[a]	6378137.0	298.257222101

Adopted by Different Organizations and Geodetic Systems
[a]China Geodetic Coordinate System 2000

Table 2.6 Helmert transformation parameters

		Origin offset			Scale	Misalignment of the coordinate axes		
		T_1	T_2	T_3	D	R_1	R_2	R_3
Source	Target	(cm)	(cm)	(cm)	10^{-9}	(0″.001)	(0″.001)	(0″.001)
ITRF90	WGS72	+6.0	−51.7	−472.3	−231	+18.3	−0.3	+547.0
ITRF90	WGS84	+6.0	−51.7	−22.3	−11	+18.3	−0.3	−7.0
ITRF94	ITRF90	+1.8	+1.2	−3.0	+0.9	0.0	0.0	0.0
ITRF94	WGS84 (G730)	−2	+2	−1	+0.2	+2.5	+1.9	−2.5
ITRF94	WGS84 (G873)	+1	−1	−2	+0.3	+0.6	+1.2	+0.7
ITRF2000	ITRF94	0.67	0.61	−1.85	1.55	0.0	0.0	0.0
WGS84	PZ-90	+47	+51	+156	−22	+15.7	+3.5	−356
ITRF2000	WGS84	[a]						
WGS84	CGCS	[b]						

Monenbruck [9] 2000
[a]New realizations of WGS84 are based on GPS data, such as WGS84 (G730, G873, and G1150). These new WGS84 realizations are coincident with ITRF2000 at about 10-cm level. For these realizations, there are no official transformation parameters. This means that one can consider that ITRF coordinates are also expressed in WGS84 at 10 cm level
[b]According to Wei [10], the China Geodetic Coordinate System 2000 realization is coincident with ITRF2000 and WGS84 (G1150). For these realizations, there is no official transformation between them

In addition to the Cartesian coordinates in the geodetic reference frame, the location of satellite or the station situated on the surface of the Earth is commonly expressed in terms of geodetic coordinates relative to a chosen reference ellipsoid. Table 2.5 summarizes the Earth's geodetic reference systems adopted by different organizations. The computation geodetic coordinate from the Cartesian coordinate is slightly involved with additional knowledge (see Chap. 3).

Except for statistical errors in the associated station coordinates, the relation among different systems may be expressed by an infinitesimal seven-parameter transformation. This is known as Helmert transformation and accounts for an offset in the adopted origin ($T_1, T_2. T_3$), a scale difference (D) and a misalignment of the coordinates axes (R_1, R_2, R_3). Table 2.6 summarizes the Helmert transformation parameters for global geodetic system.

Fig. 2.20 Station coordinate frame

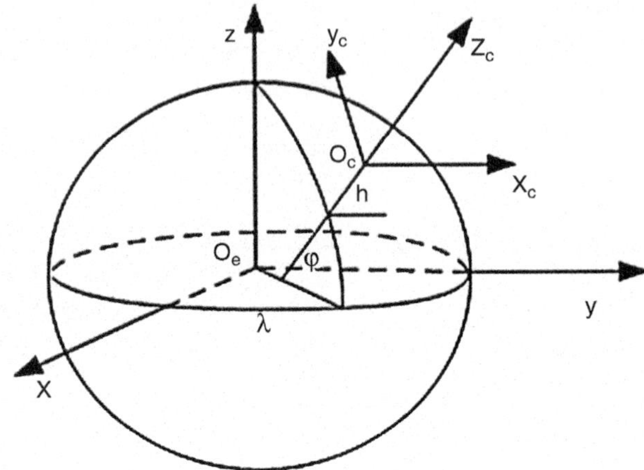

Given the coordinates in the original system, the coordinates in another geodetic system may be expressed as

$$\mathbf{r}' = \begin{pmatrix} T_1 \\ T_2 \\ T_3 \end{pmatrix} + \left(\mathbf{I}_{3\times3} + \begin{pmatrix} +D & -R_3 & +R_2 \\ +R_3 & +D & -R_1 \\ -R_2 & +R_1 & +D \end{pmatrix} \right) \mathbf{r} \tag{2.40}$$

There is a slight offset to position a satellite with the Earth-fixed coordinates relative to different geodetic frames.

2.4.8 Local Tangential Coordinate System

A natural coordinate system for describing the motion of a satellite with respect to an observer or ground station is the topocentric or local tangent coordinate system. For a given point on the Earth, this may be the center of antenna and is aligned with the local horizontal plane, with which that is tangential to the surface of the Earth at that point. And three orthogonal unit vectors are pointing to the east, north, and zenith direction, respectively, which are employed to define the reference axes of the local tangent coordinate system for a given station. Figure 2.20 illustrates the local tangent coordinate defined with the Earth-fixed coordinate. The origin is defined with the Greenwich meridian cylindrical coordinates, which are the longitude λ, the latitude φ, and the altitude h.

Where the zenith $\mathbf{z}_c$, east $\mathbf{x}_c$, and north $\mathbf{y}_c$ directions in this point are given by

$$\mathbf{z}_c = \begin{pmatrix} \cos\varphi\cos\lambda \\ \cos\varphi\sin\lambda \\ \sin\varphi \end{pmatrix}, \mathbf{x}_c = \frac{\mathbf{z}\times\mathbf{z}_c}{\|\mathbf{z}\times\mathbf{z}_c\|} = \begin{pmatrix} -\sin\lambda \\ \cos\lambda \\ 0 \end{pmatrix}, \mathbf{y}_c = \frac{\mathbf{z}_c\times\mathbf{x}_c}{\|\mathbf{z}_c\times\mathbf{x}_c\|} = \begin{pmatrix} -\sin\varphi\cos\lambda \\ -\sin\varphi\sin\lambda \\ \cos\varphi \end{pmatrix}$$

With these three directions, define the orthogonal transformation matrix from the local tangential coordinate to the Earth-centered-fixed frame (ECF) as

$$\mathbf{M}_{\mathrm{TTC}} = \left[\mathbf{x}_c, \mathbf{y}_c, \mathbf{z}_c\right] \tag{2.41}$$

The corresponding coordinate of a ground station in ECF, according to a chosen reference ellipsoid, is

$$\mathbf{R} = \begin{bmatrix} X \\ Y \\ Z \end{bmatrix} = \begin{bmatrix} G_1 \cos\lambda \\ G_1 \sin\lambda \\ G_2 \end{bmatrix} \tag{2.42}$$

where

$$G_1 = \left(\frac{R_\oplus}{\sqrt{1 - e_\oplus^2 \sin^2\varphi}} + h\right) \cdot \cos\varphi, \tag{2.43}$$

$$G_2 = \left(\frac{R_\oplus(1 - e_\oplus^2)}{\sqrt{1 - e_\oplus^2 \sin^2\varphi}} + h\right) \cdot \sin\varphi \tag{2.44}$$

Here, $R_\oplus$ and $e_\oplus^2$ are parameters related to the reference ellipsoid of the Earth. For example, if take the WGS84 as a reference ellipsoid, then

$$R_\oplus = 6378137.0\,\mathrm{m}, \quad e_\oplus^2 = 0.00669437999014.$$

Suppose there is a satellite with the position vector $\mathbf{r}_{\mathrm{ECF}}$ and the velocity vector $\dot{\mathbf{r}}_{\mathrm{ECF}}$ in the J2000.0 reference frame and their projection in the TTC reference frame are $\mathbf{r}_{\mathrm{TTC}}$ and $\dot{\mathbf{r}}_{\mathrm{TTC}}$, respectively, and then the coordinate transformation expressions satisfy

$$\mathbf{r}_{\mathrm{TTC}} = \mathbf{M}_{\mathrm{TTC}}^T(\mathbf{r}_{\mathrm{ECF}} - \mathbf{R}) \tag{2.45}$$

$$\dot{\mathbf{r}}_{\mathrm{TTC}} = \mathbf{M}_{\mathrm{TTC}}^{\mathrm{T}} \cdot \dot{\mathbf{r}}_{\mathrm{ECF}} \tag{2.46}$$

For the description of antenna tracking and pointing directions, the Cartesian coordinates are commonly supplemented by the topocentric distance, line-of-sight velocity, azimuth, and elevation angles. The azimuth gives the angle between the projection of the station satellite vector on the horizontal plane and the north direction. It is counted positively from the north to the east as illustrated in Fig. 2.21. The elevation E, on the other hand, describes the angle between the topocentric satellite vector and the horizontal plane.

Suppose there is a satellite with the position projection $\mathbf{r}_{\mathrm{TTC}} = (x_c, y_c, z_c)^T$ and velocity vector $\dot{\mathbf{r}}_{\mathrm{TTC}} = (\dot{x}_c, \dot{y}_c, \dot{z}_c)^T$ in the station coordinate frame. The

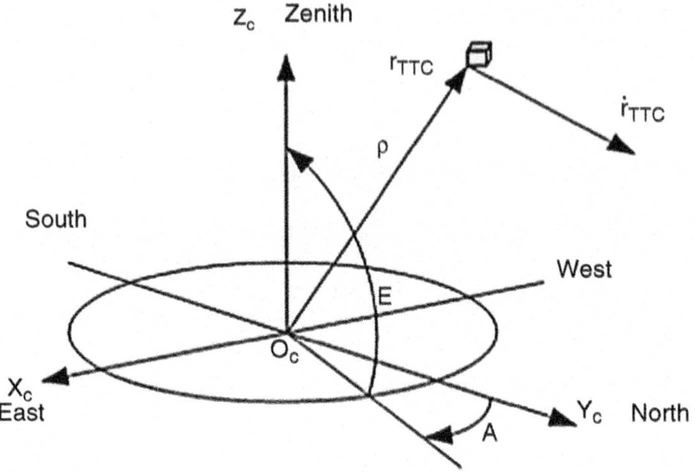

Fig. 2.21 Measurements in station coordinate frame

line-of-sight tracking distance and antenna pointing direction are based on the conversion below:

$$\rho = \|\mathbf{r}_{\mathrm{TTC}}\| = \sqrt{x_c^2 + y_c^2 + z_c^2} \tag{2.47}$$

$$\dot{\rho} = \frac{1}{\rho}(\mathbf{r}_{\mathrm{TTC}} \cdot \dot{\mathbf{r}}_{\mathrm{TTC}}) = \frac{1}{\rho}(x_c\dot{x}_c + y_c\dot{y}_c + x_c\dot{z}_c) \tag{2.48}$$

The azimuth and elevation angles satisfy

$$A = \arctan\left(\frac{x_c}{y_c}\right) \in [0, 2\pi] \tag{2.49}$$

$$E = \arcsin\left(\frac{z_c}{\rho}\right) \in \left[-\frac{\pi}{2}, \frac{\pi}{2}\right] \tag{2.50}$$

Suppose there is a ground station with its cylindrical coordinate reference in the WGS84 reference ellipsoid.

$$\lambda = 30.0°, \varphi = 34.0°, h = 1000.0\,\mathrm{m}$$

The corresponding coordinate of the origin of ground station in ECF, according to (2.42) is

$$\mathbf{R} = \begin{pmatrix} 4584814.154552 \\ 2467043.6863154 \\ 3547005.7566842 \end{pmatrix} (\mathrm{m})$$

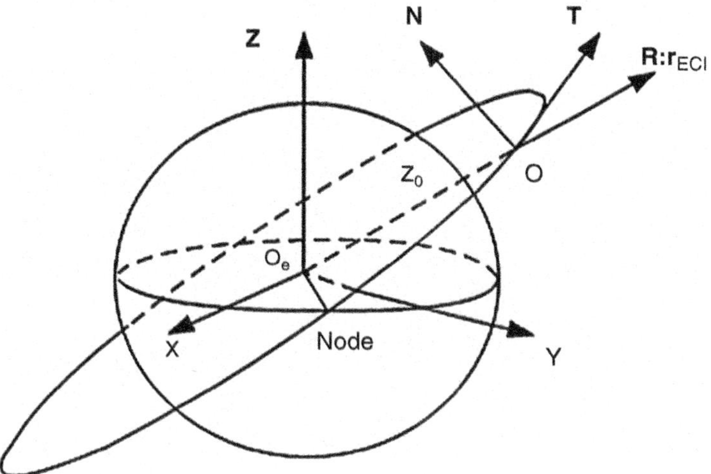

Fig. 2.22 Satellite RTN coordinate system

The satellite with the position vector $\mathbf{r}_{\mathrm{ECI}}$ and the velocity vector $\dot{\mathbf{r}}_{\mathrm{ECI}}$ in the J2000.0 reference frame can be projected as $\mathbf{r}_{\mathrm{TTC}}$, $\dot{\mathbf{r}}_{\mathrm{TTC}}$ in TTC reference frame at the given epoch 12 h in UTC, May 1, 2006, according to relations (2.41, 2.42, 2.43, 2.44, 2.45, and 2.46).

$$\mathbf{r}_{\mathrm{TTC}} = \begin{pmatrix} -33917440.104868 \\ -13937949.904587 \\ 14427971.152700 \end{pmatrix} (\mathrm{m}), \quad \dot{\mathbf{r}}_{\mathrm{TTC}} = \begin{pmatrix} -0.07996149 \\ -0.33249759 \\ -0.12656709 \end{pmatrix} (\mathrm{m/s})$$

The corresponding line-of-sight tracking distance and antenna pointing directions are calculated by relation (2.47, 2.48, 2.49, and 2.50).

$$\rho = 39405907.455523(\mathrm{m}), A = 247.660399°, E = 21.477588° \dot{\rho} = 0.1400886(\mathrm{m/s})$$

2.4.9 Orbit RTN Coordinate System

The orbit radial/tangential/normal coordinate system is commonly abbreviated as RTN, upon which the perturbation forces imposed on satellite are projected and by which the famous Gauss Lagrange equations are established and the variations of the orbit elements are expressed as a function of the three components of the perturbation acceleration in the orbit radial, tangential, and normal reference frame.

The coordinate takes the mass center of the satellite as origin. The primary direction points along the radius of satellite, and it takes the orbit plane as the reference plane as illustrated in Fig. 2.22.

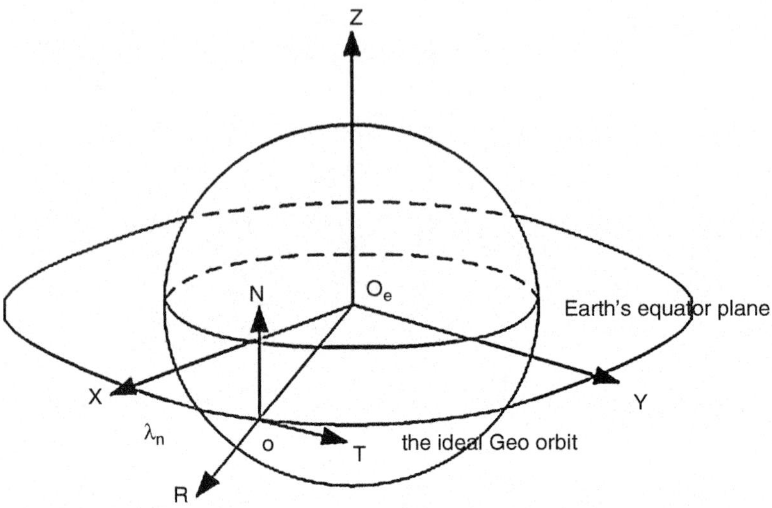

Fig. 2.23 Nominal radial, tangential, and normal reference frames

Suppose there is a satellite with the position vector $\mathbf{r}_{\mathrm{ECI}}$ and the velocity vector $\dot{\mathbf{r}}_{\mathrm{ECI}}$ in the J2000.0 reference frame, and then the radial, the tangential, and the normal can be determined by the expression below.

$$\mathbf{R} = \frac{\mathbf{r}_{\mathrm{ECI}}}{\|\mathbf{r}_{\mathrm{ECI}}\|}, \mathbf{T} = \frac{(\mathbf{r}_{\mathrm{ECI}} \times \dot{\mathbf{r}}_{\mathrm{ECI}}) \times \mathbf{r}_{\mathrm{ECI}}}{\|(\mathbf{r}_{\mathrm{ECI}} \times \dot{\mathbf{r}}_{\mathrm{ECI}}) \times \mathbf{r}_{\mathrm{ECI}}\|}, \mathbf{N} = \frac{(\mathbf{r}_{\mathrm{ECI}} \times \dot{\mathbf{r}}_{\mathrm{ECI}})}{\|(\mathbf{r}_{\mathrm{ECI}} \times \dot{\mathbf{r}}_{\mathrm{ECI}})\|} \tag{2.51}$$

With these three directions define the orthogonal transformation matrix from the orbit RNT to the ECI as

$$\mathbf{M}_{\mathrm{RTN}} = [\mathbf{R}, \mathbf{T}, \mathbf{N}] \tag{2.52}$$

In particular, the geostationary satellite should reside at the nominal longitude λ_n, and keep steps along orbit with the rotation of the Earth. In order to express the motion of a geostationary satellite relative to the nominal location, the nominal point radial, tangential, and normal coordinates may be deployed as illustrated in Fig. 2.23, in which the actual geostationary satellite motion near the nominal point can be projected in the nominal radial, tangential, and normal reference frames.

2.4.10 *Satellite-Fixed Orbit Coordinate System*

The orbit coordinate system $O - \mathbf{x}_o\mathbf{y}_o\mathbf{z}_o$, with which the attitude of satellite is described and stabilized, takes the center of satellite as the origin. The $O\mathbf{z}_o$ is from the satellite to the center of the Earth, which is commonly abbreviated to Nadir;

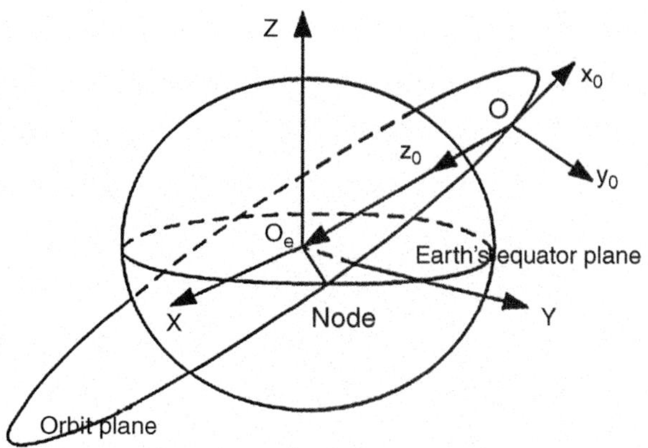

Fig. 2.24 The orbit coordinate system

the $O\mathbf{y}_o$ points along the negative direction of the orbit angular momentum; the $O\mathbf{x}_o$ lies in the orbit plane pointing to the motion direction, and they form the orthogonal frame as illustrated in Fig. 2.24.

Suppose there is a satellite with the position vector $\mathbf{r}_{\mathrm{ECI}}$ and the velocity vector $\dot{\mathbf{r}}_{\mathrm{ECI}}$ in the J2000.0 reference frame, and then the orbit coordinate system can be determined by the expression below.

$$\mathbf{x}_o = \frac{\mathbf{r}_{\mathrm{ECI}} \times (\dot{\mathbf{r}}_{\mathrm{ECI}} \times \mathbf{r}_{\mathrm{ECI}})}{\|\mathbf{r}_{\mathrm{ECI}} \times (\dot{\mathbf{r}}_{\mathrm{ECI}} \times \mathbf{r}_{\mathrm{ECI}})\|}, \mathbf{y}_o = \frac{(\dot{\mathbf{r}}_{\mathrm{ECI}} \times \mathbf{r}_{\mathrm{ECI}})}{\|(\dot{\mathbf{r}}_{\mathrm{ECI}} \times \mathbf{r}_{\mathrm{ECI}})\|}, \mathbf{z}_o = -\frac{\mathbf{r}_{\mathrm{ECI}}}{\|\mathbf{r}_{\mathrm{ECI}}\|} \tag{2.53}$$

With these three directions, define the orthogonal transformation matrix from the orbit coordinate frame to the ECI frame as

$$\mathbf{M}_{xyz} = \left[\mathbf{x}_o, \mathbf{y}_o, \mathbf{z}_o\right] \tag{2.54}$$

For three-axis-stabilized satellite, the attitude control system often uses the following notation for attitude control: the $O\mathbf{x}_o$-axis is the roll axis, the $O\mathbf{y}_o$-axis is the pitch axis, and the $O\mathbf{z}_o$-axis is the yaw axis.

2.4.11 Satellite-Fixed East/South/Down Coordinate Frame

Another satellite orbit-oriented frame is the satellite-fixed East/South/Down (ESD) coordinate frame, which is usually used as the frame to describe the attitude of the geostationary satellite. The ESD coordinate system takes the center of satellite as the origin and the local horizontal plane as the primary plane. The $O\mathbf{x}_{\mathrm{E}}$-axis lies on the local horizontal plane and points eastward, the $O\mathbf{y}_{\mathrm{S}}$-axis also lies on the primary plane and points southward, and the $O\mathbf{z}_{\mathrm{D}}$-axis points to the nadir.

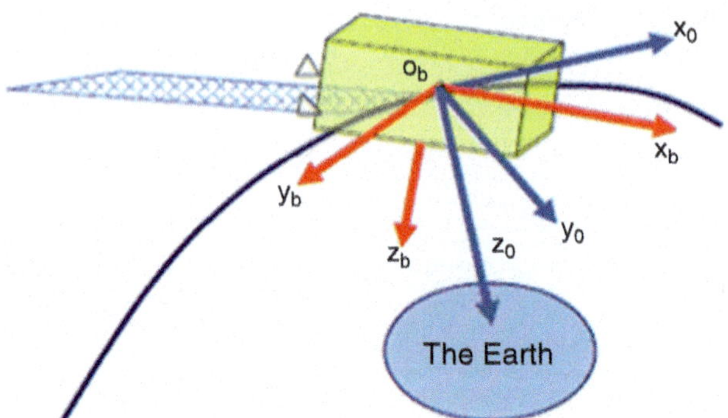

Fig. 2.25 Spacecraft body frame with the three-axis attitude

Suppose there is a satellite with the position vector $\mathbf{r}_{\text{ECI}}$ and the velocity vector $\dot{\mathbf{r}}_{\text{ECI}}$ in the J2000.0 reference frame, and then the ESD frame can be determined by the expression below.

$$\mathbf{x}_{\text{E}} = \frac{\mathbf{z} \times \mathbf{r}_{\text{ECI}}}{\|\mathbf{z} \times \mathbf{r}_{\text{ECI}}\|}, \mathbf{y}_{\text{S}} = \frac{(\mathbf{z} \times \mathbf{r}_{\text{ECI}}) \times \mathbf{r}_{\text{ECI}}}{\|(\mathbf{z} \times \mathbf{r}_{\text{ECI}}) \times \mathbf{r}_{\text{ECI}}\|}, \mathbf{z}_{\text{D}} = -\frac{\mathbf{r}_{\text{ECI}}}{\|\mathbf{r}_{\text{ECI}}\|} \tag{2.55}$$

Here, $\mathbf{z} = (0 \quad 0 \quad 1)^T$ indicates the normal direction of the equator plane. With these three directions, define the orthogonal transformation matrix from the East/South/Down coordinate frame to the ECI frame as

$$\mathbf{M}_{\text{ESD}} = [\mathbf{x}_{\text{E}}, \mathbf{y}_{\text{S}}, \mathbf{z}_{\text{D}}] \tag{2.56}$$

For three-axis-stabilized satellite operated by many organizations, the attitude control system often uses the following notation for attitude control: the $O\mathbf{x}_{\text{E}}$-axis is the roll axis, the $O\mathbf{y}_{\text{S}}$-axis is the pitch axis, and the $O\mathbf{z}_{\text{D}}$-axis is the yaw axis.

2.4.12 *Satellite Body Coordinate System*

The satellite body coordinate system is aligned to the satellite's principal axes. Three axes of this system relative to a nominal reference frame define the attitude of satellite. It takes the mass center of satellite as the origin of frame. The $o_b\mathbf{x}_{\text{b}}$-axis points to the head of satellite along the vertical symmetry axis. The $o_b\mathbf{z}_{\text{b}}$-axis lies in the vertical symmetry plane of satellite and is perpendicular to the vertical symmetry axis. The $o_b\mathbf{y}_{\text{b}}$-axis is the normal direction of the vertical symmetry plane of satellite. The attitude defined in relation to a reference frame which depends on the pointing mode is changeable with the mission designation. The following reference frames are commonly used as the nominal reference: the orbit coordinate system, the orbit East/South/Down coordinate system, and the Earth-centered inertial coordinate system. Figure 2.25 illustrates the satellite body coordinate system ($o_b - \mathbf{x}_{\text{b}}\mathbf{y}_{\text{b}}\mathbf{z}_{\text{b}}$) and the orbit coordinate frame ($o_b - \mathbf{x}_{\text{o}}\mathbf{y}_{\text{o}}\mathbf{z}_{\text{o}}$).

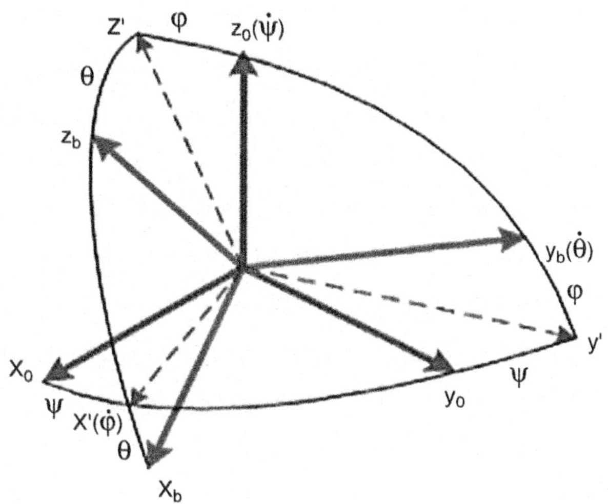

Fig. 2.26 The yaw-roll-pitch rotation presentation

Satellite attitude can be described by placing the satellite body system within a reference frame and then following its evolution with time. According to Euler's theory, any rotation about a point can be represented by a rotation about a dedicated axis in space. The attitude can be described through any of the following representations, such as rotation matrix, Euler angles, and the quaternion. Each of presentation has both advantages and disadvantages. In this section, the attitude presented for the three-axis-stabilized satellites is in terms of two different rotation sequences. They are the yaw-roll-pitch rotation presentation and the pitch-roll-yaw rotation presentation. It is important to realize that the rotation matrix doesn't rely on the rotation presentation, but only the Euler angle definition depends on the rotation sequence. With three Euler angles, there is in existence eight different rotation sequences. The choice of the dedicated sequence depends on the mission requirements.

2.4.12.1 The Yaw-Roll-Pitch Rotation Presentation

For the first rotation of yaw angle ψ, the $\mathbf{x_e}$-axis scans with the yaw axis $\mathbf{z_o}$ rotation anticlockwise until the $\mathbf{x_o}$-axis intersects the plane $\mathbf{x_b z_b}$. For the second rotation of roll angle φ, it takes the roll axis $\mathbf{x}'$ as the rotation axis and rotates anticlockwise until the $\mathbf{y}'$-axis is coincident with the $\mathbf{y_b}$-axis. For the third rotation of pitch angle θ, it takes the pitch axis $\mathbf{y_o}$, which now is coincident with the body fixed axis $\mathbf{y_b}$, as the rotation axis, and rotates anticlockwise until the $\mathbf{z}'$-axis is coincident with the $\mathbf{z_b}$. See Fig. 2.26.

The attitude transformation matrix corresponding to the rotation sequence is

$$\mathbf{M}_{3\_1\_2} = \mathbf{M}_{\mathbf{y}}[\theta] \cdot \mathbf{M}_{\mathbf{x}}[\varphi] \cdot \mathbf{M}_{\mathbf{z}}[\psi]$$
$$\begin{bmatrix} \cos\theta\cos\psi - \sin\theta\sin\varphi\sin\psi & \cos\theta\sin\psi + \sin\theta\sin\varphi\cos\psi & -\sin\theta\cos\varphi \\ -\cos\varphi\sin\psi & \cos\varphi\cos\psi & \sin\varphi \\ \sin\theta\cos\psi + \cos\theta\sin\varphi\sin\psi & \sin\theta\sin\psi - \cos\theta\sin\varphi\cos\psi & \cos\theta\cos\varphi \end{bmatrix} \tag{2.57}$$

and the quaternion denotation is

$$\mathbf{M}_{3-1-2} = \mathbf{M}[q_\theta] \cdot \mathbf{M}[q_\varphi] \cdot \mathbf{M}[q_\psi] \tag{2.58}$$

here

$$\begin{aligned} \mathbf{q}_\psi &= \mathbf{q}(\mathbf{e}_\mathbf{z}, \psi) = \left[0, 0, \sin\frac{\psi}{2}, \cos\frac{\psi}{2}\right]^{\mathrm{T}} \\ \mathbf{q}_\varphi &= \mathbf{q}(\mathbf{e}_\mathbf{x}, \varphi) = \left[\sin\frac{\varphi}{2}, 0, 0, \cos\frac{\varphi}{2}\right]^{\mathrm{T}} \\ \mathbf{q}_\theta &= \mathbf{q}(\mathbf{e}_\mathbf{y}, \theta) = \left[0, \sin\frac{\theta}{2}, 0, \cos\frac{\theta}{2}\right]^{\mathrm{T}} \end{aligned} \tag{2.59}$$

When the attitude transformation matrix is represented with the attitude quaternion $\mathbf{q} = [q_0, q_1, q_2, q_3]$, it is

$$\mathbf{M}[\mathbf{q}] = \begin{pmatrix} q_1^2 - q_2^2 - q_3^2 + q_0^2 & 2(q_1q_2 - q_3q_0) & 2(q_1q_3 + q_2q_0) \\ 2(q_1q_2 + q_3q_0) & -q_1^2 + q_2^2 - q_3^2 + q_0^2 & 2(q_2q_3 - q_1q_0) \\ 2(q_1q_3 - q_2q_0) & 2(q_2q_3 + q_1q_0) & -q_1^2 - q_2^2 + q_3^2 + q_0^2 \end{pmatrix} \tag{2.60}$$

The relation between the Euler parameters and the quaternion according to this rotation sequence is listed in the following conversions:

$$\psi = \arctan\left(\frac{2(q_3q_4 - q_1q_2)}{q_4^2 - q_1^2 + q_2^2 - q_3^2}\right) \tag{2.61}$$

$$\varphi = \arcsin(2(q_2q_3 + q_1q_4)) \tag{2.62}$$

$$\theta = \arctan\left(\frac{2(q_2q_4 - q_1q_3)}{q_4^2 - q_1^2 - q_2^2 + q_3^2}\right) \tag{2.63}$$

On the contrary, the conversions from the Euler parameters to the quaternion are as follows:

$$\mathbf{q}=\begin{bmatrix} q_1 \\ q_2 \\ q_3 \\ q_4 \end{bmatrix}=\mathbf{Q}(\mathbf{q}_\psi)\cdot\mathbf{Q}(\mathbf{q}_\varphi)\cdot\mathbf{q}_\theta=\begin{bmatrix} \sin\frac{\psi}{2}\cos\frac{\varphi}{2}\sin\frac{\theta}{2}+\cos\frac{\psi}{2}\sin\frac{\varphi}{2}\cos\frac{\theta}{2} \\ \cos\frac{\psi}{2}\cos\frac{\varphi}{2}\sin\frac{\theta}{2}-\sin\frac{\psi}{2}\sin\frac{\varphi}{2}\cos\frac{\theta}{2} \\ -\cos\frac{\psi}{2}\sin\frac{\varphi}{2}\sin\frac{\theta}{2}+\sin\frac{\psi}{2}\cos\frac{\varphi}{2}\cos\frac{\theta}{2} \\ \sin\frac{\psi}{2}\sin\frac{\varphi}{2}\sin\frac{\theta}{2}+\cos\frac{\psi}{2}\cos\frac{\varphi}{2}\cos\frac{\theta}{2} \end{bmatrix} \tag{2.64}$$

The quaternion, as a parameterization of the attitude, is more compact than the Euler angles to carry out the computer calculation, but the Euler angles have the advantage to carry out the physical definitions. The attitude rotation motion equation according to yaw-roll-pitch sequence follows the expression listed below.

$$\mathbf{M_y}[\theta]\cdot\{\dot{\theta}\mathbf{e_y}+\mathbf{M_x}[\varphi]\cdot[\dot{\varphi}\mathbf{e_x}+\mathbf{M_z}[\psi]\cdot\dot{\psi}\mathbf{e_z}]\}=\begin{bmatrix} w_x \\ w_y \\ w_z \end{bmatrix} \tag{2.65}$$

where the rotation rate in each axis is expressed with the vector $\boldsymbol{\omega}=(\omega_x,\omega_y,\omega_z)^{\mathrm{T}}$ to carry out some reckoning. The Euler angles following the motion equation with this rotation sequence are listed below.

$$\begin{bmatrix} \dot{\psi} \\ \dot{\varphi} \\ \dot{\theta} \end{bmatrix}=\frac{1}{\cos\varphi}\begin{bmatrix} -\sin\theta & 0 & \cos\theta \\ \cos\theta\cos\varphi & 0 & \sin\theta\cos\varphi \\ \sin\theta\sin\varphi & \cos\varphi & -\cos\theta\sin\varphi \end{bmatrix}\cdot\begin{bmatrix} w_x \\ w_y \\ w_z \end{bmatrix} \tag{2.66}$$

and the corresponding attitude motion equation represented by the quaternion is

$$\begin{bmatrix} \dot{q}_1 \\ \dot{q}_2 \\ \dot{q}_3 \\ \dot{q}_4 \end{bmatrix}=\frac{1}{2}\begin{bmatrix} 0 & w_z & -w_y & w_x \\ -w_z & 0 & w_x & w_y \\ w_y & -w_x & 0 & w_z \\ -w_x & -w_y & -w_z & 0 \end{bmatrix}\cdot\begin{bmatrix} q_1 \\ q_2 \\ q_3 \\ q_4 \end{bmatrix} \tag{2.67}$$

2.4.12.2 The Pitch-Roll-Yaw Rotation Presentation

For the first rotation of pitch angle θ, it takes the pitch axis $\mathbf{y_o}$ as the spinning axis and rotates anticlockwise until the axis $\mathbf{z_o}$ intersects with the plane $\mathbf{y_o z_b}$. For the

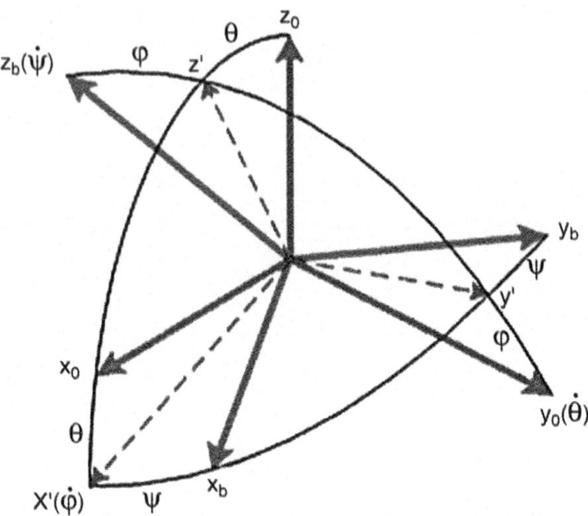

Fig. 2.27 The pitch-roll-yaw rotation presentation

second rotation of roll angle φ, it takes the roll axis $\mathbf{x}'$ as the spinning axis and rotates anticlockwise until the axis $\mathbf{y_o}$ intersects with the plane $\mathbf{x_b y_b}$. For the third rotation of yaw angle ψ, it takes the yaw axis $\mathbf{z_b}$ and rotates anticlockwise until the axis $\mathbf{y}'$ coincident with the $\mathbf{y_b}$. See Fig. 2.27.

The attitude transformation matrix corresponding to the rotation sequence is

$$\mathbf{M}_{2-1-3} = \mathbf{M_z}[\psi] \cdot \mathbf{M_x}[\varphi] \cdot \mathbf{M_y}[\theta] =$$
$$\begin{bmatrix} \cos\psi\cos\theta + \sin\psi\sin\varphi\sin\theta & \sin\psi\cos\varphi & -\cos\psi\sin\theta + \sin\psi\sin\varphi\cos\theta \\ -\sin\psi\cos\theta + \cos\psi\sin\varphi\sin\theta & \cos\psi\cos\varphi & \sin\psi\sin\theta + \cos\psi\sin\varphi\cos\theta \\ \cos\varphi\sin\theta & -\sin\varphi & \cos\varphi\cos\theta \end{bmatrix}$$

and the quaternion denotation is

$$\mathbf{M}_{2-1-3} = \mathbf{M}\left[\mathbf{q}_\psi\right] \cdot \mathbf{M}\left[\mathbf{q}_\varphi\right] \cdot \mathbf{M}[\mathbf{q}_\theta] \tag{2.68}$$

Here,

$$\begin{aligned} \mathbf{q}_\psi &= \mathbf{q}(\mathbf{e_z}, \psi) = \left[0, 0, \sin\frac{\psi}{2}, \cos\frac{\psi}{2}\right]^T \\ \mathbf{q}_\varphi &= \mathbf{q}(\mathbf{e_x}, \varphi) = \left[\sin\frac{\varphi}{2}, 0, 0, \cos\frac{\varphi}{2}\right]^T \\ \mathbf{q}_\theta &= \mathbf{q}\left(\mathbf{e_y}, \theta\right) = \left[0, \sin\frac{\theta}{2}, 0, \cos\frac{\theta}{2}\right]^{\mathrm{T}} \end{aligned} \tag{2.69}$$

When the attitude transformation matrix is represented with the attitude quaternion $\mathbf{q}=[q_0, q_1, q_2, q_3]$, it is

$$\mathbf{M}[\mathbf{q}] = \begin{pmatrix} q_1^2 - q_2^2 - q_3^2 + q_0^2 & 2(q_1q_2 - q_3q_0) & 2(q_1q_3 + q_2q_0) \\ 2(q_1q_2 + q_3q_0) & -q_1^2 + q_2^2 - q_3^2 + q_0^2 & 2(q_2q_3 - q_1q_0) \\ 2(q_1q_3 - q_2q_0) & 2(q_2q_3 + q_1q_0) & -q_1^2 - q_2^2 + q_3^2 + q_0^2 \end{pmatrix} \tag{2.70}$$

The relation between the Euler parameters and the quaternion according to this rotation sequence is listed in the following conversions:

$$\theta = \arctan\left(\frac{2(q_1q_3 + q_2q_4)}{q_4^2 - q_1^2 - q_2^2 + q_3^2}\right) \tag{2.71}$$

$$\varphi = \arcsin(2(q_1q_4 - q_2q_3)) \tag{2.72}$$

$$\psi = \arctan\left(\frac{2(q_1q_2 + q_3q_4)}{q_4^2 - q_1^2 + q_2^2 - q_3^2}\right) \tag{2.73}$$

On the contrary, the conversions from the Euler parameters to the quaternion are as follows:

$$\mathbf{q} = \begin{bmatrix} q_1 \\ q_2 \\ q_3 \\ q_4 \end{bmatrix} = \mathbf{Q}(\mathbf{q}_\theta) \cdot \mathbf{Q}(\mathbf{q}_\varphi) \cdot \mathbf{q}_\psi = \begin{bmatrix} -\sin\frac{\theta}{2}\cos\frac{\varphi}{2}\sin\frac{\psi}{2} + \cos\frac{\theta}{2}\sin\frac{\varphi}{2}\cos\frac{\psi}{2} \\ \cos\frac{\theta}{2}\sin\frac{\varphi}{2}\sin\frac{\psi}{2} + \sin\frac{\theta}{2}\cos\frac{\varphi}{2}\cos\frac{\psi}{2} \\ \cos\frac{\theta}{2}\cos\frac{\varphi}{2}\sin\frac{\psi}{2} + \sin\frac{\theta}{2}\sin\frac{\varphi}{2}\cos\frac{\psi}{2} \\ -\sin\frac{\theta}{2}\sin\frac{\varphi}{2}\sin\frac{\psi}{2} + \cos\frac{\theta}{2}\cos\frac{\varphi}{2}\cos\frac{\psi}{2} \end{bmatrix} \tag{2.74}$$

The quaternion, as a parameterization of the attitude, are more compact than the Euler angles to carry out the computer calculation, but the Euler angles have the advantage to carry out the physical definitions. The attitude rotation motion equation according to yaw-roll-pitch sequence is

$$\mathbf{M}_\mathbf{z}[\psi] \cdot \{\dot{\psi}\mathbf{e}_\mathbf{z} + \mathbf{M}_\mathbf{x}[\varphi] \cdot [\dot{\varphi}\mathbf{e}_\mathbf{x} + \mathbf{M}_\mathbf{y}[\theta] \cdot \dot{\theta}\mathbf{e}_\mathbf{y}]\} = \begin{bmatrix} w_x \\ w_y \\ w_z \end{bmatrix} \tag{2.75}$$

where the rotation rate in each axis is expressed with the vector $\boldsymbol{\omega}=(\omega_x, \omega_y, \omega_z)^\mathrm{T}$ to carry out some reckoning. The Euler angles following the motion equation with this rotation sequence are listed below.

$$\begin{bmatrix} \dot{\theta} \\ \dot{\varphi} \\ \dot{\psi} \end{bmatrix} = \frac{1}{\cos\varphi} \begin{bmatrix} \sin\psi & \cos\psi & 0 \\ \cos\psi\cos\varphi & -\sin\psi\cos\varphi & 0 \\ \sin\psi\sin\varphi & \cos\psi\sin\varphi & \cos\varphi \end{bmatrix} \cdot \begin{bmatrix} \omega_x \\ \omega_y \\ \omega_z \end{bmatrix} \tag{2.76}$$

And the corresponding attitude motion equation represented with the quaternion is

$$\begin{bmatrix} \dot{q}_1 \\ \dot{q}_2 \\ \dot{q}_3 \\ \dot{q}_4 \end{bmatrix} = \frac{1}{2} \begin{bmatrix} 0 & \omega_z & -\omega_y & \omega_x \\ -\omega_z & 0 & \omega_x & \omega_y \\ \omega_y & -\omega_x & 0 & \omega_z \\ -\omega_x & -\omega_y & -\omega_z & 0 \end{bmatrix} \cdot \begin{bmatrix} q_1 \\ q_2 \\ q_3 \\ q_4 \end{bmatrix} \tag{2.77}$$

In general, the three-axis-stabilized satellite has few excursions relative to its nominal reference frame. In case of small Euler angle situation, we can treat $\sin(x) = x$ and $\cos(x) = 1$, so the attitude matrix can be specialized without reference to the rotation sequence.

$$\mathbf{M}_b = \begin{bmatrix} 1 & \psi & -\theta \\ -\psi & 1 & \varphi \\ \theta & -\varphi & 1 \end{bmatrix} \tag{2.78}$$

2.5 The Kepler Orbit

2.5.1 Kepler Orbit Elements

Supposed that an object is considered as a point mass, the only force taken into account is the inverse-of-square Newtonian attraction force, and the rounded celestial body is spherical uniform mass distributed. Under those conditions, the motion of the object in an inertial reference frame centered at the mass center of the celestial body is called the Kepler motion. Its trajectory follows the three famous Kepler laws and is depicted with six basic elements as illustrated in Figs. 2.28 and 2.29, which show the size, shape, and orientation of the dedicated trajectory or the orbit in line with the inertial reference frame.

a: semi-major axis of the orbit, with the unit of meter or kilometer.

e: eccentricity. There are three families of orbit motion: $e < 1$, the ellipse; $e = 1$, the parabola; and $e > 1$, the hyperbola.

i: inclination, with the unit of degree. If the inclination of an orbit satisfies $0 \leq i < 90°$, the direction of the motion is clockwise in terms of the rotation of the celestial body; if it satisfies $90° \leq i < 180°$, the direction of the motion is anti-clockwise, and the orbit is called retrograde orbit.

Ω: right ascension of the ascending node (RAAN), with the unit of degree. By inclination and RAAN, the orientation of orbit plane relative to inertial space is defined.

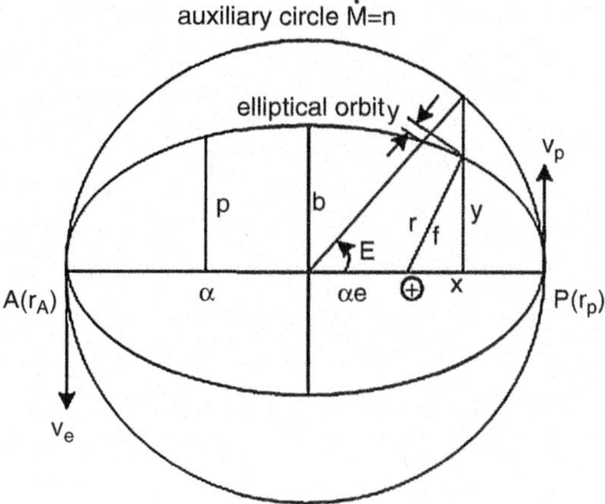

Fig. 2.28 The orbit plane elements of Kepler orbit

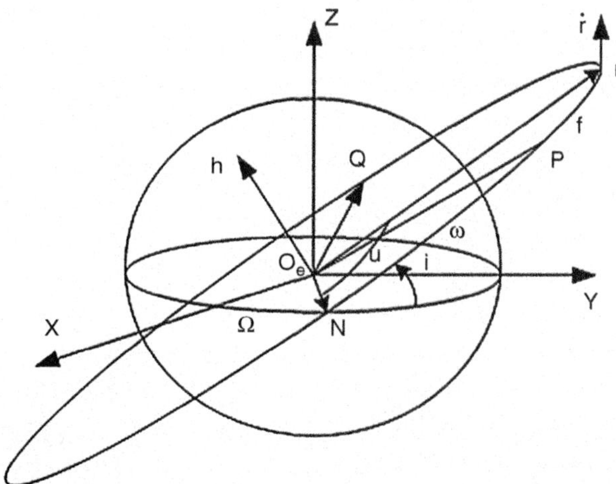

Fig. 2.29 Kepler orbit element in inertial space

ω: argument of perigee (AP), with the unit of degree. By argument of perigee and eccentricity, the shape of orbit relative to inertial space is defined.

M: mean anomaly defines the orbit position of the moving object along time.

Some transformation relations are listed in Table 2.7, which will be helpful for readers to carry out some calculations.

2.5.2 The Kepler Orbit with Motion States

The Kepler orbit elements represent the size, the shape, and the orientation of the dedicated trajectory or the orbit states in line with inertial reference frame. The convention relations from the motion states to the Kepler orbit elements are described below by taking the elliptical orbit as an example.

Table 2.7 The two-dimensional parameters of Kepler orbit

Argument	Definition	Transformation relation
r	Radius	$r=\frac{a(1-e^2)}{1+e\cos f}=\frac{p}{1+e\cos f}=a(1-e\cos E)$
$\dot{r}=\frac{dr}{dt}$	Radius velocity	$\dot{r}=\frac{d}{dt}r=\sqrt{\frac{\mu}{a(1-e^2)}}e\sin f$
v	Energy formula	$v=\sqrt{\frac{\mu}{a(1-e^2)}}\cdot\sqrt{\sin^2 f+(e+\cos f)^2}$ $=\sqrt{\mu\left(\frac{2}{r}-\frac{1}{a}\right)}$
γ	Flight path angle	$\sin\gamma=\frac{r}{v}\dot{f}=\frac{1+e\cos f}{\sqrt{1+e^2+2e\cos f}}$ $\cos\gamma=\frac{1}{v}\dot{r}=\frac{e\sin f}{\sqrt{1+e^2+2e\cos f}}$
r_p	Radius at perigee	$r_p=a(1-e)$
v_p	Velocity at perigee	$v_p=\sqrt{\frac{\mu}{a}}\cdot\sqrt{\frac{1+e}{1-e}}$
r_a	Radius at apogee	$r_a=a(1+e)$
v_a	Velocity at apogee	$v_a=\sqrt{\frac{\mu}{a}}\cdot\sqrt{\frac{1-e}{1+e}}$
E	Eccentric anomaly	$\sin E=\frac{\sqrt{1-e^2}\sin f}{1+e\cos f}$, $\cos E=\frac{e+\cos f}{1+e\cos f}$ $E_0=M$ $E_{i+1}=M+e\sin(E_i)$ (sequence iterative method) $E_0=M$ $E_{i+1}=E_i-\frac{E_i-e\sin E_i-M}{1-e\cos E_i}$ (Newton iterative method)
f	True anomaly	$\sin f=\frac{\sqrt{1-e^2}\sin E}{1-e\cos E}$, $\cos f=\frac{\cos E-e}{1-e\cos E}$
$\dot{f}=\frac{d}{dt}f$	Rate of true anomaly	$\dot{f}=\frac{1}{r}\sqrt{\frac{\mu}{a(1-e^2)}}(1+e\cos f)$
M	Kepler equation	$M=E-e\sin E$ $\dot{M}=n=\sqrt{\frac{\mu}{a^3}}$
$\frac{f}{2}$	Anomaly transformation	$\tan\left(\frac{f}{2}\right)=\left(\frac{1+e}{1-e}\right)^{\frac{1}{2}}\tan\left(\frac{E}{2}\right)$
p:	Semilatus rectum	$p=a(1-e^2)=b\sqrt{1-e^2}$
b	Semi-minor axis	$b=a\sqrt{1-e^2}$
n	Mean motion	$n=\frac{2\pi}{T}=\sqrt{\frac{\mu}{a^3}}$
T	Period	$T=2\pi\sqrt{\frac{a^3}{\mu}}$
u	Argument of the latitude	$u=\omega+f$
$\mathbf{h}$	Orbit momentum	$\mathbf{h}=\mathbf{r}\times\dot{\mathbf{r}},\ \mathbf{h}=\begin{pmatrix}h_x\\h_y\\h_z\end{pmatrix}=h\begin{pmatrix}\sin i\sin\Omega\\-\sin i\cos\Omega\\\cos i\end{pmatrix}$
h	Angular momentum	$h=r^2\dot{f}=\sqrt{p\mu}=\sqrt{\mu a(1-e^2)}$
$\mathbf{r}$	Position vector	$\mathbf{r}=r\cos f\cdot\mathbf{P}+r\sin f\cdot\mathbf{Q}$ $\mathbf{r}=a(\cos E-e)\mathbf{P}+a\sqrt{1-e^2}\sin E\cdot\mathbf{Q}$

(continued)

Table 2.7 (continued)

Argument	Definition	Transformation relation
$\dot{\mathbf{r}}$	Velocity vector	$\dot{\mathbf{r}} = \sqrt{\frac{\mu}{a(1-e^2)}}[-\sin f \cdot \mathbf{P} + (e+\cos f)\cdot \mathbf{Q}]$ $\dot{\mathbf{r}} = \sqrt{\frac{\mu a}{r^2}}\left(-\sin E \cdot \mathbf{P} + \sqrt{1-e^2}\cos E \cdot \mathbf{Q}\right)$
P	Perigee direction	$\mathbf{P} = \begin{pmatrix} +\cos\omega\cos\Omega - \sin\omega\cos i\sin\Omega \\ +\cos\omega\sin\Omega + \sin\omega\cos i\cos\Omega \\ +\sin\omega\sin i \end{pmatrix}$
Q	A direction from the center of attraction body perpendicular to the line with apogee to perigee point ($f = 90°$)	$\mathbf{Q} = \begin{pmatrix} -\sin\omega\cos\Omega - \cos\omega\cos i\sin\Omega \\ -\sin\omega\sin\Omega - \cos\omega\cos i\cos\Omega \\ +\cos\omega\sin i \end{pmatrix}$
N	A direction points to the ascension node ($u = 0°$)	$\mathbf{N} = \begin{pmatrix} \cos\Omega \\ \sin\Omega \\ 0 \end{pmatrix}$
e	Eccentricity vector (the magnitude is orbit eccentricity, the direction points to the perigee)	$\mathbf{e} = -\frac{\mathbf{r}}{r} + \frac{\dot{\mathbf{r}}\times(\mathbf{r}\times\dot{\mathbf{r}})}{\mu} = -\frac{\mathbf{r}}{r} + \frac{\dot{\mathbf{r}}\times\mathbf{h}}{\mu}$

μ: the Earth's gravity constant, $\mu = 398600.4415\ \mathrm{km}^3/\mathrm{s}^2$(JGM − 3)

2.5.2.1 The Conversions from Motion States to Kepler Orbit Elements

Suppose at a particular epoch, a satellite is of the position vector $\mathbf{r}$ and velocity $\dot{\mathbf{r}}$, respectively.

Semi-major axis

$$a = \left(\frac{2}{r} - \frac{v^2}{\mu}\right)^{-1}, r = \|\mathbf{r}\|, v = \|\dot{\mathbf{r}}\| \tag{2.79}$$

Eccentricity

$$e = \sqrt{1 - \frac{p}{a}}, p = \frac{h^2}{\mu}, h = \|\mathbf{r}\times\dot{\mathbf{r}}\| \tag{2.80}$$

Inclination

$$\mathbf{h} = (h_x, h_y, h_z)^{\mathrm{T}} = \mathbf{r}\times\dot{\mathbf{r}} \tag{2.81}$$

$$\sin(i) = \sqrt{\left(\frac{h_x}{h}\right)^2 + \left(\frac{h_y}{h}\right)^2}, \cos(i) = \left(\frac{h_z}{h}\right) \tag{2.82}$$

Right ascension of the ascending node (RAAN)

$$\sin(\Omega) = \frac{h_x}{\sqrt{h_x^2 + h_y^2}}, \ \cos(\Omega) = \frac{-h_y}{\sqrt{h_x^2 + h_y^2}} \tag{2.83}$$

Argument of perigee

$$\omega = \arccos\left(\frac{\mathbf{N} \cdot \mathbf{e}}{e}\right) \tag{2.84}$$

$$\mathbf{N} = \begin{pmatrix} \cos\Omega \\ \sin\Omega \\ 0 \end{pmatrix}, \vec{e} == -\frac{\mathbf{r}}{r} + \frac{\dot{\mathbf{r}} \times \mathbf{h}}{\mu} \tag{2.85}$$

Mean anomaly

$$M = E - e\sin E \tag{2.86}$$

$$\sin E = \frac{\sqrt{1-e^2}\sin f}{1 + e\cos f}, \ \cos E = \frac{e + \cos f}{1 + e\cos f} \tag{2.87}$$

Having determined the eccentric anomaly, the true anomaly is obtained from In case $e \neq 0$,

$$f = \arccos\left(\frac{\mathbf{r} \cdot \mathbf{e}}{re}\right) \tag{2.88}$$

In case $e = 0, i \neq 0$,

$$f = \arccos\left(\frac{\mathbf{r} \cdot \mathbf{N}}{r \cdot \|\mathbf{N}\|}\right) \tag{2.89}$$

In case $e = 0, i = 0$,

$$f = \arccos\left(\frac{r_x}{r}\right) \tag{2.90}$$

For example, an Earth-orbiting satellite located at

$$\mathbf{r} = (+20000.0, \ +2000.0, \ -6000.0)\text{km}$$

and moving at a velocity of

$$\dot{\mathbf{r}} = (+1.7, \ +2.5, \ -4.0)(\text{km/s})$$

The corresponding Kepler orbit elements are
Semi-major axis $a = 30983.175$(km)
Eccentricity $e = 0.6524539$
Inclination $i = 56.40432°$
RAAN $\Omega = 174.273153°$
Arg. of perigee $\omega = 96.637968°$
Mean anomaly $M = 27.847385°$

2.5.2.2 Conversion from Kepler Orbit Element to Motion States

Suppose the Kepler orbit elements of a satellite at a particular epoch are ($ae i\Omega\omega M$), and then the corresponding motion states at the inertial reference frame are

$$\mathbf{r} = a(\cos E - e) \cdot \mathbf{P} + a\sqrt{1 - e^2} \sin E \cdot \mathbf{Q} \tag{2.91}$$

$$\dot{\mathbf{r}} = \sqrt{\frac{\mu a}{r^2}} \left(- \sin E \cdot \mathbf{P} + \sqrt{1 - e^2} \cos E \cdot \mathbf{Q} \right) \tag{2.92}$$

Here,

$$\mathbf{P} = \begin{pmatrix} + \cos\omega \cos\Omega - \sin\omega \cos i \sin\Omega \\ + \cos\omega \sin\Omega + \sin\omega \cos i \cos\Omega \\ + \sin\omega \sin i \end{pmatrix} \tag{2.93}$$

$$\mathbf{Q} = \begin{pmatrix} - \sin\omega \cos\Omega - \cos\omega \cos i \sin\Omega \\ - \sin\omega \sin\Omega - \cos\omega \cos i \cos\Omega \\ + \cos\omega \sin i \end{pmatrix} \tag{2.94}$$

The eccentric anomaly is obtained by Newton iterative method from Kepler equation

$$E_0 = M, E_{i+1} = E_i - \frac{E_i - e \sin E_i - M}{1 - e \cos E_i} \tag{2.95}$$

For example, the Kepler orbit elements of an earth-orbiting satellite are listed below.

a (km)	e	i (°)	Ω (°)	ω (°)	M (°)
27905.0	0.003	54.75	60.0	90.0	50.0

The corresponding motion states are

$$\mathbf{r} = (-19607.649, -13410.453, 14539.490)\text{km}$$

$$\dot{\mathbf{r}} = (0.239, -2.94086, -2.37348)(\text{km/s})$$

It is well known that the Kepler six-element parameter is tightly related to the current motion states of the satellite with time and describes the size, shape, and

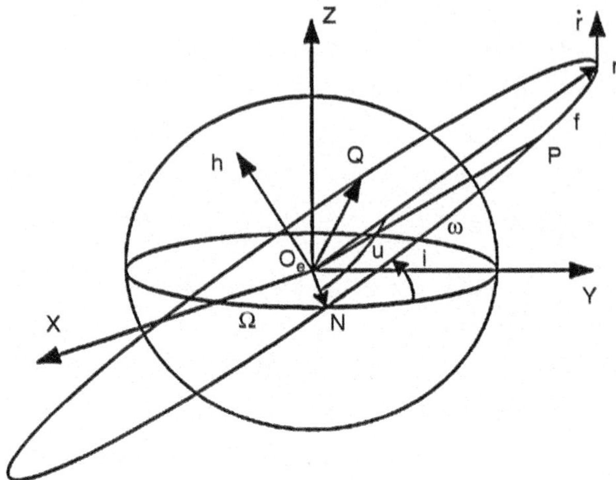

Fig. 2.30 Orbit in different celestial sphere-oriented frame

orientation of the dedicated trajectory or the orbit in line with the inertial reference frame at dedicated time. Owing to the advantages, we can figure out the imagination of satellite motion in the space with Kepler element and describe the motion states with position and velocity vectors. So, in general, the Kepler elements serve as the parameters to analyze the motion of satellite within perturbation situation.

2.5.3 *The Kepler Orbit with Reference System*

As discussed in the above section, the Kepler elements show differences in line with different coordinate frames. Usually, the J2000.0 ECI, the mean equator and equinox of epoch (Mean of Date) and the true equator and equinox of epoch (True of Date) are taken as the coordinate frames to depict the orbit motion of the Earth-round satellites. With the Earth-centered coordinate frame $O_e - \mathbf{XYZ}$ and $O_e - \mathbf{X'Y'Z'}$, a satellite will be of the same orbit in size and shape (a, e), but the orbit plane will orient to different directions owing to different reference plane relative to inertial space as Fig. 2.30 illustrates.

Suppose a satellite with the position and velocity vectors of $\mathbf{r}_{\mathrm{ECI}}$ and $\dot{\mathbf{r}}_{\mathrm{ECI}}$, respectively, the motion states of the satellite in the coordinate frames of the Mean of Date (mean equator and equinox of the epoch) and the True of Date (true equator and equinox of the epoch) follow the conventions.

$$\mathbf{r}_{\mathrm{MOD}} = \mathbf{P}(T) \cdot \mathbf{r}_{\mathrm{ECI}}, \dot{\mathbf{r}}_{\mathrm{MOD}} = \mathbf{P}(T) \cdot \dot{\mathbf{r}}_{\mathrm{ECI}}$$
$$\mathbf{r}_{\mathrm{TOD}} = \mathbf{N}(T) \cdot \mathbf{P}(T) \cdot \mathbf{r}_{\mathrm{ECI}}, \dot{\mathbf{r}}_{\mathrm{TOD}} = \mathbf{N}(T) \cdot \mathbf{P}(T) \cdot \dot{\mathbf{r}}_{\mathrm{ECI}}$$

For example, the Kepler orbit elements in different coordinate systems at epoch 12 h in UTC, January 1, 2006, are listed at Table 2.8.

Table 2.8 Kepler orbit parameters referenced different coordinate frame

Coordinate frame	Mean equator and equinox of J2000	Mean equator and equinox	True equator and equinox
Semi-major axis (km)	42167.064	42167.064	42167.064
Eccentricity	0.000065	0.000065	0.000065
Inclination (°)	0.047109 °	0.08152595 °	0.081774025 °
Right ascension of the ascending node (°)	286.361234 °	279.4312408 °	281.195305 °
Argument of perigee (°)	55.214915 °	62.2260147 °	60.461473 °
Mean anomaly (°)	34.064274 °	34.064273998 °	34.064274 °

Pay attention that only if the orbit parameters are projected on the true equator and equinox of the epoch can the relative motion of the satellite with the Earth motion be displayed clearly, so the orbit parameters of the geostationary satellite are always described according to the true equator and equinox of the epoch reference system.

2.5.4 The Station Keeping Element

An ideal geostationary orbit is a circle orbit whose orbit plane is identical to the equator of the Earth, which means that the inclination and the eccentricity would be equal to zero. If the inclination and eccentricity are almost zero, it is meaningless for geostationary orbit to measure the right ascension of ascending node and the argument of apogee with the Kepler orbit elements. For example, a geostationary satellite located at the longitude λ_n, its Kepler orbit parameters at epoch (T) look like

$$a = 42164.2 \text{ km}$$

$$e = 0$$

$$i = 0$$

$$\left.\begin{matrix}\Omega \\ \omega\end{matrix}\right\} \text{arbitrary within 0–360°.}$$

$$M = \lambda_n + \theta(T) - (\Omega + \omega)$$

where $\theta(T)$ is the mean sidereal angle at epoch T. For example, on 0 h in UTC, Jan. 1, 2009, the mean sidereal angle is 100.6615°. Suppose that the direction of apogee of orbit is oriented to the solar direction and the orbit plane is located with the right ascension of ascending node $\Omega = 270.0\,°$, at epoch T the right longitude of the Solar is 281.502°, so the orbit parameters may be as follows:

$$a = 42164.2 \text{ km}$$
$$e = 0$$
$$i = 0$$
$$\Omega = 270.0°$$
$$\omega = 11.502°$$
$$M = \lambda_n - 180.8405°$$

In reality, the ideal geostationary orbit only exists in mathematical conception, as well as the satellite residing at nominal longitude will not stay absolutely in the same position relative to the Earth because additional forces acting on it will change the shape of the orbit, the orientation of the orbit plane, and the spacecraft longitude. Anyway, the perfect geostationary orbit is useful as an approximate description of the real case. In order to avoid the singularity of the Kepler orbit parameters measuring the geostationary orbit, the station keeping elements are induced to depict the perturbation motion of geostationary satellite.

2.5.4.1 Semi-major Discrepancy (Δa) and Longitude Drift Rate (D)

The longitude drift rate is highly related to the semi-major discrepancy relative to the synchronous semi-major axis a_s, whose value is almost constant subjected to the non-spherical terms of the Earth's gravitation field.

$$\Delta a = a - a_s$$

According to the orbit mean rate of the satellite, the longitude drift rate follows

$$D = \left(\sqrt{\frac{\mu}{a^3}} - \sqrt{\frac{\mu}{a_s^3}}\right) \tag{2.96}$$

With function tailor expansion formula

$$\begin{aligned}\left(\frac{a_s}{x}\right)^{\frac{3}{2}} &= \left(\frac{a_s + (x - a_s)}{a_s}\right)^{-\frac{3}{2}} = \left(1 + \frac{(x - a_s)}{a_s}\right)^{-\frac{3}{2}} \\ &\cong 1 - \frac{3}{2}\left(\frac{x - a_s}{a_s}\right) + \frac{15}{8}\left(\frac{x - a_s}{a_s}\right)^2 - \frac{35}{16}\left(\frac{x - a_s}{a_s}\right)^3 + o(\cdot)\end{aligned}$$

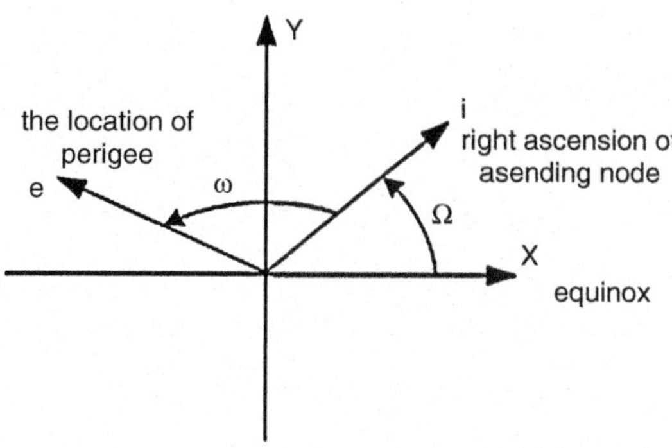

Fig. 2.31 The eccentricity and inclination vector

the daily longitude drift rate satisfies

$$
\begin{aligned}
D &= \left(\sqrt{\frac{\mu}{a^3}} - \sqrt{\frac{\mu}{a_s^3}}\right) \cdot \left(\frac{360^\circ}{86164.0}\right) \cdot 86400.0 \\
&\approx -\frac{3}{2} \cdot \frac{\Delta a}{a_s} \cdot 360.9860(^\circ/\text{day})
\end{aligned}
\tag{2.97}
$$

The drift rate is counted positively in the eastward direction. If $\Delta a = 0$, then $D = 0$. If $\Delta a > 0$, then $D < 0$, which means that the semi-major axis' increment results in that the satellite rotates slowly relative to the spin of the Earth. By contraries, the semi-major axis' decrement results in that the satellite runs faster than the spin of the Earth. One kilometer of semi-major discrepancy induces the longitude drift rate of 0.0128° per day.

2.5.4.2 Eccentricity Vector

As the eccentricity approaches zero, the perigee's location becomes indeterminable under the classical Kepler orbit parameters; in order to study the variation of eccentricity as well as the perigee's orientation, the eccentricity vector is defined as

$$
\mathbf{e} = \begin{pmatrix} e_x \\ e_y \end{pmatrix} = \begin{pmatrix} e\cos(\Omega + \omega) \\ e\sin(\Omega + \omega) \end{pmatrix} \tag{2.98}
$$

Figure 2.31 shows the vector, whose magnitude is equal to the orbit eccentricity and whose direction points to the location of perigee along the line of apsides.

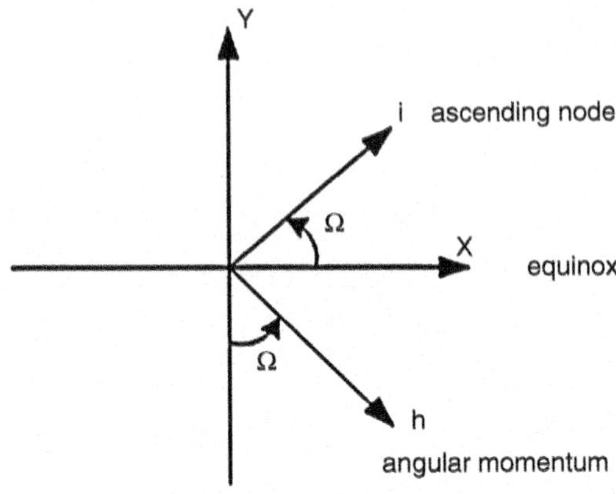

Fig. 2.32 The angular momentum and inclination vector

2.5.4.3 Inclination Vector

Similarly, as the inclination approaches zero, the ascending node becomes undeterminable. It is therefore necessary to define the inclination vector to study simultaneously the variation of inclination and the right ascension of ascending node. Figure 2.32 illustrates the vector, whose magnitude is equal to the orbit inclination and whose direction is identical to the line of nodes orienting toward the orbit ascending node.

$$\mathbf{i} = \begin{pmatrix} i_x \\ i_y \end{pmatrix} = \begin{pmatrix} i\cos(\Omega) \\ i\sin(\Omega) \end{pmatrix} \tag{2.99}$$

An alternative definition adopted for the inclination vector is aligning to the orbit angle momentum, whose components are

$$\mathbf{h} = \begin{pmatrix} +\sin i \sin\Omega \\ -\sin i \cos\Omega \\ \cos i \end{pmatrix}$$

When $i \cong 0$, $\sin(i) \cong i$ and $\cos(i) \cong 1$, the components within primary plane become

$$\mathbf{h} = \begin{pmatrix} +i\sin\Omega \\ -i\cos\Omega \end{pmatrix}$$

Under this definition, the momentum vector logs behind the inclination vector with 90°. For example, when the right ascension $\Omega = 90°$, the momentum vector points to the vernal equinox, and when $\Omega = 270°$, the momentum vector points to the autumnal equinox.

2.5.4.4 Right Longitude and Geocentric Longitude

Similarly, the mean anomaly as a time-dependent element also becomes undeterminable when both the inclination and eccentricity become zero. It is necessary to induce the mean right longitude and true right longitude to describe the relative drift motion to the nominal allocation.

$$\bar{l} = \Omega + \omega + M, l = \Omega + \omega + f$$

and the corresponding mean and true geocentric longitude are given by

$$\bar{\lambda} = \bar{l} - \theta(T), \lambda = l - \theta(T)$$

where $\theta(T)$ is the mean sidereal time, which gives the first-order approximate representation under a small eccentricity and inclination condition as

$$l = \bar{l} + 2e \sin M, \lambda = \bar{\lambda} + 2e \sin M$$

It may be observed that the true longitude oscillates about the mean longitude over the period of one day with the amplitude of $2e$ in radian.

Other forms of the station keeping element can be found in the literature [4, 5]. In general, the station keeping element in different forms are all given under the true equator and equinox reference frame, with which the inclination with the true equator reflects the drift motion along the north and south direction. For example, the Kepler classical elements of a geostationary satellite at epoch Jan. 1, 2006 (UTC) are

$$a_{\text{TOD}} = 42167063.7506(\text{m})$$
$$e_{\text{TOD}} = 0.000065$$
$$i_{\text{TOD}} = 0.081774025°$$
$$\Omega_{\text{TOD}} = 281.195305°$$
$$\omega_{\text{TOD}} = 60.461473°$$
$$M_{\text{TOD}} = 34.064274°\backslash$$

The corresponding station keeping elements are

$$\Delta a = 2.8640(\text{km})$$
$$D = -0.0368(°/\text{day})$$
$$e_x = 6.1697 \times 10^{-5}, e_y = -2.0456 \times 10^{-5}$$
$$i_x = 0.0159°, i_y = -0.0802°$$
$$l = 15.7211°, \lambda = 336.4432°$$

References

1. International Earth Rotation and Reference System Service (IERS). www.iers.org/IERS/EN/IERSHome/home.html?__nnn=true. Accessed 20 Feb 2013
2. Lieske JH, Lederle T, Fricke W et al (1977) Expressions for the precession quantities based upon the IAU system of astronomical constants. Astron Astrophys 58:1–16
3. Lieske JH (1979) Precession matrix based on IAU system of astronomical constants. Astron Astrophys 73:282–284
4. Newcomb S (1898) Tables of the motion of the Earth on its axis and around the Sun. Astron Pap Am Ephemeris XI:1–170
5. Kinoshita H (1977) Theory of the rotation of the rigid earth. Celest Mech 15:277–326
6. Wahr JM (1981) The forced nutations of an elliptical, rotating, elastic, and oceanless earth. Geophys J R Astron Soc 64:705–728
7. Seidelmann PK (1982) 1980 IAU theory of nutation: the final report of the IAU Working Group on Nutation. Celest Mech 27:79–106
8. Aoki S et al (1982) The new definition of universal time. Astron Astrophys 105:359–361
9. Montenbruck O, Gill E (2000) Satellite orbits – models, methods, and application. Springer, Berlin/Heidelberg
10. Ziqing W (2008) China geodetic coordinate system 2000 and its comparison with WGS84. J Geodesy Geodyn 28(5):1–5 (in Chinese)

Chapter 3
The Motion of Geostationary Satellite

Abstract There is no absolute stationary orbit for the geostationary satellite to reside in. Special attention we pay in this chapter to the geostationary satellite's relative motion to the Earth's rotation motion. We will illustrate the orbit motion of real geostationary satellite with the rotational Earth in inertial space.

3.1 Introduction

As rounding about the Earth, the geostationary orbit is depicted by the station keeping elements introduced in the last section. The station keeping element is identified to the Kepler classical element just to avoid the singularity with nearly zero inclination and eccentricity, which means that a geostationary satellite circles the Earth as do the Earth-round satellite viewed from inertial space. Special attention we will pay in this chapter to its relative motion to the Earth's rotation. Due to the minor offsets between the real and ideal geostationary orbit, the geostationary satellite is not stationary in terms of the terminological meaning. Since the eccentricity is not strictly equal to zero, which results in that the geostationary satellite is of uneven motion rate, and causes the geostationary satellite runs faster than the spin rate of the Earth and drifts eastward relative to the nominal longitude at perigee point, and on the contrary, it runs slower than the spin rate of the Earth and drifts westward relative to the nominal longitude near the apogee point. Since the inclination of geostationary satellite is not strictly equal to zero, which results in that its orbit plane is not identical with the Earth's equatorial plane, the geostationary satellite trespasses the equatorial plane twice one day. In general, there is no absolute stationary orbit for geostationary satellite to reside in. In this chapter, we will illustrate the orbit motion of geostationary satellite with the rotational Earth in inertial space.

H. Li, *Geostationary Satellites Collocation*, DOI 10.1007/978-3-642-40799-4_3,

3.2 The Geostationary Orbit in Inertial Space

The Kepler orbit elements $\{a, e, i, \Omega, \omega, M\}$ depict the motion of satellite in terms of inertial reference at a given epoch. They are in accordance with the motion Cartesian states $\mathbf{r}$ and $\dot{\mathbf{r}}$ at the same epoch. For the sake of analyzing the characteristics of geostationary orbit, some spherical parameters will be introduced for referencing the Earth-centered celestial sphere as illustrated in Fig. 3.1.

r, the geocentric distance; α, the right ascension; δ, the declination
v, the velocity; γ, the velocity tilt angle; β, the velocity azimuth

1. The spherical and Cartesian parameters

Suppose the motion Cartesian states $\{\mathbf{r}, \dot{\mathbf{r}}\}$ at a given epoch are

$$\mathbf{r} = \begin{pmatrix} x \\ y \\ z \end{pmatrix}, \quad \dot{\mathbf{r}} = \begin{pmatrix} v_x \\ v_y \\ v_z \end{pmatrix}$$

and the corresponding spherical polar position components are

$$r = \|\mathbf{r}\| = \sqrt{x^2 + y^2 + z^2} \tag{3.1}$$

$$\alpha = \arctan\left(\frac{y}{r} / \frac{x}{r}\right) \in [0, 2\pi] \tag{3.2}$$

$$\delta = \operatorname{asin}\left(\frac{z}{r}\right) \in \left[-\frac{\pi}{2}, \frac{\pi}{2}\right] \tag{3.3}$$

and the corresponding spherical polar velocity components are

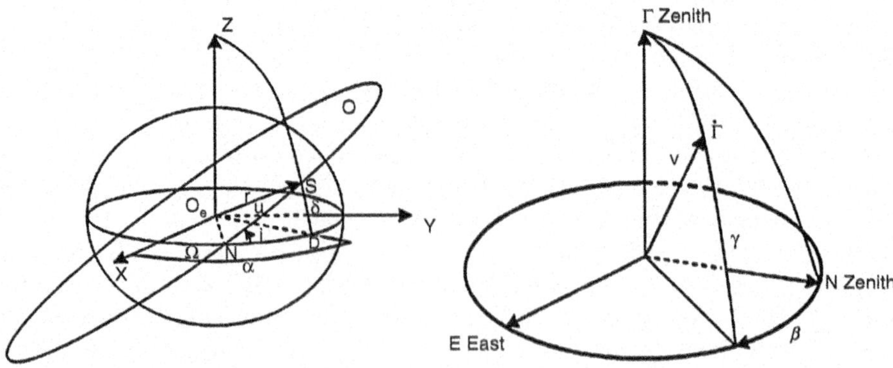

Fig. 3.1 The spherical polar parameters

$$v = \|\dot{\mathbf{r}}\| = \sqrt{v_x^2 + v_y^2 + v_z^2} \tag{3.4}$$

$$\gamma = \frac{\pi}{2} - \arccos\left(\frac{\mathbf{r} \cdot \dot{\mathbf{r}}}{r \cdot v}\right) \in \left[-\frac{\pi}{2}, \frac{\pi}{2}\right] \tag{3.5}$$

$$\beta = \arccos\left(\frac{(\mathbf{r} \times \dot{\mathbf{r}}) \cdot (\mathbf{r} \times \mathbf{z})}{\|(\mathbf{r} \times \dot{\mathbf{r}}) \cdot (\mathbf{r} \times \mathbf{z})\|}\right) \in [0, \pi] \tag{3.6}$$

On the contrary, suppose the spherical polar parameters are $\{r, \alpha, \delta, v, \gamma, \beta\}$ and the corresponding Cartesian states $\mathbf{r}$ and $\dot{\mathbf{r}}$ components in the Earth-centric reference frame are

$$\mathbf{r} = \begin{pmatrix} x \\ y \\ z \end{pmatrix} = \begin{pmatrix} r\cos\delta\cos\alpha \\ r\cos\delta\sin\alpha \\ \sin\delta \end{pmatrix} \tag{3.7}$$

$$\dot{\mathbf{r}} = \begin{pmatrix} v_x \\ v_y \\ v_z \end{pmatrix} = \mathbf{M} \cdot \begin{pmatrix} v\cos\gamma\sin\beta \\ v\cos\gamma\cos\beta \\ v\sin\gamma \end{pmatrix} \tag{3.8}$$

Here

$$\mathbf{M} = \begin{bmatrix} -\cos\alpha\sin\delta & -\sin\alpha & \cos\delta\cos\alpha \\ \sin\alpha\sin\delta & \cos\alpha & \cos\delta\sin\alpha \\ \cos\delta & 0 & \sin\delta \end{bmatrix} \tag{3.9}$$

2. The spherical parameters and the Kepler orbit

Suppose the Kepler orbit parameters at a given epoch are $\{a, e, i, \Omega, \omega, M\}$, and then the relation between corresponding geocentric distance and the semi-major axis, the eccentricity and the true anomaly is

$$r = \frac{a(1 - e^2)}{1 + e\cos f} \tag{3.10}$$

As the satellite passes perigee $f = 0$, the minimum geocentric distance will occur, and the value is $r_p = a(1 - e)$, while as the satellite passes apogee $f = 180°$, the maximum geocentric distance will occur, and the value is $r_a = a(1 + e)$. As illustrated in Fig. 3.2, the relation between the spherical parameters and the Kepler orbit parameters is

$$\sin\delta = \sin(\omega + f)\sin i \tag{3.11}$$

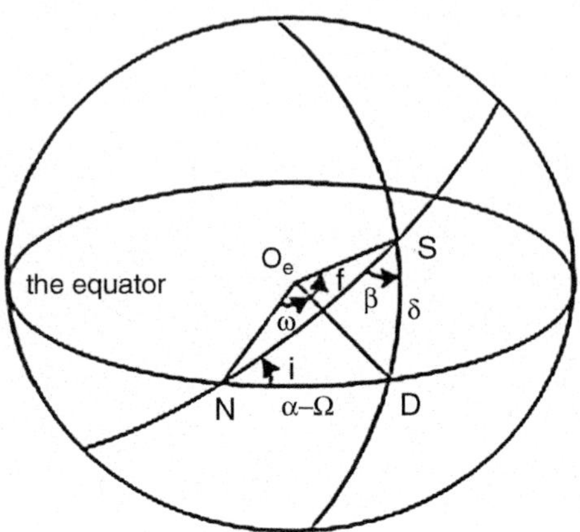

Fig. 3.2 The spherical triangle NDS

$$\cos(\alpha-\Omega) = \frac{\cos(\omega+f)}{\cos\delta} \tag{3.12}$$

$$\sin(\alpha-\Omega) = \sin(\omega+f)\frac{\cos i}{\cos\delta} \tag{3.13}$$

$$\cos\beta = \sin i \cos(\alpha-\Omega) \tag{3.14}$$

According to expression (3.14), when $\alpha-\Omega=0$, the satellite passes the ascension node of orbit plane, the velocity azimuth which defines the angle between the local northward $\beta=90°-i$ and the corresponding right declination $\delta=0$; when $\alpha-\Omega=90°$, the satellite passes the northern tropic of orbit, the velocity azimuth $\beta=90°$, and the corresponding right declination is equal to orbit inclination, $\delta=i$; when $\alpha-\Omega=180°$, the satellite passes the descent point, the velocity azimuth $\beta=90°+i$, and the right declination is identical to zero; when $\alpha-\Omega=270°$, the satellite passes the southern tropic of orbit, the velocity azimuth $\beta=90°$, and the corresponding right declination is identical to the inclination of orbit.

The magnitude of velocity satisfies

$$v = \sqrt{\frac{\mu}{a(1-e^2)}}\cdot\sqrt{\sin^2 f + (e+\cos f)^2} = \sqrt{\mu\left(\frac{2}{r}-\frac{1}{a}\right)} \tag{3.15}$$

When the satellite is at the perigee point, the maximum velocity satisfies

$$v_p = \sqrt{\frac{\mu}{a}}\cdot\frac{1}{\sqrt{1+e}\cdot\sqrt{1-e}}\cdot\sqrt{(1+e)^2} = \sqrt{\frac{\mu}{a}}\cdot\sqrt{\frac{1+e}{1-e}} \tag{3.16}$$

While the satellite is at the apogee point, the minimum velocity satisfies

$$v_a = \sqrt{\frac{\mu}{a}} \cdot \frac{1}{\sqrt{1+e} \cdot \sqrt{1-e}} \cdot \sqrt{(1-e)^2} = \sqrt{\frac{\mu}{a}} \cdot \sqrt{\frac{1-e}{1+e}}, \tag{3.17}$$

When $f=90°$ or $f=270°$, the satellite is of the average velocity, and the magnitude is

$$\bar{v} = \sqrt{\frac{\mu}{a}} \cdot \sqrt{\frac{1+e^2}{1-e^2}} \tag{3.18}$$

The velocity tilt angle γ, which is defined as the intersection angle between the velocity vector and the local tangential plane, satisfies the following expressions:

$$\sin\gamma = \frac{e\sin f}{\sqrt{1+e^2+2e\cos f}}, \tag{3.19}$$

$$\cos\gamma = \frac{1+e\cos f}{\sqrt{1+e^2+2e\cos f}}, \tag{3.20}$$

When the satellite is at the perigee point, i.e., $f=0$, the velocity tilt angle satisfies $\sin\gamma=0, \cos\gamma=1$, which means $\gamma=0$.

When the satellite is at the apogee point, that is, $f=180$, the velocity tilt angle satisfies $\sin\gamma=0, \cos\gamma=1$, which means $\gamma=0$.

When the true anomaly satisfies $f=90°$, the velocity tilt angle satisfies the expressions

$$\sin\gamma = e/\sqrt{1+e^2}, \quad \cos\gamma = 1/\sqrt{1+e^2} \tag{3.21}$$

which means that the velocity tilt angle is dependent on the orbit eccentricity. In case of elliptic orbit, the range will satisfy

$$\gamma = \arctan(e) \in [0, 45°), 0 \le e < 1$$

When the true anomaly satisfies $f=270°$, the velocity tilt angle satisfies the expressions

$$\sin\gamma = -e/\sqrt{1+e^2}, \quad \cos\gamma = 1/\sqrt{1+e^2}$$

which means that the velocity tilt angle is dependent on the eccentricity of orbit. In case of elliptic orbit, the range will satisfy

$$\gamma = a\tan(-e) \in (-45°, 0], \quad 0 \le e < 1$$

If and only if the satellite is in a perfect circle orbit, the velocity angle always satisfies $\gamma=0°$.

3.3 The Geostationary Orbit Relative to the Earth

The perfect geostationary orbit is a mathematical conception that could be realized only based on that the Earth is a spherical symmetric body, and the spacecraft is not influenced by other forces except the central gravity attraction from the Earth, and the central body rotates along its spin axis with a constant angular velocity. Unfortunately, we have no ideal condition for a satellite to circle in a perfect geostationary orbit.

The real geostationary orbit always has a little bias from the perfect one. Owing to the semi-major axis offset, the orbit rate is out of synchronization with the rotation speed of the Earth, and the eccentricity offset causes the inhomogeneous rotation speed of the satellite, as well as the inclination offset causes that the orbit plane is not identical to the equatorial plane. Therefore, viewed from the ground, the real geostationary satellite is not absolutely stationary but has some oscillations in both longitudinal and latitudinal directions. As the title suggested, in this section we try to depict the above motion of geostationary orbit relative to the Earth.

Hence, in this section, we focus on the real orbit motion relative to the ideal geostationary orbit. In order to linearize the relative equation, some approximate treatments will be deployed to simplify the equations below:

$$\begin{aligned} &a = a_s + \Delta a, \quad f \cong E \cong M, \quad e^2 \cong 0, \\ &e \cdot \Delta a \cong 0, \quad \sin(i) \cong i, \quad \cos(i) \cong 1 \end{aligned}$$

The Cartesian position parameters of a satellite in inertial reference satisfy the expressions below:

$$\mathbf{r} = \frac{a(1-e^2)}{1+e\cos f} \cdot \begin{pmatrix} \cos\Omega\cos(\omega+f) - \sin\Omega\sin(\omega+f)\cos i \\ \sin\Omega\cos(\omega+f) + \cos\Omega\sin(\omega+f)\cos i \\ \sin(\omega+f)\sin i \end{pmatrix} \tag{3.22}$$

3.3.1 *Linearization of Geocentric Distance*

Since $a = a_s + \Delta a$, and with some approximate treatments, i.e., $e^2 \cong 0$, $e \cdot \Delta a \cong 0$, the geocentric distance becomes

$$\begin{aligned} r &= \frac{a(1-e^2)}{1+e\cos f} \cong \frac{a}{1+e\cos f} = \frac{a(1-e\cos f)}{1-e^2\cos^2 f} \\ &= a(1-e\cos f) = (a_s+\Delta a)(1-e\cos f) \\ &\cong a_s + \Delta a - e a_s \cos f \end{aligned} \tag{3.23}$$

and the corresponding time is related to the distance r by the relation

$$r = a_s + \Delta a - e a_s \cos\left(\omega_e\left(t - t_p\right)\right) \tag{3.24}$$

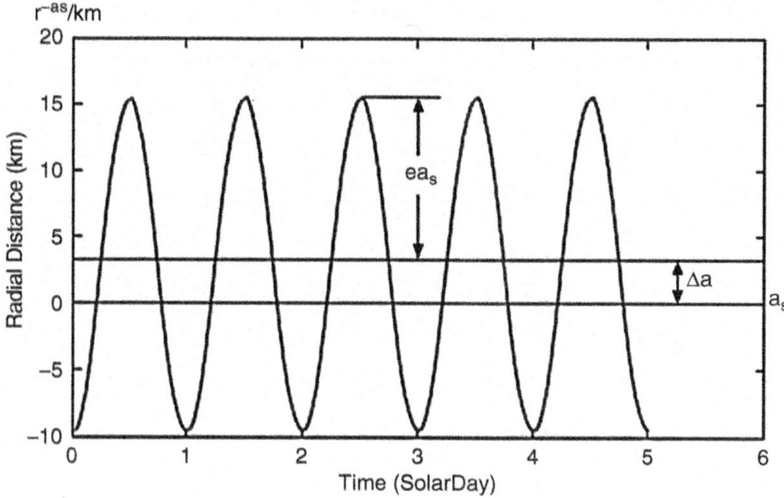

Fig. 3.3 The radial distance versus time

Figure 3.3 illustrates the relative geocentric distance between the real satellite orbit with $\Delta a \neq 0, e \neq 0$ conditions and the ideal geostationary orbit. When the satellite passes the perigee point, the relative distance satisfies $\Delta r_p = r - a_s = \Delta a - ea_s$. When the satellite passes the apogee point, the relative distance satisfies $\Delta r_a = r - a_s = \Delta a + ea_s$.

The real geostationary orbit is of an eccentricity offset e *(nonzero)*. If the semi-major axis satisfies the condition below, the real geostationary orbit intersects with the ideal one:

$$a \geq a_s(1 - e) \text{ and } a \leq a_s(1 + e)$$

3.3.2 Linearization of the True Anomaly

Neglecting the high-order terms of nonzero eccentricity, from the angular moment equation, we get

$$\dot{f} = \frac{1}{r^2}\sqrt{\mu a(1 - e^2)} \cong \frac{1}{r^2}\sqrt{\mu a} \tag{3.25}$$

And in conformity with the perfect geostationary orbit, then exists

$$\sqrt{\mu} = \omega_e \sqrt{\mu a_s} \tag{3.26}$$

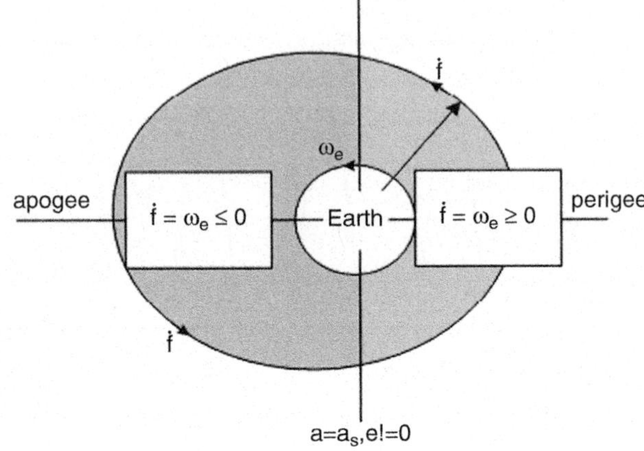

Fig. 3.4 Geosynchronous orbit with a nonzero eccentricity

Hence, (3.25) becomes

$$\dot{f} = \frac{1}{r^2}\omega_e a_s^{\frac{3}{2}}\sqrt{a} = \omega_e\left(\frac{a_s}{a}\right)^{\frac{3}{2}}\left(\frac{a}{r}\right)^2 \tag{3.27}$$

and with some approximate treatments

$$\left(\frac{a}{r}\right) = 1 + e\cos f \Rightarrow \left(\frac{a}{r}\right)^2 = (1 + e\cos f)^2 \tag{3.28}$$

From the above relation, then the angular moment equation becomes the linearization form:

$$\dot{f} = \omega_e\left(\frac{a_s}{a}\right)^{\frac{3}{2}}(1 + e\cos f)^2 \tag{3.29}$$

$$\cong \omega_e\left(1 - \frac{3}{2}\left(\frac{\Delta a}{a_s}\right)\right)(1 + 2e\cos f) \cong \omega_e\left(1 - \frac{3}{2}\left(\frac{\Delta a}{a_s}\right) + 2e\cos f\right) \tag{3.30}$$

From expression (3.30), the relative rotation between the real and ideal geostationary orbits contains two parts: The first part is a secular term, which is caused by the semi-major axis deviation. The second part is a daily-period oscillation, which is caused by the eccentricity of the real orbit. Figure 3.4 illustrates the relative rotation with a nonzero eccentricity of the real orbit.

When the satellite passes quadrants IV and I of the orbit plane, i.e., $\dot{f} - \omega_e \cong 2e\cos f \geq 0$, which means that the satellite runs faster than the rotation of the Earth, it results in an eastward drift motion viewed from the ground. The maximum eastward drift rate occurs when the satellite is at the perigee point, and the maximum relative drift rate satisfies $\dot{f} - \omega_e \cong 2e$. When the satellite passes quadrants II and III of the orbit plane, i.e.,$\dot{f} - \omega_e \cong 2e\cos f \leq 0$, which means that the satellite runs slower than the rotation of the Earth, it results in a westward drift motion viewed from the ground. The maximum westward drift rate occurs when the satellite is at the apogee point and satisfies $\dot{f} - \omega_e \cong -2e$.

Integrate expression (3.30) and utilize the following relation:

$$\frac{\mathrm{d}}{\mathrm{d}t}\left(\sin \omega_e (t - t_p)\right) = \omega_e \cos \omega_e (t - t_p) \tag{3.31}$$

Then the true anomaly becomes the linearization form:

$$\begin{aligned} f &= \int_{t_p}^{t} \dot{f}\,\mathrm{d}t = \int_{t_p}^{t} \omega_e \left(1 - \frac{3}{2}\left(\frac{\Delta a}{a_s}\right)\right) dt + 2e \int_{t_p}^{t} \frac{\mathrm{d}}{\mathrm{d}t}\left(\sin \omega_e (t - t_p)\right)\mathrm{d}t \\ &= \omega_e (t - t_p)\left(1 - \frac{3}{2}\left(\frac{\Delta a}{a_s}\right)\right) + 2e \sin\left(\omega_e (t - t_p)\right) \end{aligned} \tag{3.32}$$

3.3.3 *Linearization of Right Ascension and Longitude*

Neglecting the high-order terms of oscillation caused by the inclination, from Eq. (3.22), we get

$$\frac{X}{r} \cong \cos\Omega \cos(\omega + f) - \sin\Omega \sin(\omega + f) = \cos(\Omega + \omega + f) \tag{3.33}$$

and

$$\frac{Y}{r} \cong \sin\Omega \cos(\omega + f) + \cos\Omega \sin(\omega + f) = \sin(\Omega + \omega + f) \tag{3.34}$$

Then the right ascension and longitude of geostationary satellite are obtained from Eqs. (3.33) and (3.34).

$$l = \arctan\left(\frac{Y}{r} \Big/ \frac{X}{r}\right) = \Omega + \omega + f \tag{3.35}$$

$$\lambda = l - (G_0 + \omega_e (t - t_0)) = \Omega + \omega + f - (G_0 + \omega_e (t - t_0)) \tag{3.36}$$

Then the right ascension and longitude of the real geostationary satellite with time can be expressed by substituting with relation (3.32).

$$l = \Omega + \omega + f \tag{3.37}$$

$$= \Omega + \omega + \omega_e(t - t_p) - \frac{3}{2}\left(\frac{\Delta a}{a_s}\right)\omega_e(t - t_p) + 2e\sin\left(\omega_e(t - t_p)\right)$$

$$= \Omega + \omega + M - \frac{3}{2}\left(\frac{\Delta a}{a_s}\right)\omega_e(t - t_p) + 2e\sin\left(\omega_e(t - t_p)\right) \tag{3.38}$$

and

$$\begin{aligned}
\lambda &= \Omega + \omega + f - (G_0 + \omega_e(t - t_0)) \\
&= \Omega + \omega + \omega_e(t - t_p) - (G_0 + \omega_e(t - t_0)) - \frac{3}{2}\left(\frac{\Delta a}{a_s}\right)\omega_e(t - t_p) + 2e\sin\left(\omega_e(t - t_p)\right) \\
&= \Omega + \omega + \omega_e(t_0 - t_p) - G_0 - \frac{3}{2}\left(\frac{\Delta a}{a_s}\right)\omega_e(t - t_p) + 2e\sin\left(\omega_e(t - t_p)\right) \\
&= \Omega + \omega + M_0 - G_0 - \frac{3}{2}\left(\frac{\Delta a}{a_s}\right)\omega_e(t - t_p) + 2e\sin\left(\omega_e(t - t_p)\right) \\
&= \lambda_0 - \frac{3}{2}\left(\frac{\Delta a}{a_s}\right)\omega_e(t - t_p) + 2e\sin\left(\omega_e(t - t_p)\right)
\end{aligned} \tag{3.39}$$

From expression (3.39), the longitude drift motion of the real satellite relative to the nominal longitude contains two parts: The first part is a secular term, which is caused by the semi-major axis deviation; the second part is a daily-period oscillation, which is caused by nonzero eccentricity of the real orbit. Figure 3.5 illustrates the longitude drift motion of the real satellite relative to the nominal longitude. Because of the semi-major axis deviation, i.e., $\Delta a \neq 0$, the secular term satisfies $D = -\frac{3}{2}\left(\frac{\Delta a}{a_s}\right)\omega_e$. When $\Delta a \geq 0$, indicating the semi-major axis of the real orbit is greater than that of the ideal one and the satellite resided in the real orbit will run slower than the one in the ideal orbit, the relative drift rate satisfies $D \leq 0$ and a westward motion relative to the nominal longitude is shown. When $\Delta a \leq 0$, indicating the semi-major axis of the real orbit is smaller than that of the ideal one and the satellite resided in the real orbit will run faster than the one in the ideal orbit, the drift rate satisfies $D \geq 0$ and an eastward motion relative to the nominal longitude is shown.

Figure 3.5 illustrates that the relative longitude drifts from the nominal longitude, which contains two parts: The first part is a secular drift term, whose value is

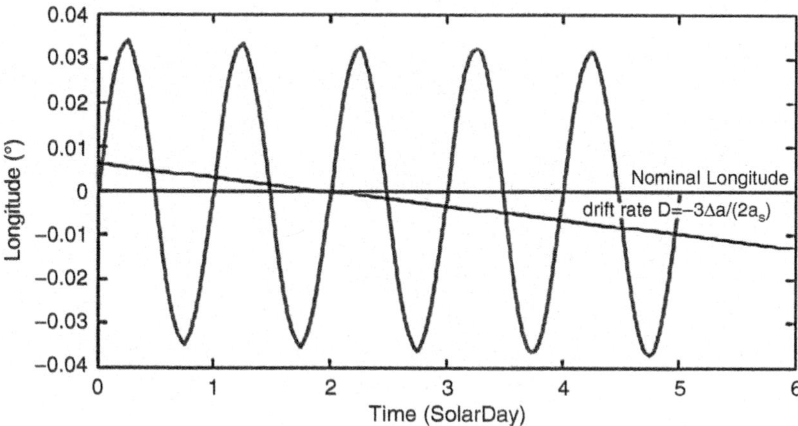

Fig. 3.5 Secular drift and daily libration

$-\frac{3}{2}\left(\frac{\Delta a}{a_s}\right)\omega_e$; the second part is a daily-period oscillation, whose amplitude is $2e$ in radian.

If we define mean longitude as an average longitude in one sidereal day, the mean longitude follows the motion

$$\overline{\lambda} = \overline{\lambda}_0 - \frac{3}{2}\left(\frac{\Delta a}{a_s}\right)\omega_e\left(t - t_p\right) = \overline{\lambda}_0 + D\left(t - t_p\right) \tag{3.40}$$

while the osculating longitude is

$$\overline{\lambda} = \overline{\lambda} + 2e\sin\left(\omega_e\left(t - t_p\right)\right) \tag{3.41}$$

3.3.4 Linearization of Relative Declination

Neglecting the high-order terms of oscillation caused by the inclination, from expression (3.22), we get

$$\frac{Z}{r} = i \cdot \sin\left(\omega + f\right) \tag{3.42}$$

The declination relative to the equatorial plane is related to the argument of perigee as

$$\varphi \cong \sin\varphi = \frac{Z}{r} = i \cdot \sin\left(\omega + f\right) \tag{3.43}$$

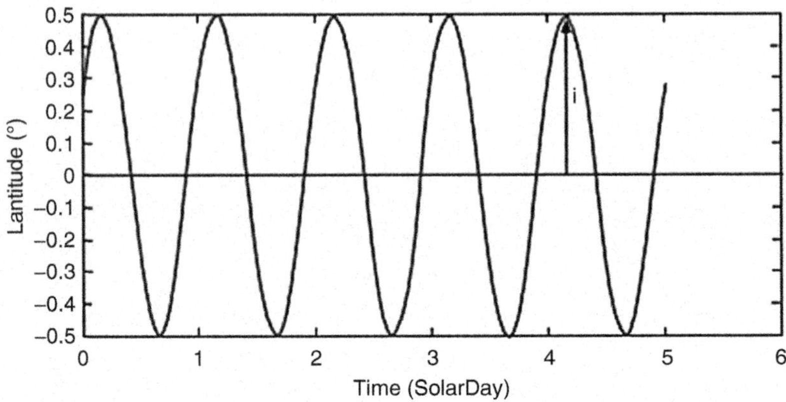

Fig. 3.6 The declination's daily libration motion

and with time

$$\varphi = i \cdot \sin\left(\omega + \omega_e\left(t - t_p\right)\right) \tag{3.44}$$

When $i \neq 0$, the latitude history of the real satellite relative to the equatorial plane with the inclination deviation is illustrated in Fig. 3.6.

3.4 The Truth of "8"-Shape Subsatellite

Even though the subsatellite of the real geostationary orbit is depicted as an "8" shape in many references, the truth is that only under very special conditions, the real geostationary orbit experiences an "8"-shape trajectory. This section explores under what conditions the orbit of the real geostationary satellite will show an "8"-shape trajectory.

As illustrated in Fig. 3.7, suppose a real geostationary satellite is located at the nominal longitude λ_N. If its orbit is of same semi-major axis and eccentricity with the ideal geostationary orbit, then the satellite is of a constant rotation rate, which is identical to the rotation rate of the Earth, i.e., $\dot{f} = n = \omega_e$. Through a time interval t, the satellite has traveled from N to S along the orbit plane, while the Earth's primary plane has scanned from G_0 to G_t along the equatorial plane, forming a spherical triangle NDS, and satisfies the following relation:

$$\cos(i) = \cot(\omega_e t) \cdot \cot\left(\frac{\pi}{2} - (\lambda - \lambda_N - \omega_e t)\right) \tag{3.45}$$

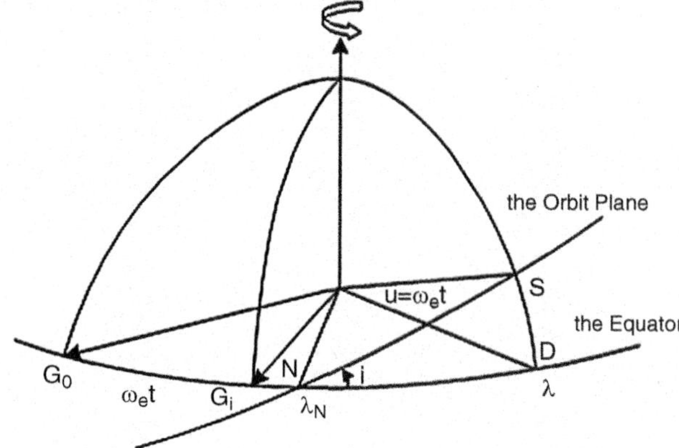

Fig. 3.7 Longitude libration induced by nonzero inclination

which is simplified as

$$\tan(\lambda - \lambda_N - \omega_e t) = \cos(i)\tan(\omega_e t)$$

$$\cos(i) = \frac{\tan(\Delta\lambda + \omega_e t)}{\tan(\omega_e t)} = \frac{\sin(\Delta\lambda + \omega_e t)}{\cos(\Delta\lambda + \omega_e t)} \cdot \frac{\cos(\omega_e t)}{\sin(\omega_e t)}$$

By making use of triangle function relation,

$$\begin{aligned} 1 - \cos(i) &= -\frac{(\sin(\Delta\lambda + \omega_e t)\cos(\omega_e t) - \cos(\Delta\lambda + \omega_e t)\sin(\omega_e t))}{\cos(\Delta\lambda + \omega_e t)\sin(\omega_e t)} \\ &= -\frac{\sin(\Delta\lambda + \omega_e t - \omega_e t)}{\cos(\Delta\lambda + \omega_e t)\sin(\omega_e t)} = -\frac{\sin(\Delta\lambda)}{\cos(\Delta\lambda + \omega_e t)\sin(\omega_e t)} \end{aligned}$$

and finally we get

$$1 - \cos(i) = \frac{\Delta\lambda}{\frac{1}{2}\sin(2\omega_e t)}$$

and

$$\cos(i) \cong 1 - \frac{i^2}{2} + o(i^4)$$

The longitude libration induced by the nonzero inclination satisfies the following relation:

$$\Delta\lambda = -\frac{i^2}{4}\sin(2\omega_e t) \tag{3.46}$$

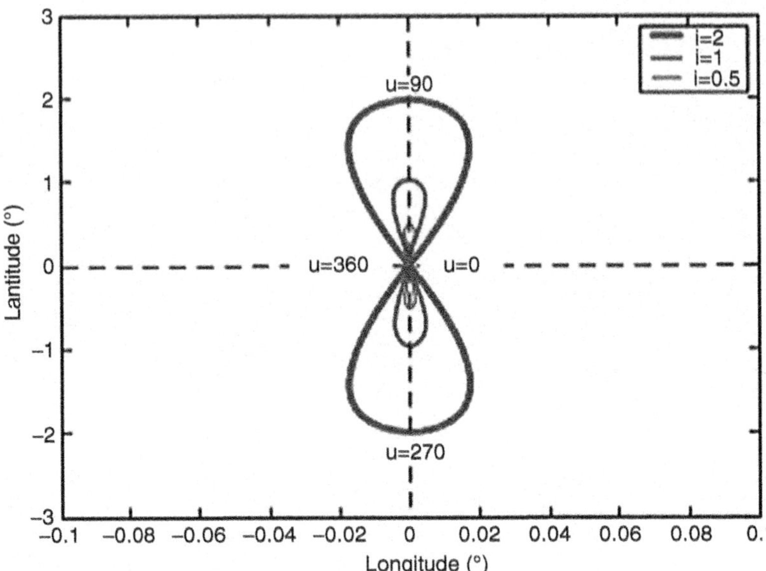

Fig. 3.8 "8"-Shape satellite track with nonzero inclination

Hence, the maximum libration caused by the inclination is $(i^2/4)$ in radian. For example, in general, the maximum inclination of the real geostationary orbit satisfies $i_{\max}=0.1°$. According to expression (3.46), the maximum libration is $\Delta\lambda_{\text{inc}}=4°.3633\times10^{-5}$ in degrees, which is much smaller than the longitude libration caused by the eccentricity. For instance, if the eccentricity is kept to satisfy $e_{\max}=10^{-3}$, then the maximum longitude libration will be $\Delta\lambda_{\text{ecc}}=0.1146°$ in degrees. It can be seen that the longitude libration induced by the inclination is a more ignorable factor compared to the one that caused by the eccentricity.

However, sometimes the routine inclination compensation maneuvers will be unscheduled during the end of the lifespan of geostationary satellite; the influence will become significant. For instance, when $i=1°$, $\Delta\lambda=0.0044°$, and when $i=2°$, $\Delta\lambda=0.0175°$.

In consideration of the longitude libration induced by the inclination of orbit, the relative longitude drift follows the following expression:

$$\Delta\lambda=-\frac{3}{2}\left(\frac{\Delta a}{a_s}\right)\omega_e\left(t-t_p\right)+2e\sin\left(\omega_e\left(t-t_p\right)\right)-\frac{i^2}{4}\sin\left(2\omega_e t\right) \tag{3.47}$$

$$\Delta\varphi=i\cdot\sin\left(\omega+\omega_e\left(t-t_p\right)\right) \tag{3.48}$$

Only when the particular case occurs, i.e., $i\neq0$, $\Delta a=0$, $e=0$, and $\omega=0$, the longitude and latitude libration becomes very special, which satisfies the "8"-shape restrictive conditions as illustrated in Fig. 3.8.

$$\Delta\lambda = -\frac{i^2}{4}\sin(2\omega_e t), \tag{3.49}$$

$$\Delta\varphi = i \cdot \sin(\omega_e t), \tag{3.50}$$

3.5 The Relative Motion with Nominal Longitude

In view of the relative motion with the nominal longitude, the nominal longitude originated radian-tangential-normal reference is defined. It takes the nominal point as the origin, which is located at $(a_s, \lambda_N, 0)$ in the Earth Greenwich Meridian Fixed system (see Chap. 2). The radial deviation Δr from the nominal point is measured along the radial direction, the tangential deviation ΔT from the nominal point is measured along the latitude direction, and the normal deviation ΔN from the nominal point is measured along the longitude direction. Figure 3.9 illustrates the nominal originated radian-tangential-normal reference, which shows an ideal nominal point-oriented orthogonal coordinate frame. In this section, we will study the relative motion with the nominal longitude by projecting the real geostationary satellite's motion to the following three planes: the equator plane TOR, the meridian plane RON, and the local horizontal plane TON.

From the above description, the relative motions along the local radial, tangential, normal direction are given by

$$\Delta r = \Delta a - ea_s \cos\left(\omega_e\left(t - t_p\right)\right) \tag{3.51}$$

$$\begin{aligned}\Delta T &= \Delta\lambda \cdot a_s \\ &= -\frac{3}{2}\Delta a\omega_e\left(t - t_p\right) + 2a_s e\sin\left(\omega_e\left(t - t_p\right)\right) - \frac{i^2}{4}a_s\sin(2\omega_e t)\end{aligned} \tag{3.52}$$

$$\Delta N = \Delta\varphi \cdot a_s = i \cdot a_s \sin\left(\omega + \omega_e\left(t - t_p\right)\right) \tag{3.53}$$

Some cases will be discussed based on the relative equations above.

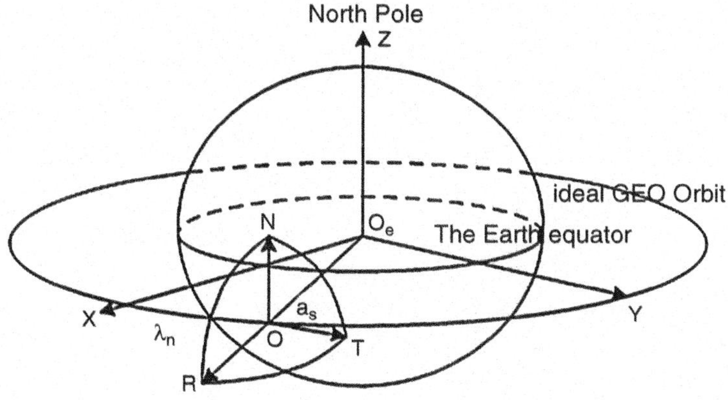

Fig. 3.9 Nominal point-originated orthogonal coordinate frame

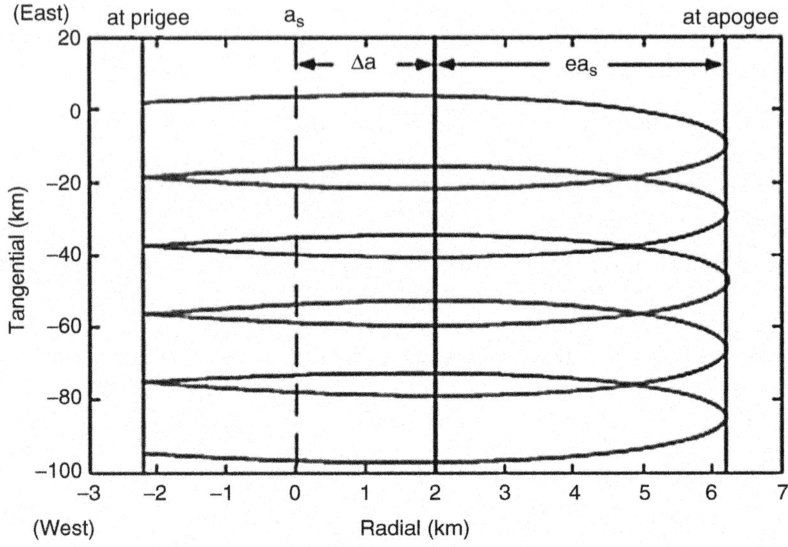

Fig. 3.10 Orbit motion projected on the equator plane

3.5.1 The Orbit Motion Projected on the Equator Plane

In this section, we will discuss the orbit motion projected on the local equator plane. In consideration of the equations above, neglecting the half-daily-period compartment induced by the inclination, the projection equation along the local equator plane takes the following form:

$$\left(\frac{\Delta r-\Delta a}{ea_s}\right)^2+\left(\Delta T+\frac{\frac{3}{2}\Delta a\omega_e\left(t-t_p\right)}{2ea_s}\right)^2=1 \tag{3.54}$$

The equation shows that the projection motion on the equator plane is an elliptic formation. Its origin is at point $\left(\Delta a,\ -\frac{3}{2}\Delta a\omega_e\left(t-t_p\right)\right)$. Its semi-minor axis is located along the radial direction with the length of ea_s, and its semi-major axis is located along the tangential direction with the length of $2ea_s$. Its origin drifts along the tangential direction with time. Figure 3.10 illustrates the projection motion on the equator plane, where the origin of the ellipse moves westward along the tangential direction and the drift rate is about $9.4248\cdot\Delta a$ kilometers (is identical to the unit of the semi-major axis).

1. $\Delta a=0, e\neq 0$

In this case, the real orbit is a strict geosynchronous orbit. The projection equation along the local equator plane is

$$\left(\frac{\Delta r}{ea_s}\right)^2+\left(\frac{\Delta T}{2ea_s}\right)^2=1 \tag{3.55}$$

The equation above indicates that the satellite resided in this orbit rotates clockwise along an ellipse on the radial and tangential plane. The origin locates at the nominal point; the semi-minor axis is along the radial direction, with the length of ea_s; and the semi-major axis is along the tangential direction, with the length of $2ea_s$.

2. $\Delta a \neq 0, e = 0$

In this case, the real orbit is a strict round orbit. The projection equation along the local equator plane is

$$\Delta r = \Delta a \tag{3.56}$$

$$\Delta T = \frac{3}{2}\Delta a \omega_e (t - t_p) \tag{3.57}$$

The equation above shows that the satellite resided in this orbit drifts along a line at a speed of $9.4248 \cdot \Delta a$ from nominal point eastward when $\Delta a < 0$ or westward when $\Delta a > 0$.

3. $\Delta a = 0, e = 0$

In this case, the real orbit is a strict geosynchronous round orbit, and the projection of the satellite resided in this orbit keeps stable at the nominal longitude.

3.5.2 The Orbit Motion Projected on the Meridian Plane

In this section, we will discuss the orbit motion projected on the local meridian plane. In consideration of the equations above, neglecting the half-daily-period compartment induced by the inclination, the projection equation along the local meridian plane takes the following form:

$$\Delta r = \Delta a - ea_s \cos\left(\omega_e (t - t_p)\right), \tag{3.58}$$

$$\Delta N = i \cdot a_s \sin\left(\omega + \omega_e (t - t_p)\right) \tag{3.59}$$

Given the argument of perigee as ω, the relative motion projected on the local meridian plane can be realized with an elliptic equation by

$$\left(\frac{\Delta r = \Delta a}{e \cdot a_s}\right)^2 + \left(\frac{\Delta N + \frac{i}{e}(\Delta r = \Delta a)\sin\omega}{i \cdot a_s \cos\omega}\right)^2 = 1$$

Figure 3.11 illustrates the orbit motion projected on the meridian plane with different arguments of perigee.

1. $\omega = 0°$ or $\omega = 180°$

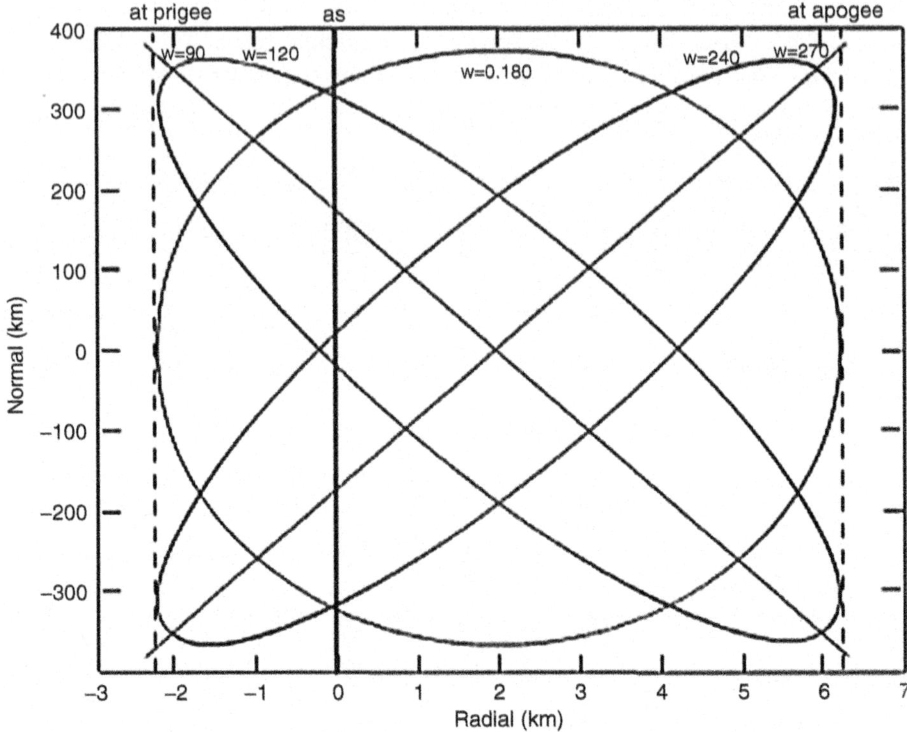

Fig. 3.11 The orbit motion projected on the meridian plane

When the argument of perigee satisfies $\omega = 0°$,

$$\sin\left(\omega + \omega_e\left(t - t_p\right)\right) = \sin\left(\omega_e\left(t - t_p\right)\right), \cos\omega = 1$$

And $\omega = 180°$,

$$\sin\left(\omega + \omega_e\left(t - t_p\right)\right) = \sin\left(\omega_e\left(t - t_p\right)\right), \cos\omega = 1$$

Then the relative motion projected on the local meridian plane satisfies the following elliptic equation:

$$\left(\frac{\Delta r - \Delta a}{ea_s}\right)^2 + \left(\frac{\Delta N}{ia_s}\right)^2 = 1, \tag{3.60}$$

which means that when the direction of perigee is parallel to the direction of the right ascension, the relative motion projected on the local meridian plane is an ellipse, whose center is at the point $[\Delta r, \Delta N] = [\Delta a, 0]$. When $e \geq i$ (inclination is in radian), the semi-major axis is along the radial direction, with the length of ea_s, and the semi-minor axis is along the normal direction, with the length of ia_s. When $e \leq i$, the semi-major axis is along the radial direction, with the length of ia_s, and the semi-minor axis is along the radial direction, with the length of ea_s.

2. $\omega = 90°$

When the argument of perigee satisfies $\omega = 90°$, then

$$\sin\left(\omega + \omega_e\left(t - t_p\right)\right) = \cos\left(\omega_e\left(t - t_p\right)\right)$$

The projection equation along the local meridian plane takes the form

$$\Delta_r = \Delta a - ea_s \cos\left(\omega_e\left(t - t_p\right)\right)$$
$$\Delta N = i \cdot a_s \cos\left(\omega_e\left(t - t_p\right)\right)$$

And

$$\frac{\Delta r - \Delta a}{\Delta N} = -\frac{ea_s}{ia_s} = -\frac{e}{i} \tag{3.61}$$

which means that when the direction of perigee is perpendicular to the direction of right ascension, the relative motion projected on the local meridian plane is a line and its slope equals to $\left(-\frac{e}{i}\right)$. When the satellite is at the perigee point, the radial deviation $\Delta r = \Delta a - e \cdot a_s$, and the maximum normal deviation satisfies $\Delta N = i \cdot a_s$. When the satellite is at the apogee point, the radial deviation $\Delta r = \Delta a + e \cdot a_s$, and the maximum normal deviation satisfies $\Delta N = -i \cdot a_s$.

3. $\omega = 270°$

When the argument of perigee satisfies $\omega = 270°$, then

$$\sin\left(\omega + \omega_e\left(t - t_p\right)\right) = -\cos\left(\omega_e\left(t - t_p\right)\right) \tag{3.62}$$

The projection equation along the local meridian plane takes the form

$$\Delta r = \Delta a - ea_s \cos\left(\omega_e\left(t - t_p\right)\right) \tag{3.63}$$
$$\Delta N = -i \cdot a_s \cos\left(\omega_e\left(t - t_p\right)\right) \tag{3.64}$$

since

$$\frac{\Delta r - \Delta a}{\Delta N} = \frac{ea_s}{ia_s} = \frac{e}{i}, \tag{3.65}$$

which means that when the direction of perigee is perpendicular to the direction of right ascension, the relative motion projected on the local meridian plane is a line and its slope is equal to $\left(+\frac{e}{i}\right)$. When the satellite is at the perigee point, the radial deviation $\Delta r = \Delta a - e \cdot a_s$, and the maximum normal deviation $\Delta N = -i \cdot a_s$. When the satellite is at the apogee point, the radial deviation $\Delta r = \Delta a + e \cdot a_s$, and the maximum normal deviation $\Delta N = i \cdot a_s$.

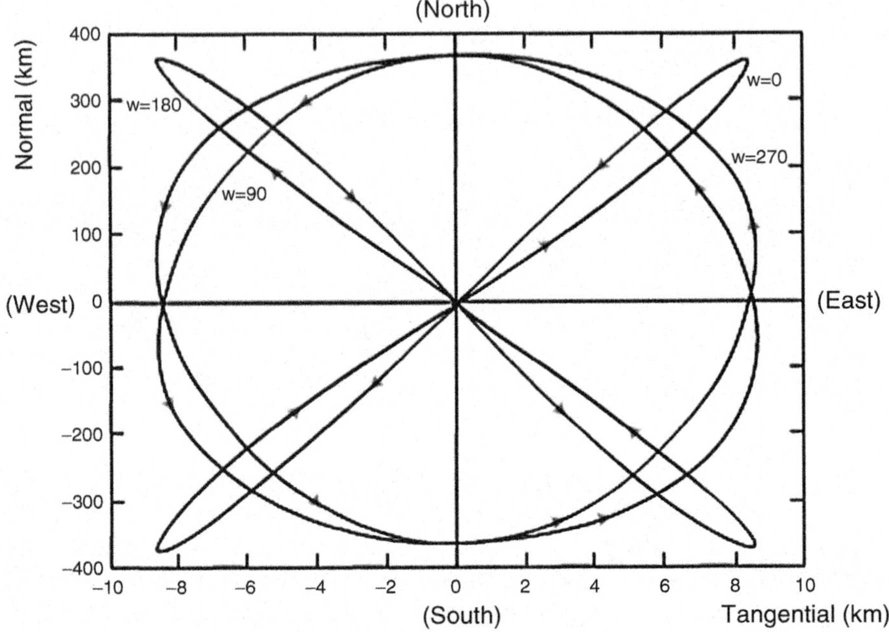

Fig. 3.12 The orbit motion projected on horizontal plane

3.5.3 Relative Motion Projected on the Local Horizontal Plane

In this section, we will discuss the relative motion projected on the local tangential plane. The projection equation along the local tangential plane takes the following form:

$$\Delta T = -\frac{3}{2}\Delta a\omega_e\left(t-t_p\right) + 2a_s e\sin\left(\omega_e\left(t-t_p\right)\right) - \frac{i^2}{4}a_s\sin\left(2\omega_e t\right) \tag{3.66}$$

$$\Delta N = i\cdot a_s\sin\left(\omega+\omega_e\left(t-t_p\right)\right) \tag{3.67}$$

1. $\Delta a = 0,\ e \neq 0, i \neq 0$

In this case, the real orbit is a strict geosynchronous orbit. The tangential deviation induced by the inclination is much smaller than that caused by the eccentricity. Neglecting the third term induced by the inclination, the equation takes the following form:

$$\Delta T = 2ea_s\sin\left(\omega_e\left(t-t_p\right)\right), \tag{3.68}$$

$$\Delta N = i\cdot a_s\sin\left(\omega+\omega_e\left(t-t_p\right)\right) \tag{3.69}$$

Figure 3.12 illustrates the relative motion projected on the local horizontal plane with different arguments of perigee.

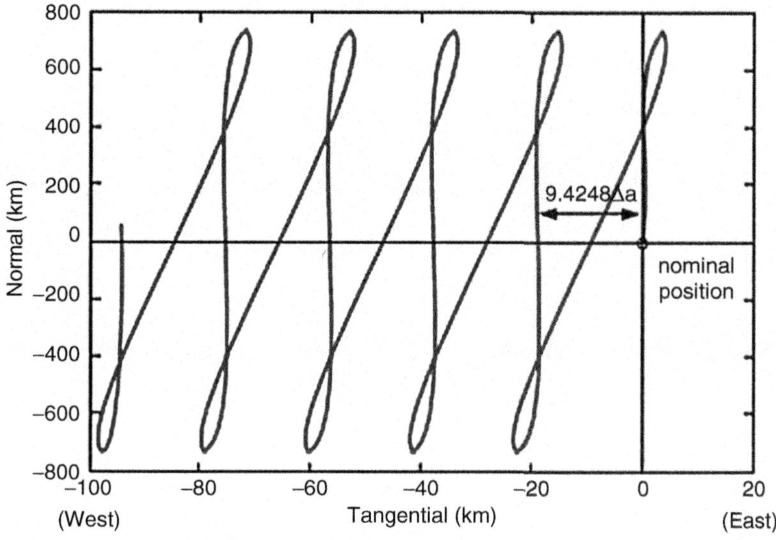

Fig. 3.13 The projection on horizontal plane ($\omega = 0$)

(a) $\omega = 0$

When the argument of perigee satisfies $\omega = 0$, the perigee of orbit will point to the right ascension, and the relative motion projected on the local tangential plane takes the following form:

$$\Delta T = \frac{2e}{i} \cdot \Delta N, \quad \Delta N \in [-i \cdot a_s, i \cdot a_s], \tag{3.70}$$

As illustrated in Fig. 3.12, the relative motion projected on the local tangential plane takes the form of a sloped "8" formation in consideration of the drift motion caused by the inclination, and the tilt slope caused by the eccentricity is

$$\arctan\left(\frac{2e}{i}\right) \tag{3.71}$$

(b) $\omega = 180°$

When the argument of perigee satisfies $\omega = 180°$, the perigee of orbit will point to the right descent, and the relative motion projected on the local tangential plane takes the following form:

$$\Delta T = -\frac{2e}{i} \cdot \Delta N, \quad \Delta N \in [-i \cdot a_s, i \cdot a_s], \tag{3.72}$$

As illustrated in Fig. 3.13, the relative motion projected on the local tangential plane takes the form of a sloped "8" formation and the tilt slope caused by eccentricity is

$$\frac{\pi}{2} + a\tan\left(\frac{2e}{i}\right)$$

(c) $\omega = 90°$, or $270°$

When the argument of perigee satisfies $\omega = 90°$, or $270°$, which means that the direction of perigee is perpendicular to the direction of right ascension, then

$$\sin\left(\omega + \omega_e\left(t - t_p\right)\right) = \pm\cos\left(\omega_e\left(t - t_p\right)\right)$$

The relative motion projected on the local tangential plane takes the following form:

$$\begin{aligned} \Delta T &= 2ea_s \sin\left(\omega_e\left(t - t_p\right)\right) \\ \Delta N &= i \cdot a_s \cos\left(\omega_e\left(t - t_p\right)\right) \end{aligned}$$

and it is simplified as

$$\left(\frac{\Delta T}{2e \cdot a_s}\right)^2 + \left(\frac{\Delta N}{i \cdot a_s}\right)^2 = 1$$

As illustrated in Fig. 3.13, when the direction of perigee is perpendicular to the direction of right ascension, the relative motion projected on the local tangential plane is an ellipse, whose center is at the nominal point. When $2e \geq i$ (inclination in radian), its semi-major axis is along the tangential direction with the length of $2ea_s$, and its semi-minor axis is along the normal direction with the length of ia_s. When $2e \leq i$, its semi-major axis is along the normal direction with the length of ia_s, and its semi-minor axis is along the radial direction with the length of $2ea_s$.

2. $\Delta a \neq 0, e \neq 0, i \neq 0$

In this case, the real orbit is a true picture of a real geostationary orbit. The deviation induced by the inclination is much smaller than that caused by the eccentricity. From (3.66), by neglecting the compartment containing the inclination, the equation takes the following form:

$$\begin{aligned} \Delta T &= -\frac{3}{2}\Delta a\omega_e\left(t - t_p\right) + 2a_s e \sin\left(\omega_e\left(t - t_p\right)\right) \\ \Delta N &= i \cdot a_s \sin\left(\omega + \omega_e\left(t - t_p\right)\right) \end{aligned}$$

(a) $\omega = 0°$

When the argument of perigee satisfies $\omega = 0°$, with

$$\sin\left(\omega + \omega_e\left(t - t_p\right)\right) = \sin\left(\omega_e\left(t - t_p\right)\right),$$

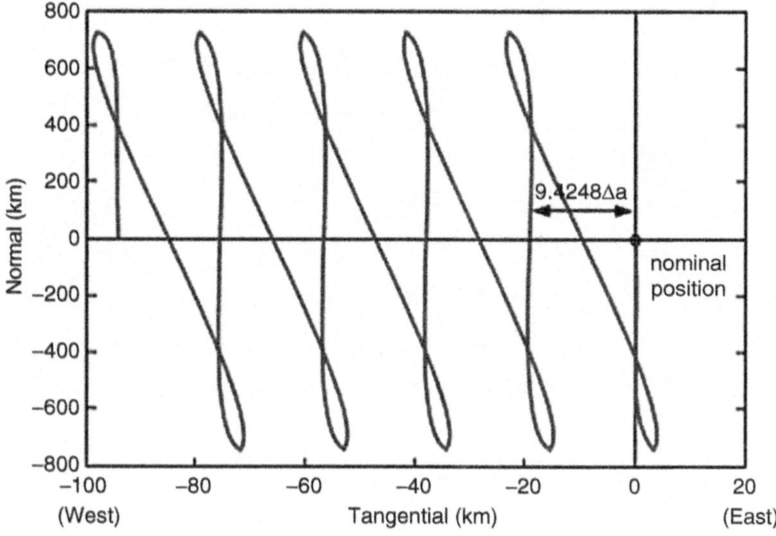

Fig. 3.14 The projection on horizontal plane ($\omega = 180°$)

the projection motion on the local tangential plane satisfies

$$\Delta T = \frac{2e}{i} \cdot \Delta N - \frac{3}{2} \Delta a \cdot \omega_e (t - t_p) \tag{3.73}$$

Being of no synchronous characteristics, the satellite drifts along the tangential direction with a speed of $9.4248 \cdot \Delta a$ per day. The projection motion on the local tangential plane looks like a line, with the slope about $\left(\frac{2e}{i}\right)$. Figure 3.13 illustrates the scenery in which the semi-major deviation $\Delta a = +2$ km, the inclination $i = 1.0°$, and the eccentricity $e = 3.0 \times 10^{-4}$.

(b) $\omega = 180°$

When the argument of perigee satisfies $\omega = 180°$, with

$$\sin\left(\omega + \omega_e(t - t_p)\right) = -\sin\left(\omega_e(t - t_p)\right),$$

the projection motion on the local tangential plane satisfies

$$\Delta T = -\frac{2e}{i} \cdot \Delta N - \frac{3}{2} \Delta a \cdot \omega_e (t - t_p) \tag{3.74}$$

The satellite drifts along the tangential direction with a speed of $9.4248 \cdot \Delta a$ per day. The projection motion on the local tangential plane looks like a line, with the slope about $\left(-\frac{2e}{i}\right)$. Figure 3.14 illustrates the scenery in which the semi-major deviation $\Delta a = +2$ km, the inclination $i = 1.0°$, and the eccentricity $e = 3.0 \times 10^{-4}$.

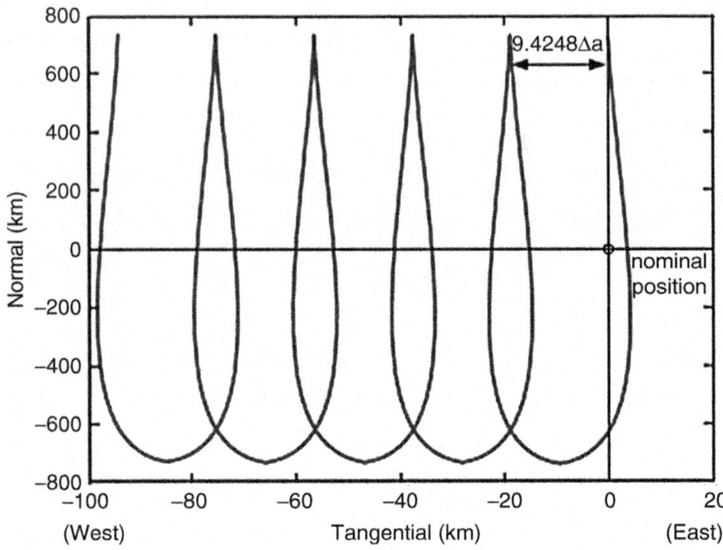

Fig. 3.15 The projection on horizontal plane ($\omega = 90°$)

(c) $\omega = 90°$

When the argument of perigee satisfies $\omega = 90°$, with

$$\sin\left(\omega + \omega_e\left(t - t_p\right)\right) = \cos\left(\omega_e\left(t - t_p\right)\right),$$

the projection motion on the local tangential plane satisfies

$$\Delta T = -\frac{3}{2}\Delta a\omega_e\left(t - t_p\right) + 2a_s e\sin\left(\omega_e\left(t - t_p\right)\right)$$
$$\Delta N = i \cdot a_s\cos\left(\omega_e\left(t - t_p\right)\right)$$

and

$$\left(\Delta T + \frac{\frac{3}{2}\Delta a\omega_e\left(t - t_p\right)}{2ea_s}\right)^2 + \left(\frac{\Delta N}{i \cdot a_s}\right)^2 = 1 \tag{3.75}$$

Figure 3.15 illustrates the scenery in which the semi-major deviation $\Delta a = +2$ km, the inclination $i = 1.0°$, and the eccentricity $e = 3.0 \times 10^{-4}$.

(d) $\omega = 270°$

When the argument of perigee satisfies $\omega = 270°$, with

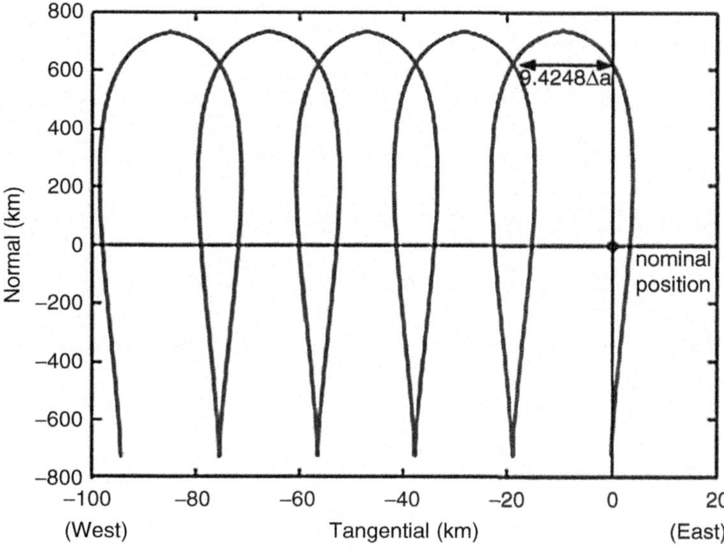

Fig. 3.16 The projection on horizontal plane ($\omega = 270°$)

$$\sin\left(\omega + \omega_e\left(t - t_p\right)\right) = \cos\left(\omega_e\left(t - t_p\right)\right),$$

the projection motion on the local tangential plane satisfies

$$\begin{aligned} \Delta T &= -\frac{3}{2}\Delta a\omega_e\left(t - t_p\right) + 2a_s e \sin\left(\omega_e\left(t - t_p\right)\right) \\ \Delta N &= -i \cdot a_s \cos\left(\omega_e\left(t - t_p\right)\right) \end{aligned}$$

and

$$\left(\frac{\Delta T + \frac{3}{2}\Delta a\omega_e\left(t - t_p\right)}{2ea_s}\right)^2 + \left(\frac{\Delta N}{i \cdot a_s}\right)^2 = 1 \tag{3.76}$$

Figure 3.16 illustrates the scenery in which the semi-major deviation $\Delta a = +2$ km, the inclination $i = 1.0°$, and the eccentricity $e = 3.0 \times 10^{-4}$.

The geostationary satellite circles the Earth as the same as other satellites around the Earth viewed from inertial space. In this chapter we pay special attention to the satellite motion relative to the Earth's rotation. Due to the minor offset between the real orbit and the ideal geostationary orbit, the geostationary satellite is not stationary in terms of the terminological meaning. The eccentricity which is not strictly equal to zero will result in uneven motion rate. The inclination which is not strictly equal to zero, which means that the orbit plane is not identical with the Earth's equatorial plane, will cause that the real geostationary satellite trespasses the equatorial plane twice a day. In general, there is no absolute stationary orbit for the geostationary satellite to reside in. In this chapter, we have illustrated the orbit motion of the real geostationary satellite with the rotational Earth.

Chapter 4
Geostationary Orbit Perturbation

Abstract Performing mathematical analysis and getting concise conclusions may help readers understand the physical realities no matter what educational backgrounds they have. The main strength in this chapter is to discuss the reasons why the geostationary orbit is unstable and how the evolutions of the geostationary orbit elements are caused by perturbation factors. All of the discussions are based on the famous Lagrange equation of planetary motion. No more additional variable transformation and advanced physical background are needed for understanding the equation.

4.1 Introduction

So far we have discussed the characteristics of the geostationary satellite in the assumed spherical symmetrical field of gravity. We have also analyzed the relative motion induced by the minor offset with the ideal geostationary. Any minor offset of the orbit elements will result in that the geostationary satellite moves from its stable resting position to various directions. For example, the semi-major axis offset brings on long-term drift motion toward the tangential direction; the eccentricity offset brings on a periodical libration motion toward the radial and tangential directions; the inclination offset brings on a periodical libration along the normal direction. It's inevitable that the real geostationary orbit may generate those minor offsets out of the ideal geostationary orbit naturally.

In this chapter, we will discuss the reasons why these offsets arise and the evolutions of the orbit elements caused by those natural resources. Although there are many books [1–5] concerning the perturbation motion of the Earth round orbits, this work aims only at the specification of the geostationary orbit. All of the discussions are based on the famous Lagrange equation of planetary motion. No more additional variable transformation and advanced physical background are needed for understanding the equation.

H. Li, *Geostationary Satellites Collocation*, DOI 10.1007/978-3-642-40799-4_4,

4.2 Natural Evolution Motion Scenery

For in-orbit geostationary satellites, the orbit elements are not kept unchangeable. For example, the satellite located at 125° east longitude will drift away from its initial nominal position after 20 days unless we do some necessary maneuvers. Figure 4.1 illustrates that it drifts westward with acceleration and arrives at 105° east longitude in half of a year.

As illustrated in Fig. 4.2, the longitude drift rate changes nearly linearly, and the slope coefficient relies on the nominal longitude of the satellite.

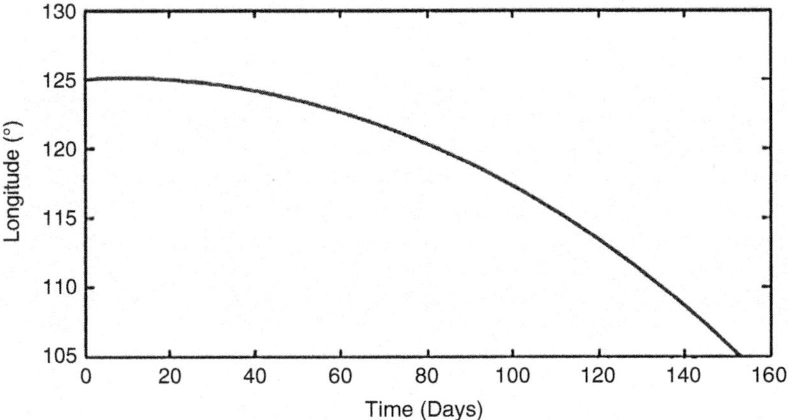

Fig. 4.1 The natural evolution of longitude

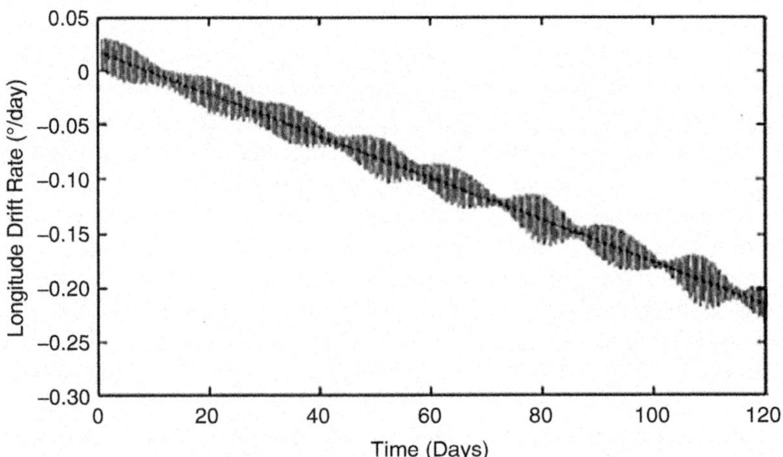

Fig. 4.2 The natural evolution of longitude drift rate

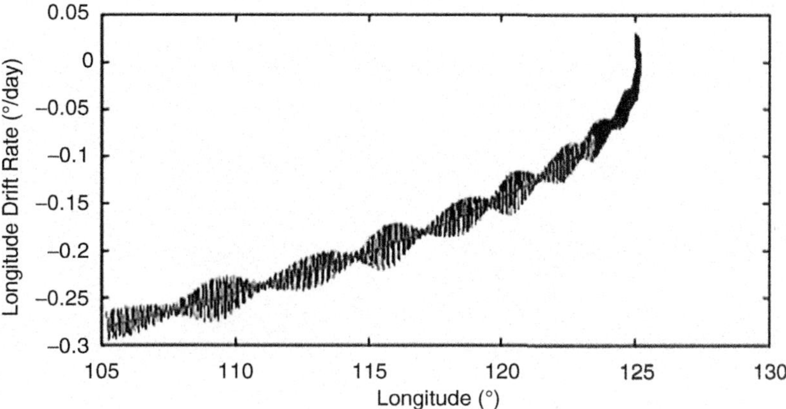

Fig. 4.3 Longitude drift rate versus longitude

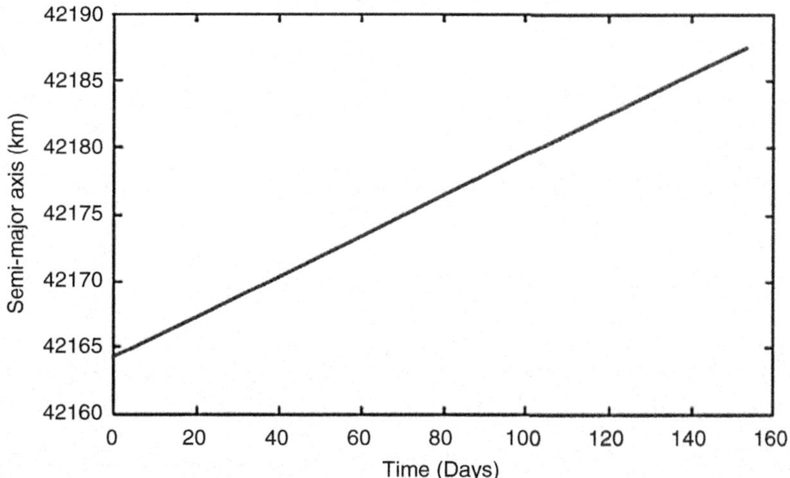

Fig. 4.4 Semi-major axis over approximately one half year

Figure 4.3 shows the phase picture of the longitude and the longitude drift experiences is in the shape of a parabola.

At the same time, after 160 days of perturbation motion, the semi-major axis will increase from 42,165.8 km of the nominal semi-major axis (different from 42,164.2 km of Kepler geostationary orbit radius) to 42,187.5 km as shown in Fig. 4.4.

The eccentricity of geostationary orbit won't keep equal to zero either. Not only the value of eccentricity but also the direction pointing to the perigee node alters because of perturbation forces. Figure 4.5 shows that in polar coordinates with the vernal equinox axis, the natural evolution of the eccentricity vector $(e, \Omega+\omega)$ in 6 months draws approximately a half roundness curve.

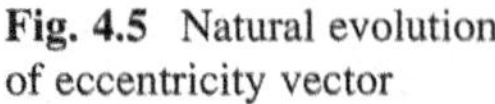

Fig. 4.5 Natural evolution of eccentricity vector

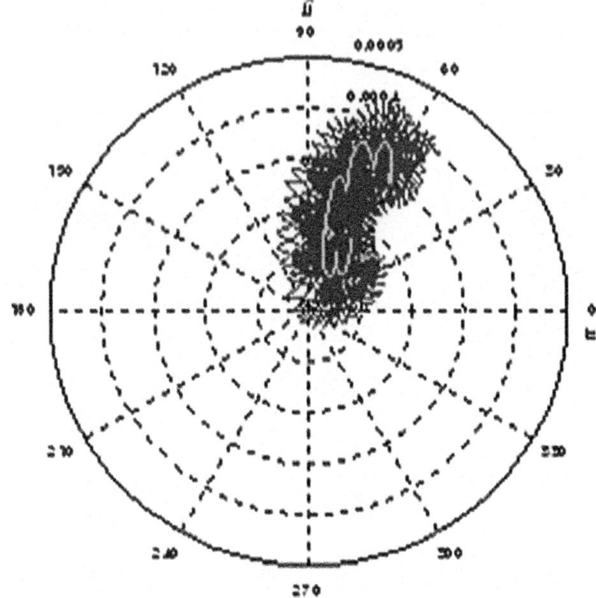

Fig. 4.6 Natural evolution of inclination vector

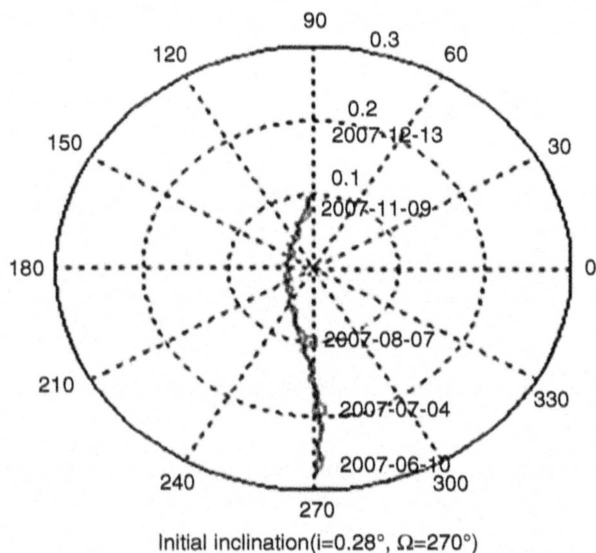

For the inclination of geostationary orbit, not only the magnitude but also the right ascension of the ascending node (the direction pointing to the ascension node) alters because of perturbation forces, too. Figure 4.6 shows that in polar coordinates with the vernal equinox axis, the inclination vector (i, Ω) increases 0.45° toward $+i_y$ direction in 6 months.

From the presentation of natural evolutions of geostationary orbit elements, we can conclude that the real geostationary orbit changes continuously:

1. The real geostationary orbit radius is not equal to the orbit radius given from Kepler law of two-body motion.
2. The geostationary satellite does not stay steadily in its resting position but drifts away in parabola because of eastward or westward perturbing acceleration.
3. The semi-major axis drifts with a secular and some long-period terms.
4. The inclination is not equal to zero strictly but changes approximately linearly with time.
5. The eccentricity is not equal to zero strictly but drifts in some complicated mode.

All of these motions are generated from perturbation forces. In the geostationary orbit, the perturbation forces mainly consist of the non-spherical part of the Earth's gravitational attraction, the gravitational attraction of the Sun and Moon, and the solar radiation pressure. To analyze how perturbation forces act on geostationary satellites and change the values of orbit elements, we will derive the Lagrange equation of perturbation motion with station keeping elements in this section.

4.3 Lagrange Equation for Station Keeping Elements

Besides the Earth's central gravitational attraction, there are many perturbation forces acting on the geostationary satellite all the time. These perturbation forces include the nonhomogeneous and non-spherical part of the Earth's gravitational attraction, the attractions from the third-body, such as the Sun and Moon, and the solar radiation pressure. Because of those perturbation forces, the semi-major axis, the period, the eccentricity, the right ascension of the ascending node, and the inclination change with time. Owning to the accumulation of perturbation acceleration, the geostationary satellite gradually deviates from its ideal resting position.

Define the satellite's instantaneous position vector in the Earth-centric inertial system as $\mathbf{r}$ and its velocity vector as $\dot{\mathbf{r}}$. According to the Newton's first law and with an additional function R of perturbations acting on the satellite, the instantaneous position and velocity vectors satisfy the following differential equation:

$$\begin{cases} \dfrac{\mathrm{d}\mathbf{r}}{\mathrm{d}t} = \dot{\mathbf{r}} \\ \dfrac{\mathrm{d}\dot{\mathbf{r}}}{\mathrm{d}t} = -\dfrac{\mu}{r^3}\mathbf{r} + \mathrm{grad}(R) \end{cases} \tag{4.1}$$

If $R = 0$, that is, the satellite orbit obeys Kepler law of two-body motion, then the orbit semi-major axis, the period, the eccentricity, the right ascension of the ascending node, and the inclination won't change with time. If $R \neq 0$, that is, the satellite does not move in accordance with the law of two-body motion anymore, then these orbit elements change with time. The Kepler orbit elements corresponding to the instantaneous position vector $\mathbf{r}$ and velocity vector $\dot{\mathbf{r}}$ at any moment are named as osculating orbit elements at that moment. The evolution of osculating orbit elements $\{T, a, e, i, \Omega, \omega, M\}$ and their relations to perturbation function R are described with the famous Lagrange equation of planetary motion:

$$\begin{aligned}
\frac{\mathrm{d}a}{\mathrm{d}t} &= \frac{2}{na}\frac{\partial R}{\partial M} \\
\frac{\mathrm{d}e}{\mathrm{d}t} &= \frac{1-e^2}{na^2 e}\frac{\partial R}{\partial M} - \frac{\sqrt{1-e^2}}{na^2 e}\frac{\partial R}{\partial \omega} \\
\frac{\mathrm{d}i}{\mathrm{d}t} &= \frac{\cot i}{na^2\sqrt{1-e^2}}\frac{\partial R}{\partial \omega} - \frac{\csc i}{na^2\sqrt{1-e^2}}\frac{\partial R}{\partial \Omega} \\
\frac{\mathrm{d}\Omega}{\mathrm{d}t} &= \frac{1}{na^2\sqrt{1-e^2}\sin i}\frac{\partial R}{\partial i} \\
\frac{\mathrm{d}\omega}{\mathrm{d}t} &= \frac{\sqrt{1-e^2}}{na^2 e}\frac{\partial R}{\partial e} - \frac{\cot i}{na^2\sqrt{1-e^2}}\frac{\partial R}{\partial i} \\
\frac{\mathrm{d}M}{\mathrm{d}t} &= n - \frac{2}{na}\frac{\partial R}{\partial a} - \frac{1-e^2}{na^2 e}\frac{\partial R}{\partial e}
\end{aligned} \tag{4.2}$$

By introducing approximate relations under the geostationary orbit condition to linearize the above equations, we can derive the Lagrange equations of perturbation motion for station keeping elements of geostationary orbit.

4.3.1 Lagrange Equation for the Drift Vector

Among station keeping elements, the semi-major axis a (or drift rate D) and the mean longitude λ are defined as drift vector (a, λ) or (D, λ). The mean longitude and Kepler orbit elements satisfy the equation

$$\lambda = \omega + \Omega + M - \theta(t)$$

Converting the equation to the differential form, we can derive

$$\begin{aligned}
\frac{\mathrm{d}\lambda}{\mathrm{d}t} &= \frac{d}{\mathrm{d}t}(\omega + \Omega + M - \theta(t)) \\
&= \frac{\mathrm{d}\omega}{\mathrm{d}t} + \frac{\mathrm{d}\Omega}{\mathrm{d}t} + \frac{\mathrm{d}M}{\mathrm{d}t} - \frac{\mathrm{d}\theta(t)}{\mathrm{d}t} = \frac{\mathrm{d}\omega}{\mathrm{d}t} + \frac{\mathrm{d}\Omega}{\mathrm{d}t} + \frac{\mathrm{d}M}{\mathrm{d}t} - \omega_e
\end{aligned}$$

In the differential equation, ω_e means the angular velocity of the Earth's rotation. From Lagrange equation (4.2) and only keeping first-order terms of e and i, we convert the equation to

$$\frac{\partial R}{\partial M}=\frac{\partial R}{\partial \lambda}\cdot\frac{\partial \lambda}{\partial M}=\frac{\partial R}{\partial \lambda}\cdot\frac{\partial}{\partial M}(\omega+\Omega+M-\theta(t))=\frac{\partial R}{\partial \lambda}$$
$$\frac{d\omega}{dt}+\frac{d\Omega}{dt}=\frac{1}{na^2e}\cdot\frac{\partial R}{\partial e}$$
$$\frac{dM}{dt}=n-\frac{2}{na}\frac{\partial R}{\partial a}-\frac{1}{na^2e}\frac{\partial R}{\partial a}$$

Now we derive the Lagrange equation for the drift vector (a,λ) of the geostationary orbit:

$$\begin{cases}\dfrac{da}{dt}=\dfrac{2}{na}\dfrac{\partial R}{\partial \lambda}\\[2mm] \dfrac{d\lambda}{dt}=\dfrac{d\omega}{dt}+\dfrac{d\Omega}{dt}+\dfrac{dM}{dt}-\omega_e=(n-\omega_e)-\dfrac{2}{na}\dfrac{\partial R}{\partial a}\end{cases}\cdot \tag{4.3}$$

From

$$\frac{dD}{dt}=-\frac{3}{2}\left(\frac{1}{a_s}\right)\frac{da}{dt}$$

the Lagrange equation for the drift vector (D,λ) of geostationary orbit follows the following expression:

$$\begin{cases}\dfrac{dD}{dt}=-\dfrac{3}{2}\left(\dfrac{1}{a_s}\right)\dfrac{da}{dt}=-\dfrac{3}{2}\left(\dfrac{1}{a_s}\right)\left(\dfrac{2}{na}\right)\dfrac{\partial R}{\partial \lambda}\\[2mm] \dfrac{d\lambda}{dt}=(n-\omega_e)-\dfrac{2}{na}\dfrac{\partial R}{\partial a}\end{cases} \tag{4.4}$$

4.3.2 *Lagrange Equation for the Eccentricity Vector*

The eccentricity vector defines the value of orbit eccentricity and its direction points from the Earth's center to the orbit perigee:

$$\mathbf{e}=\begin{pmatrix}e_x\\ e_y\end{pmatrix}=\begin{pmatrix}e\cos(\Omega+\omega)\\ e\sin(\Omega+\omega)\end{pmatrix}$$

Converting the equation to the differential form, we can derive the eccentricity vector expressed as a function of time:

$$\frac{\mathrm{d}e_x}{\mathrm{d}t} = \cos(\Omega+\omega)\cdot\frac{\mathrm{d}e}{\mathrm{d}t} - e\sin(\Omega+\omega)\left(\frac{\mathrm{d}\Omega}{\mathrm{d}t}+\frac{\mathrm{d}\omega}{\mathrm{d}t}\right) \tag{4.5}$$

$$\frac{\mathrm{d}e_y}{\mathrm{d}t} = \sin(\Omega+\omega)\cdot\frac{\mathrm{d}e}{\mathrm{d}t} + e\cos(\Omega+\omega)\left(\frac{\mathrm{d}\Omega}{\mathrm{d}t}+\frac{\mathrm{d}\omega}{\mathrm{d}t}\right) \tag{4.6}$$

From Lagrange equation (4.2) and only keeping first-order terms of e and i, we convert the equation to

$$\frac{\mathrm{d}e}{\mathrm{d}t} = -\frac{1}{na^2e}\frac{\partial R}{\partial\omega},\ \frac{\mathrm{d}\omega}{\mathrm{d}t}+\frac{\mathrm{d}\Omega}{\mathrm{d}t} = \frac{1}{na^2e}\cdot\frac{\partial R}{\partial e}$$

Introduce total differential formula with multivariable function:

$$\frac{\partial R}{\partial\omega} = \frac{\partial R}{\partial e_x}\cdot\frac{\partial e_x}{\partial\omega}+\frac{\partial R}{\partial e_y}\cdot\frac{\partial e_y}{\partial\omega},\quad \frac{\partial R}{\partial e} = \frac{\partial R}{\partial e_x}\cdot\frac{\partial e_x}{\partial e}+\frac{\partial R}{\partial e_y}\cdot\frac{\partial e_y}{\partial e}$$

and perform the differential to the eccentricity vector with respect to ω and e:

$$\frac{\partial e_x}{\partial\omega} = -e\sin(\Omega+\omega),\quad \frac{\partial e_y}{\partial\omega} = e\cos(\Omega+\omega)$$

$$\frac{\partial e_x}{\partial e} = \cos(\Omega+\omega),\quad \frac{\partial e_y}{\partial e} = \sin(\Omega+\omega)$$

So we can derive

$$\begin{aligned}\frac{\mathrm{d}e}{\mathrm{d}t} &= -\frac{1}{na^2e}\frac{\partial R}{\partial\omega} = -\frac{1}{na^2e}\left(\frac{\partial R}{\partial e_x}\cdot\frac{\partial e_x}{\partial\omega}+\frac{\partial R}{\partial e_y}\cdot\frac{\partial e_y}{\partial\omega}\right)\\ &= \frac{1}{na^2}\left(\sin(\Omega+\omega)\frac{\partial R}{\partial e_x}-\cos(\Omega+\omega)\frac{\partial R}{\partial e_y}\right)\end{aligned}$$

$$\begin{aligned}\frac{\mathrm{d}\omega}{\mathrm{d}t}+\frac{\mathrm{d}\Omega}{\mathrm{d}t} &= \frac{1}{na^2e}\cdot\frac{\partial R}{\partial e} = \frac{1}{na^2e}\cdot\left(\frac{\partial R}{\partial e_x}\cdot\frac{\partial e_x}{\partial e}+\frac{\partial R}{\partial e_y}\cdot\frac{\partial e_y}{\partial e}\right)\\ &= \frac{1}{na^2e}\cdot\left(\cos(\Omega+\omega)\frac{\partial R}{\partial e_x}+\sin(\Omega+\omega)\frac{\partial R}{\partial e_y}\right)\end{aligned}$$

Replace Eqs. (4.5) and (4.6) with the expression above:

$$\begin{aligned}\frac{\mathrm{d}e_x}{\mathrm{d}t} &= \cos(\Omega+\omega)\frac{1}{na^2}\left(\sin(\Omega+\omega)\frac{\partial R}{\partial e_x} - \cos(\Omega+\omega)\frac{\partial R}{\partial e_y}\right) \\ &\quad - e\sin(\Omega+\omega)\frac{1}{na^2 e}\left(\cos(\Omega+\omega)\frac{\partial R}{\partial e_x} + \sin(\Omega+\omega)\frac{\partial R}{\partial e_y}\right) \\ &= -\frac{1}{na^2}\frac{\partial R}{\partial e_y}\end{aligned}$$

$$\begin{aligned}\frac{\mathrm{d}e_y}{\mathrm{d}t} &= \sin(\Omega+\omega)\frac{1}{na^2}\left(\sin(\Omega+\omega)\frac{\partial R}{\partial e_x} - \cos(\Omega+\omega)\frac{\partial R}{\partial e_y}\right) \\ &\quad - e\cos(\Omega+\omega)\frac{1}{na^2 e}\left(\cos(\Omega+\omega)\frac{\partial R}{\partial e_x} + \sin(\Omega+\omega)\frac{\partial R}{\partial e_y}\right) \\ &= \frac{1}{na^2}\frac{\partial R}{\partial e_x}\end{aligned}$$

Now the Lagrange equation for the eccentricity vector of geostationary orbit is given by

$$\begin{cases}\dfrac{\mathrm{d}e_x}{\mathrm{d}t} = -\dfrac{1}{na^2}\dfrac{\partial R}{\partial e_y} \\ \dfrac{\mathrm{d}e_y}{\mathrm{d}t} = \dfrac{1}{na^2}\dfrac{\partial R}{\partial e_x}\end{cases}. \tag{4.7}$$

4.3.3 Lagrange Equation for the Inclination Vector

The inclination vector equals the value of orbit inclination and its direction points from the Earth's center to the orbit ascending node. The vector is defined as

$$\mathbf{i} = \begin{pmatrix} i_x \\ i_y \end{pmatrix} = \begin{pmatrix} i\cos(\Omega) \\ i\sin(\Omega) \end{pmatrix}$$

The inclination vector can be expressed as a function of time. Converting the equation to the differential form, we can derive

$$\frac{\mathrm{d}i_x}{\mathrm{d}t} = \frac{d}{\mathrm{d}t}(i\cos(\Omega)) = \cos(\Omega)\frac{\mathrm{d}i}{\mathrm{d}t} - i\sin(\Omega)\frac{\mathrm{d}\Omega}{\mathrm{d}t} \tag{4.8}$$

$$\frac{\mathrm{d}i_y}{dt}=\frac{d}{dt}(i\sin(\Omega))=\sin(\Omega)\frac{\mathrm{d}i}{dt}+i\cos(\Omega)\frac{\mathrm{d}\Omega}{\mathrm{d}t} \tag{4.9}$$

From Lagrange equation (4.2) and only keeping first-order terms of e and i, we convert the equation to

$$\frac{\mathrm{d}i}{\mathrm{d}t}=-\frac{1}{ina^2}\frac{\partial R}{\partial\Omega},\quad \frac{\mathrm{d}\Omega}{\mathrm{d}t}=\frac{1}{ina^2}\frac{\partial R}{\partial i}$$

Introduce total differential formula with multivariable function; then

$$\frac{\partial R}{\partial i}=\frac{\partial R}{\partial i_x}\frac{\partial i_x}{\partial i}+\frac{\partial R}{\partial i_y}\frac{\partial i_y}{\partial i},\quad \frac{\partial R}{\partial\Omega}=\frac{\partial R}{\partial i_x}\frac{\partial i_x}{\partial\Omega}+\frac{\partial R}{\partial i_y}\frac{\partial i_y}{\partial\Omega}$$

Perform the differential to the inclination vector (i_x, i_y) with respect to i and Ω; then

$$\begin{aligned}\frac{\partial i_x}{\partial i}&=\cos(\Omega),\quad \frac{\partial i_x}{\partial\Omega}=-i\sin(\Omega)\\ \frac{\partial i_y}{\partial i}&=\sin(\Omega),\quad \frac{\partial i_y}{\partial\Omega}=i\cos(\Omega)\end{aligned}$$

Replace Eqs. (4.10) and (4.11) with the expression above:

$$\begin{aligned}\frac{\mathrm{d}i}{\mathrm{d}t}&=-\frac{1}{ina^2}\frac{\partial R}{\partial\Omega}=-\frac{1}{ina^2}\left(\frac{\partial R}{\partial i_x}\frac{\partial i_x}{\partial\Omega}+\frac{\partial R}{\partial i_y}\frac{\partial i_y}{\partial\Omega}\right)\\ &=-\frac{1}{ina^2}\left(-i\sin(\Omega)\frac{\partial R}{\partial i_x}+i\cos(\Omega)\frac{\partial R}{\partial i_y}\right)\end{aligned}$$

$$\frac{\mathrm{d}\Omega}{\mathrm{d}t}=\frac{1}{ina^2}\frac{\partial R}{\partial i}=\frac{1}{ina^2}\left(\frac{\partial R}{\partial i_x}\frac{\partial i_x}{\partial i}+\frac{\partial R}{\partial i_y}\frac{\partial i_y}{\partial i}\right)=\frac{1}{ina^2}\left(\cos(\Omega)\frac{\partial R}{\partial i_x}+\sin(\Omega)\frac{\partial R}{\partial i_y}\right)$$

Also replace Eqs. (4.8) and (4.9) with the expression above:

$$\begin{aligned}\frac{\mathrm{d}i_x}{\mathrm{d}t}&=\cos(\Omega)\frac{\mathrm{d}i}{\mathrm{d}t}-i\sin(\Omega)\frac{\mathrm{d}\Omega}{\mathrm{d}t}\\ &=-\frac{\cos(\Omega)}{ina^2}\left(-i\sin(\Omega)\frac{\partial R}{\partial i_x}+i\cos(\Omega)\frac{\partial R}{\partial i_y}\right)-\frac{i\sin(\Omega)}{ina^2}\left(\cos(\Omega)\frac{\partial R}{\partial i_x}+\sin(\Omega)\frac{\partial R}{\partial i_y}\right)\\ &=-\frac{1}{na^2}\frac{\partial R}{\partial i_y}\end{aligned} \tag{4.10}$$

and

$$\begin{aligned}\frac{\mathrm{d}i_y}{\mathrm{d}t} &= \sin(\Omega)\frac{\mathrm{d}i}{\mathrm{d}t} + i\cos(\Omega)\frac{\mathrm{d}\Omega}{\mathrm{d}t} \\ &= -\frac{\sin(\Omega)}{ina^2}\left(-i\sin(\Omega)\frac{\partial R}{\partial i_x} + i\cos(\Omega)\frac{\partial R}{\partial i_y}\right) \\ &\quad + \frac{i\cos(\Omega)}{ina^2}\left(\cos(\Omega)\frac{\partial R}{\partial i_x} + \sin(\Omega)\frac{\partial R}{\partial i_y}\right) \\ &= \frac{1}{na^2}\frac{\partial R}{\partial i_x}\end{aligned} \tag{4.11}$$

Now the Lagrange equation for the inclination vector is given by

$$\begin{cases}\dfrac{\mathrm{d}i_x}{\mathrm{d}t} = -\dfrac{1}{na^2}\dfrac{\partial R}{\partial i_y} \\ \dfrac{\mathrm{d}i_y}{\mathrm{d}t} = \dfrac{1}{na^2}\dfrac{\partial R}{\partial i_x}\end{cases}. \tag{4.12}$$

4.4 The Earth's Non-spherical Perturbation

4.4.1 The Earth's Non-spherical Potential Function

The position of a geostationary satellite located at dedicated longitude can be expressed as

$$\mathbf{r}_{\mathrm{WGS}} = r_s \cdot \begin{pmatrix}\cos(\lambda_N) \\ \sin(\lambda_N) \\ 0\end{pmatrix}, \text{ and } \mathbf{r}_{\mathrm{ECI}} = \mathbf{M}_{\mathrm{ECI}}^{\mathrm{WGS}} \cdot \mathbf{r}_{\mathrm{WGS}}$$

According to the model of gravitational field, the gravitational acceleration acting on the geostationary satellite in the ECF coordinate is $\mathbf{a}_{\mathrm{E}}^{\mathrm{WGS}}$. Since the transfer matrix from ECF to the J2000.0 Earth-centric inertial (ECI) coordinate is $\mathbf{M}_{\mathrm{ECI}}^{\mathrm{WGS}}$, the gravitational acceleration in the J2000.0 ECI coordinate is

$$\mathbf{a}_{\mathrm{E}}^{\mathrm{ECI}} = \mathbf{M}_{\mathrm{ECI}}^{\mathrm{WGS}} \cdot \mathbf{a}_{\mathrm{E}}^{\mathrm{WGS}}$$

Table 4.1 JGM-3 Earth gravity model (3 × 3)

$n\ m$	$J_n \times 10^{-6}$	$n\ m$	$C_{nm} \times 10^{-6}$	$S_{nm} \times 10^{-6}$	$J_{nm} \times 10^{-6}$	$\lambda_{nm}(°)$
2 0	−1082.627	2 2	1.574536	−0.903868	1.815528	−14.929
3 0	2.532435	3 1	2.192799	0.2680119	2.2091169	6.968
4 0	1.619331	3 3	0.100559	0.197201	0.2213602	20.994

For simplification, the following expression is used to project the perturbing acceleration induced by the non-spherical part of the Earth's gravitational attraction into the orbit radial/tangential/normal (RTN) coordinate:

$$\mathbf{a}_{\mathrm{E}}^{\mathrm{RTN}} = \begin{pmatrix} a_R \\ a_T \\ a_N \end{pmatrix} = \left(\mathbf{M}_{\mathrm{ECI}}^{\mathrm{RTN}}\right)^{\mathrm{T}} \cdot \left(\mathbf{a}_{\mathrm{E}}^{\mathrm{ECI}} - \left(-\frac{\mu}{r_s^3}\mathbf{r}_{\mathrm{ECI}}\right)\right)$$

In the expression,

$$\mathbf{M}_{\mathrm{ECI}}^{\mathrm{RTN}} = \mathbf{M}_{\mathrm{ECI}}^{\mathrm{WGS}} \cdot \mathbf{M}_{\mathrm{WGS}}^{\mathrm{RTN}}$$

is the transfer matrix from the J2000.0 Earth-centric inertial coordinate to the RTN coordinate.

Different from the spherical symmetrical Earth and among the coefficients of the Earth's gravity $S_{n0}=0, n=0,1,\ldots,$ the function of perturbation from the non-spherical part of the Earth's gravitational attraction can be expressed as

$$R = \left(\frac{\mu}{r}\right)\left(\sum_{n=2}^{\infty}\left(\frac{R_e}{r}\right)^n\left\{J_n P_{n0}[\sin(\phi)] + \sum_{m=0}^{n} J_{nm}P_{nm}[\sin(\phi)]\cos m(\lambda - \lambda_{nm})\right\}\right)$$

In the expression,

$$J_{nm} = \sqrt{C_{nm}^2 + S_{nm}^2}, \quad \cos(m\lambda_{nm}) = \frac{C_{nm}}{J_{nm}}, \quad \sin(m\lambda_{nm}) = \frac{S_{nm}}{J_{nm}}$$

Among the coefficients of the Earth's gravity model, major perturbation coefficients are listed in Table 4.1.

And the associated Legendre polynomials are listed in Table 4.2.

For the geostationary orbit, the main perturbation function of the non-spherical part of the Earth's gravitational attraction now can be expressed as

Table 4.2 The associated Legendre polynomials and its approximations for GEO satellite

n m	$P_{nm}(\phi)$	For geostationary orbit $\sin(\phi)\approx 0, \cos(\phi)=1$
2 0	$\frac{1}{2}(3\sin^2\phi - 1)$	$-\frac{1}{2}$
2 2	$3\cos^2(\phi)$	3
3 0	$\frac{1}{2}(5\sin^3\phi - 3\sin\phi)$	0
3 1	$\frac{1}{2}\cos\phi\,(15\sin^2\phi - 3)$	$-\frac{3}{2}$
3 3	$15\cos^3\phi$	15
4 0	$\frac{1}{8}(35\sin^4\phi - 30\sin^2\phi + 3)$	$\frac{3}{8}$

$$R = \left(\frac{\mu}{r}\right)\left(\sum_{n=2}^{\infty}\left(\frac{R_e}{r}\right)^n\left\{J_n P_{n0}[\sin(\phi)] + \sum_{m=0}^{n} J_{nm}P_{nm}[\sin(\phi)]\cos m(\lambda - \lambda_{nm})\right\}\right)$$

$$= \left(\frac{\mu}{r}\right)\left\{\begin{array}{l} -\frac{1}{2}J_2\left(\frac{R_e}{r}\right)^2 + 3J_{22}\left(\frac{R_e}{r}\right)^2\cos 2(\lambda - \lambda_{22}) \\ -\frac{3}{2}J_{31}\left(\frac{R_e}{r}\right)^3\cos(\lambda - \lambda_{31}) + 15J_{33}\left(\frac{R_e}{r}\right)^3\cos 3(\lambda - \lambda_{33}) \\ +\frac{3}{8}J_4\left(\frac{R_e}{r}\right)^4 \end{array}\right\} \tag{4.13}$$

4.4.2 Real Geostationary Orbit

For the reason of the Earth's oblateness and elliptic equator plane, the satellite located in the geostationary orbit has an extra acceleration toward the radial direction. The acceleration mainly comes from the zonal term J_2 of the Earth's gravity. Due to the different effects of the tesseral term J_{22} on the satellite at a different longitude, the approximately average value of acceleration is $\mathbf{a}_R = -8.33\times 10^{-6}(\mathrm{m/s^2})$. Figure 4.7 illustrates the extra radial acceleration at a different longitude caused by the bulge of the Earth. The horizontal ordinate means the nominal longitude, where the west longitude is of negative value and the east is of positive value. The vertical ordinate means the component of the non-spherical Earth's perturbation acceleration toward the radial direction.

The effect of radial perturbation acceleration can be considered as increasing Earth's central gravitational attraction because of the bulge of the Earth. Define the

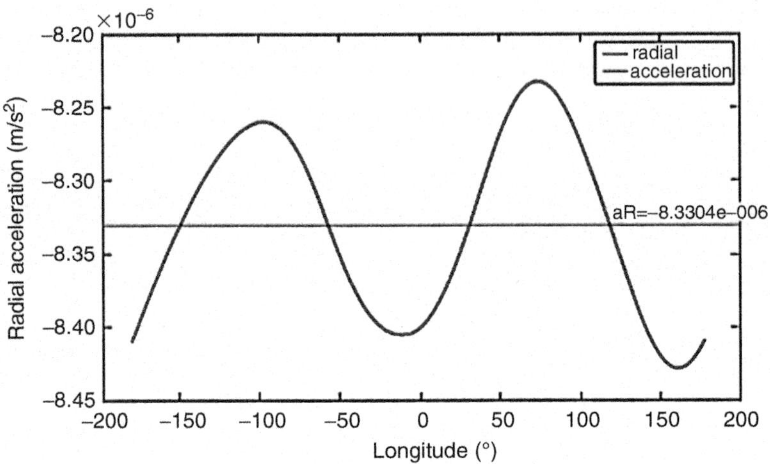

Fig 4.7 Extra radial acceleration induced by the Earth

semi-major axis with the non-spherical Earth's perturbation as a_c. By considering the Earth as a point mass or a sphere, the semi-major axis is defined as a_s. The value of a_c is different with the one of a_s. Because the orbit eccentricity is independent of the satellite's mean longitude drift, we still use the roundness orbit when we discuss how the non-spherical Earth's perturbation acceleration takes effect on the semi-major axis. Therefore, for the reason of the non-spherical Earth's perturbation, the semi-major axis a_c should be modified to keep the geostationary satellite stable, which means the real semi-major axis of geostationary orbit should satisfy

$$\frac{\mathrm{d}\lambda}{\mathrm{d}t}|_{a=a_c} = 0$$

According to Lagrange equation (4.3) of the geostationary orbit,

$$\frac{\mathrm{d}\lambda}{\mathrm{d}t} = (n - \omega_e) - \frac{2}{na}\frac{\partial R}{\partial a}$$

Obviously, if perturbation function is of $R = 0$, then a_s satisfies $\frac{\mathrm{d}\lambda}{\mathrm{d}t}|_{a=a_s} = 0$. If $R \neq 0$, in order to keep the geostationary satellite stable, the real orbit semi-major axis a_c should satisfy the equation below:

$$\frac{\mathrm{d}\lambda}{\mathrm{d}t} = (n_c - \omega_e) - \frac{2}{na_c}\frac{\partial R}{\partial a}|_{a=a_c} = 0$$

In the equation

$$n_c = \sqrt{\frac{\mu}{a_c^3}},\ \omega_e = \sqrt{\frac{\mu}{a_s}}$$

and

$$\frac{\partial R}{\partial a} = \frac{\partial R}{\partial r} = \left(\frac{\mu}{a^2}\right)\left\{\begin{array}{l} \frac{3}{2}J_2\left(\frac{R_e}{a}\right)^2 - 9J_{22}\left(\frac{R_e}{a}\right)^2\cos 2(\lambda - \lambda_{22}) \\ +6J_{31}\left(\frac{R_e}{a}\right)^3\cos(\lambda - \lambda_{31}) \\ -60J_{33}\left(\frac{R_e}{a}\right)^3\cos 3(\lambda - \lambda_{33}) - \frac{15}{8}J_4\left(\frac{R_e}{a}\right)^4 \end{array}\right\} = \left(\frac{\mu}{a^2}\right)\Gamma(a)$$

since

$$(n_c - \omega_e) = \sqrt{\frac{\mu}{a_c^3}} - \sqrt{\frac{\mu}{a_s^3}} \approx -\frac{3}{2}\sqrt{\frac{\mu}{a_c^3}}\left(\frac{a_c - a_s}{a_s}\right)$$

and

$$\frac{2}{n_c a_c}\frac{\partial R}{\partial a}\Big|_{a=a_c} = \frac{2}{n_c a_c}\left(\frac{\mu}{a_c^2}\right)\Gamma(a_c) = 2\sqrt{\frac{\mu}{a_c^3}}\Gamma(a_c)$$

so that

$$-\frac{3}{2}\sqrt{\frac{\mu}{a_c^3}}\left(\frac{a_c - a_s}{a_s}\right) = 2\sqrt{\frac{\mu}{a_c^3}}\Gamma(a_c) \Rightarrow a_c = a_s - \frac{4}{3}a_s\Gamma(a_c)$$

Introducing the approximate equations below,

$$\left(\frac{R_e}{a_c}\right)^2 \approx \left(\frac{R_e}{a_s}\right)^2, \left(\frac{R_e}{a_c}\right)^3 \approx \left(\frac{R_e}{a_s}\right)^3, \left(\frac{R_e}{a_c}\right)^4 \approx \left(\frac{R_e}{a_s}\right)^4$$

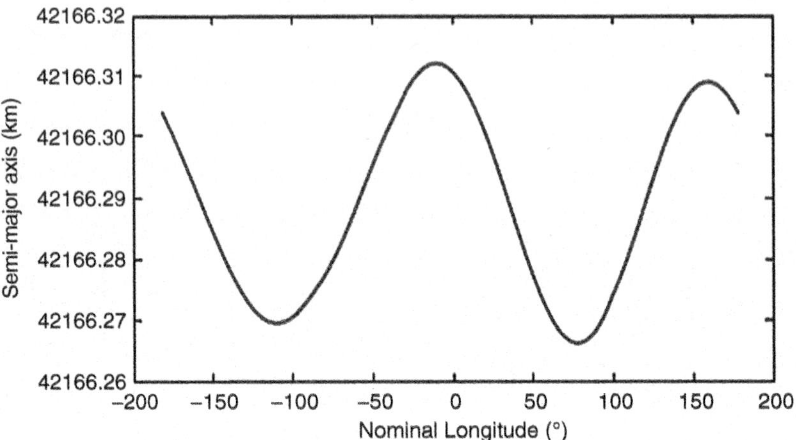

Fig. 4.8 Real semi-major axis for geostationary satellite

The approximate expression of real semi-major axis with the non-spherical Earth's perturbation is given by

$$a_c = a_s - \frac{4}{3}a_s\Gamma(a_s) = a_s + a_s\begin{pmatrix} -2J_2\left(\frac{R_e}{a_s}\right)^2 + 12J_{22}\left(\frac{R_e}{a_s}\right)^2\cos 2(\lambda - \lambda_{22}) \\ -8J_{31}\left(\frac{R_e}{a_s}\right)^3\cos(\lambda - \lambda_{31}) \\ +80J_{33}\left(\frac{R_e}{a_s}\right)^3\cos 3(\lambda - \lambda_{33}) + \frac{5}{2}J_4\left(\frac{R_e}{a_s}\right)^4 \end{pmatrix} \tag{4.14}$$

Replacing the above equation with the perturbation coefficients in Table 4.1, we can obtain the real semi-major axis of the geostationary orbit at a different longitude. Figure 4.8 shows real semi-major axis under perturbation condition is slightly different from the ones with non-perturbation force.

The contributions of non-aspheric perturbation terms on the geostationary orbit are summarized below:

J_2: contribute 2.0891 km increments.
J_4: contribute 8.9376E-5 km increments.
J_{22}: induce the semi-major axis libration within the amplitude of 0.0210 km.
J_{31}: induce the semi-major axis libration within the amplitude of 0.0026 km.
J_{33}: induce the semi-major axis libration within the amplitude of 0.0026 km.

Therefore, taking only the non-spherical Earth's perturbation into account, the real semi-major axis for geostationary satellite would be about $a_c = 42166.289$ km,

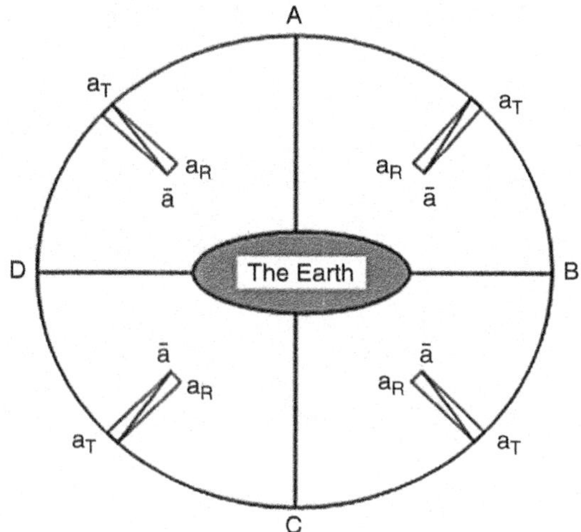

Fig. 4.9 Triaxiality of the Earth leads to an extra tangential attraction

which is greater than the one just in consideration of aspheric body. Generally, in consideration of the gravitation attractions from the Sun, Moon, and Earth together, the real semi-major axis of geostationary orbit takes the average value of about $a_c = 42165.700$ km to balance the extra perturbations.

4.4.3 Semi-major Axis Evolution

Due to the tesseral term J_{22} (main term), namely, the triaxiality of the Earth, the satellite located at the geostationary orbit has an extra gravitational acceleration toward the tangential direction. As shown in Fig. 4.9, the presence of tesseral terms in the Earth's potential leads to an extra tangential attraction that varies in magnitude and direction according to the longitude.

Being the triaxiality of the Earth, define AC as the minor axis of the Earth's elliptic equator plane and BD as the major axis. The satellite located at AB zone suffers from the extra attraction of bulge part along the major axis of the Earth's elliptic equator plane, which is of a westward tangential gravitational acceleration. The satellite located at AD zone experiences the eastward tangential acceleration. For the same reason CD zone has a westward tangential gravitational acceleration, and BC zone has an eastward tangential gravitational acceleration as illustrated in Fig. 4.10.

According to Lagrange equation, the tangential acceleration will change the semi-major axis and consequently causes inconsonance between the orbit motion and Earth's rotation angular velocity. Finally, the satellite deviates from its nominal position.

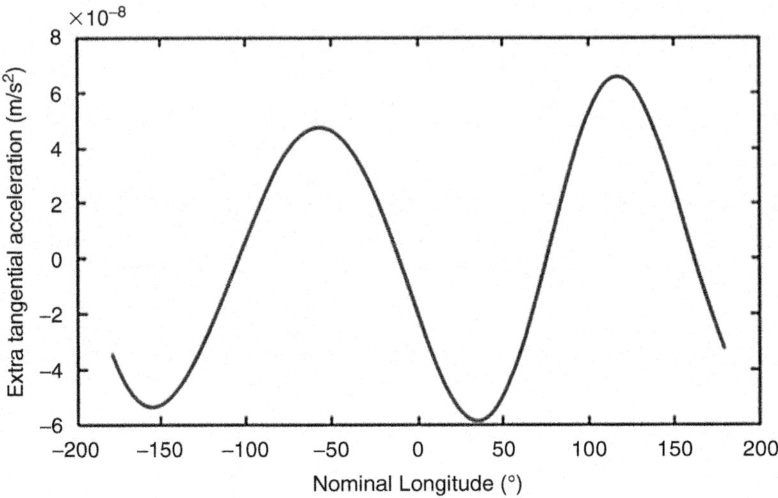

Fig. 4.10 Extra tangential acceleration due to the triaxiality of the Earth

The semi-major axis satisfies the Lagrange perturbation equation derived in the Sect. 4.3:

$$\frac{\mathrm{d}a}{\mathrm{d}t} = \frac{2}{na}\frac{\partial R}{\partial \lambda} \tag{4.15}$$

Because the real semi-major axis has balanced the perturbation of zonal term, especially the J_2 term, the extra tangential attractions from the tesseral term of the Earth become significant perturbations:

$$\frac{\partial R}{\partial \lambda} = \left(\frac{\mu}{r}\right)\begin{Bmatrix} -6J_{22}\left(\frac{R_e}{r}\right)^2 \sin 2(\lambda - \lambda_{22}) \\ +\frac{3}{2}J_{31}\left(\frac{R_e}{r}\right)^3 \sin(\lambda - \lambda_{31}) \\ -45J_{33}\left(\frac{R_e}{r}\right)^3 \sin 3(\lambda - \lambda_{33}) \end{Bmatrix} \tag{4.16}$$

Replacing Eq. (4.16) with the coefficients in Tables 4.2 and 4.3, the perturbation equation of semi-major axis induced by the non-spherical part of the Earth's gravity follows the expression below:

$$\frac{\mathrm{d}a}{\mathrm{d}t}=\frac{2}{na}\frac{\partial R}{\partial \lambda}=\frac{2}{n_c a_c}\cdot\left(\frac{\mu}{a_c}\right)\left\{\begin{array}{l} -6J_{22}\left(\dfrac{R_e}{a_c}\right)^2\sin 2(\lambda-\lambda_{22}) \\ +\dfrac{3}{2}J_{31}\left(\dfrac{R_e}{a_c}\right)^3\sin(\lambda-\lambda_{31}) \\ -45J_{33}\left(\dfrac{R_e}{a_c}\right)^3\sin 3(\lambda-\lambda_{33}) \end{array}\right\}$$
$$=-\frac{2}{3}\frac{a_c}{n_c}\cdot\left(-3\frac{\mu}{a_c^3}\right)\left\{\begin{array}{l} -6J_{22}\left(\dfrac{R_e}{a_c}\right)^2\sin 2(\lambda-\lambda_{22}) \\ +\dfrac{3}{2}J_{31}\left(\dfrac{R_e}{a_c}\right)^3\sin(\lambda-\lambda_{31}) \\ -45J_{33}\left(\dfrac{R_e}{a_c}\right)^3\sin 3(\lambda-\lambda_{33}) \end{array}\right\} \tag{4.17}$$

Denote

$$\Gamma_\lambda=-3n_c^2\left\{\begin{array}{l} -6J_{22}\left(\dfrac{R_e}{a_c}\right)^2\sin 2(\lambda-\lambda_{22}) \\ +\dfrac{3}{2}J_{31}\left(\dfrac{R_e}{a_c}\right)^3\sin(\lambda-\lambda_{31}) \\ -45J_{33}\left(\dfrac{R_e}{a_c}\right)^3\sin 3(\lambda-\lambda_{33}) \end{array}\right\} \tag{4.18}$$

so that the semi-major axis' perturbation equation of the real geostationary orbit is

$$\frac{\mathrm{d}a}{\mathrm{d}t}=-\frac{2}{3}\frac{a_c}{n_c}\cdot\Gamma_\lambda \tag{4.19}$$

The variations of the semi-major axis caused by the tesseral term of the Earth are listed as a function of nominal longitude in Table 4.3.

As illustrated in Fig. 4.11, there are four equilibrium points during the variation of semi-major axis caused by the Earth's non-spherical perturbation, where the geostationary satellite will experience almost zero tangential acceleration. These points are approximately at 104.91°W, 11.41°W, 75.05°E, and 162.08°E. These values vary a little in different contexts, owing to the different models of gravitational field applied. In this book, we apply JGM-3 model of gravitational field.

Table 4.3 The variations of the semi-major axis caused by the tesseral terms of the Earth

Longitude (°)	Variation (m/day)	Longitude (°)	Variation (m/day)
−180.00	−81.51	0.00	−50.35
−179.00	−85.12	1.00	−54.67
−178.00	−88.61	2.00	−58.95
−177.00	−91.97	3.00	−63.18
−176.00	−95.19	4.00	−67.36
−175.00	−98.27	5.00	−71.47
−174.00	−101.21	6.00	−75.52
−173.00	−104.01	7.00	−79.50
−172.00	−106.67	8.00	−83.40
−171.00	−109.17	9.00	−87.21
−170.00	−111.53	10.00	−90.94
−169.00	−113.73	11.00	−94.57
−168.00	−115.79	12.00	−98.10
−167.00	−117.69	13.00	−101.52
−166.00	−119.44	14.00	−104.83
−165.00	−121.03	15.00	−108.01
−164.00	−122.46	16.00	−111.08
−163.00	−123.75	17.00	−114.02
−162.00	−124.87	18.00	−116.82
−161.00	−125.84	19.00	−119.48
−160.00	−126.66	20.00	−122.00
−159.00	−127.32	21.00	−124.37
−158.00	−127.82	22.00	−126.59
−157.00	−128.18	23.00	−128.65
−156.00	−128.38	24.00	−130.55
−155.00	−128.43	25.00	−132.29
−154.00	−128.33	26.00	−133.85
−153.00	−128.09	27.00	−135.25
−152.00	−127.70	28.00	−136.46
−151.00	−127.17	29.00	−137.51
−150.00	−126.49	30.00	−138.36
−149.00	−125.68	31.00	−139.04
−148.00	−124.72	32.00	−139.53
−147.00	−123.64	33.00	−139.83
−146.00	−122.42	34.00	−139.95
−145.00	−121.08	35.00	−139.87
−144.00	−119.60	36.00	−139.60
−143.00	−118.01	37.00	−139.14
−142.00	−116.29	38.00	−138.49
−141.00	−114.46	39.00	−137.64
−140.00	−112.51	40.00	−136.60
−139.00	−110.45	41.00	−135.36
−138.00	−108.29	42.00	−133.94
−137.00	−106.02	43.00	−132.32
−136.00	−103.65	44.00	−130.51

(continued)

Table 4.3 (continued)

Longitude (°)	Variation (m/day)	Longitude (°)	Variation (m/day)
−135.00	−101.18	45.00	−128.52
−134.00	−98.62	46.00	−126.34
−133.00	−95.97	47.00	−123.97
−132.00	−93.24	48.00	−121.42
−131.00	−90.42	49.00	−118.69
−130.00	−87.52	50.00	−115.79
−129.00	−84.55	51.00	−112.71
−128.00	−81.51	52.00	−109.47
−127.00	−78.40	53.00	−106.06
−126.00	−75.22	54.00	−102.49
−125.00	−71.99	55.00	−98.76
−124.00	−68.70	56.00	−94.88
−123.00	−65.36	57.00	−90.85
−122.00	−61.96	58.00	−86.69
−121.00	−58.53	59.00	−82.38
−120.00	−55.05	60.00	−77.95
−119.00	−51.53	61.00	−73.39
−118.00	−47.98	62.00	−68.71
−117.00	−44.40	63.00	−63.93
−116.00	−40.79	64.00	−59.03
−115.00	−37.16	65.00	−54.04
−114.00	−33.51	66.00	−48.96
−113.00	−29.84	67.00	−43.79
−112.00	−26.16	68.00	−38.55
−111.00	−22.47	69.00	−33.23
−110.00	−18.78	70.00	−27.86
−109.00	−15.08	71.00	−22.43
−108.00	−11.38	72.00	−16.96
−107.00	−7.69	73.00	−11.44
−106.00	−4.00	74.00	−5.90
−105.00	−0.32	75.00	−0.33
−104.00	3.34	76.00	5.25
−103.00	6.99	77.00	10.83
−102.00	10.61	78.00	16.42
−101.00	14.22	79.00	21.99
−100.00	17.80	80.00	27.55
−99.00	21.35	81.00	33.08
−98.00	24.87	82.00	38.57
−97.00	28.35	83.00	44.02
−96.00	31.80	84.00	49.42
−95.00	35.21	85.00	54.76
−94.00	38.58	86.00	60.03
−93.00	41.90	87.00	65.23
−92.00	45.17	88.00	70.35
−91.00	48.39	89.00	75.37

(continued)

Table 4.3 (continued)

Longitude (°)	Variation (m/day)	Longitude (°)	Variation (m/day)
−90.00	51.56	90.00	80.30
−89.00	54.67	91.00	85.12
−88.00	57.73	92.00	89.83
−87.00	60.72	93.00	94.42
−86.00	63.65	94.00	98.89
−85.00	66.52	95.00	103.22
−84.00	69.32	96.00	107.42
−83.00	72.05	97.00	111.47
−82.00	74.70	98.00	115.36
−81.00	77.28	99.00	119.11
−80.00	79.78	100.00	122.68
−79.00	82.21	101.00	126.10
−78.00	84.55	102.00	129.34
−77.00	86.81	103.00	132.40
−76.00	88.98	104.00	135.28
−75.00	91.06	105.00	137.98
−74.00	93.06	106.00	140.49
−73.00	94.96	107.00	142.80
−72.00	96.77	108.00	144.92
−71.00	98.48	109.00	146.84
−70.00	100.10	110.00	148.56
−69.00	101.62	111.00	150.07
−68.00	103.03	112.00	151.38
−67.00	104.34	113.00	152.49
−66.00	105.55	114.00	153.38
−65.00	106.65	115.00	154.07
−64.00	107.64	116.00	154.55
−63.00	108.52	117.00	154.81
−62.00	109.30	118.00	154.87
−61.00	109.96	119.00	154.72
−60.00	110.50	120.00	154.35
−59.00	110.93	121.00	153.78
−58.00	111.25	122.00	153.01
−57.00	111.44	123.00	152.03
−56.00	111.52	124.00	150.84
−55.00	111.49	125.00	149.46
−54.00	111.33	126.00	147.88
−53.00	111.05	127.00	146.10
−52.00	110.64	128.00	144.13
−51.00	110.12	129.00	141.98
−50.00	109.47	130.00	139.63
−49.00	108.70	131.00	137.11
−48.00	107.81	132.00	134.41
−47.00	106.80	133.00	131.54
−46.00	105.66	134.00	128.50

(continued)

Table 4.3 (continued)

Longitude (°)	Variation (m/day)	Longitude (°)	Variation (m/day)
−45.00	104.39	135.00	125.30
−44.00	103.01	136.00	121.95
−43.00	101.50	137.00	118.44
−42.00	99.87	138.00	114.79
−41.00	98.12	139.00	110.99
−40.00	96.25	140.00	107.06
−39.00	94.26	141.00	103.01
−38.00	92.15	142.00	98.83
−37.00	89.92	143.00	94.54
−36.00	87.57	144.00	90.14
−35.00	85.11	145.00	85.63
−34.00	82.54	146.00	81.04
−33.00	79.86	147.00	76.35
−32.00	77.06	148.00	71.59
−31.00	74.16	149.00	66.75
−30.00	71.15	150.00	61.84
−29.00	68.05	151.00	56.88
−28.00	64.84	152.00	51.86
−27.00	61.53	153.00	46.80
−26.00	58.13	154.00	41.70
−25.00	54.64	155.00	36.57
−24.00	51.06	156.00	31.41
−23.00	47.39	157.00	26.24
−22.00	43.64	158.00	21.07
−21.00	39.82	159.00	15.89
−20.00	35.92	160.00	10.72
−19.00	31.95	161.00	5.56
−18.00	27.92	162.00	0.42
−17.00	23.83	163.00	−4.70
−16.00	19.67	164.00	−9.78
−15.00	15.47	165.00	−14.82
−14.00	11.22	166.00	−19.81
−13.00	6.93	167.00	−24.75
−12.00	2.60	168.00	−29.63
−11.00	−1.77	169.00	−34.44
−10.00	−6.16	170.00	−39.19
−9.00	−10.57	171.00	−43.85
−8.00	−15.00	172.00	−48.44
−7.00	−19.44	173.00	−52.93
−6.00	−23.89	174.00	−57.33
−5.00	−28.33	175.00	−61.64
−4.00	−32.77	176.00	−65.84
−3.00	−37.20	177.00	−69.93
−2.00	−41.61	178.00	−73.91
−1.00	−45.99	179.00	−77.77
0.00	−50.35	180.00	−81.51

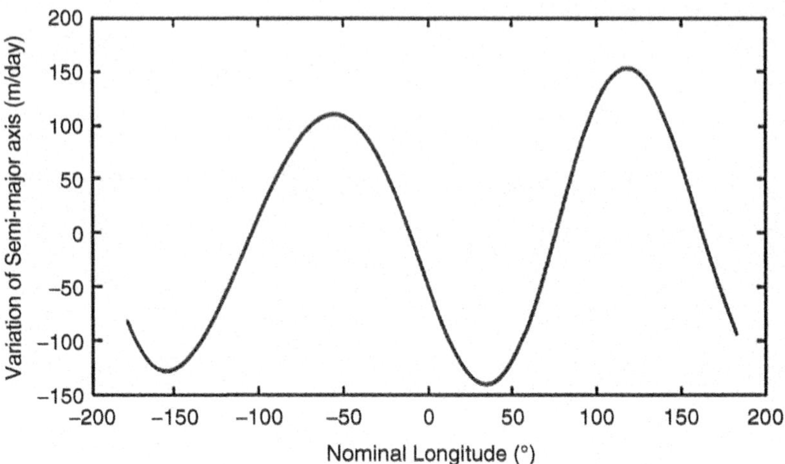

Fig. 4.11 The variation in the semi-major axis varies

4.4.4 Longitude Drift Evolution

The variation of semi-major axis causes inconsistence between orbit motion and the Earth's rotation angular velocity. The change of semi-major axis results in the drift motion of mean longitude. Define the eastward drifting as positive. If $a > a_c$, then the variation rate of the mean longitude $\frac{d\lambda}{dt} < 0$ and the satellite drifts westward; if $a < a_c$, then the variation rate of the mean longitude $\frac{d\lambda}{dt} > 0$ and the satellite drifts eastward. Denote the daily drifting rate (unit: degree/day) as D, and then

$$D = \frac{da}{dt} = -\frac{2}{3}\frac{a_c}{n_c} \cdot \Gamma_\lambda \tag{4.20}$$

$$D = \frac{d\lambda}{dt} \cdot \frac{360^\circ}{2\pi} \cdot 86400 = \frac{d\lambda}{dt} \cdot \frac{86164.09}{2\pi} \cdot \frac{86400}{86164.09} 360^\circ \tag{4.21}$$

The longitude satisfies the Lagrange perturbation equation derived in Sect. 4.3

$$\frac{d\lambda}{dt} = (n - \omega_e) - \frac{2}{na}\frac{\partial R}{\partial a} \tag{4.22}$$

and with the following relation

$$\begin{aligned} n - n_c &= \left(\sqrt{\frac{\mu}{a^3}} - \sqrt{\frac{\mu}{a_c^3}}\right) = \sqrt{\frac{\mu}{a_c^3}}\left(\left(\frac{a}{a_c}\right)^{-\frac{3}{2}} - 1\right) \\ &= n_c\left(\left(1 + \frac{a - a_c}{a_c}\right)^{-\frac{3}{2}} - 1\right) \approx n_c\left(-\frac{3}{2}\frac{a - a_c}{a_c}\right) \end{aligned} \tag{4.23}$$

and with some approximate expressions below

$$n \approx n_c - \frac{3}{2}\frac{n_c}{a_c}(a - a_c), \frac{2}{na}\frac{\partial R}{\partial a} \approx \frac{2}{n_c a_c}\frac{\partial R}{\partial a}\Big|_{a=a_c}$$

so that the longitude perturbation equation of the real geostationary orbit is

$$\begin{aligned}\frac{d\lambda}{dt} &= (n - \omega_e) - \frac{2}{na}\frac{\partial R}{\partial a} = \underbrace{(n_c - \omega_e) - \frac{2}{n_c a_c}\frac{\partial R}{\partial a}\Big|_{a=a_c}}_{=0} - \frac{3}{2}\frac{n_c}{a_c}(a - a_c) \\ &= -\frac{3}{2}\frac{n_c}{a_c}(a - a_c)\end{aligned} \tag{4.24}$$

By replacing Eq. (4.21) with the relation (4.24), the perturbation equation of longitude drift rate is given by

$$\begin{aligned}D &= -\frac{3}{2}\frac{n_c}{a_c}(a - a_c)\cdot\frac{1}{n_c}\cdot\frac{86400}{86164.09}360^\circ \\ &= -\frac{3}{2}\frac{1}{a_c}(a - a_c)\cdot 360.9856^\circ = -0.0128^\circ(a - a_c)\end{aligned} \tag{4.25}$$

If the geostationary orbit semi-major axis is 1 km greater than the nominal semi-major axis, the westward drift rate of the mean longitude $D = -0.0128$ °/day; if the orbit semi-major axis is 1 km less than the nominal semi-major axis, the eastward drift rate of the mean longitude $D = 0.0128$ °/day.

The relation among the semi-major axis perturbation motion, the mean longitude drift motion, and the gravitational tangential perturbation acceleration can be well illustrated in Fig. 4.12.

Table 4.4 concludes the direction of tangential acceleration, the evolution of the semi-major axis, and the drifting direction of mean longitude of geostationary satellite located at different regions above the equator.

4.4.5 Mean Longitude Evolution

The analysis of the above section indicates that because of the perturbation from the non-spherical part of the Earth's gravity, the orbit semi-major axis changes linearly. For the satellite located at 100.0°E degrees, the semi-major axis increases an average of 122.68 m/day. The semi-major axis increments result in that the mean longitude drifts away from the nominal allocation by

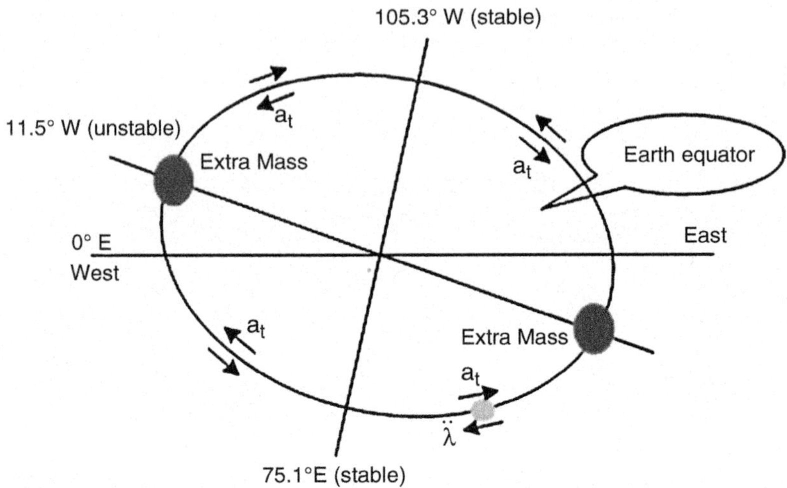

Fig. 4.12 The longitude drift motion illustration

Table 4.4 Longitude drift direction summaries

Quadrant	Longitude region	Tangential acceleration	Semi-major axis	Longitude drift direction
I	$11.5\,^\circ W - 75.1\,^\circ E$	−(West)	−(Decrease)	+(East)
II	$75.1\,^\circ E - 161.9\,^\circ E$	+(East)	+(Increase)	-(West)
III	$161.9\,^\circ W - 105.3\,^\circ W$	−(West)	−(Decrease)	+(East)
IV	$105.3\,^\circ W - 11.5\,^\circ W$	+(East)	+(Increase)	−(West)

$$\frac{\mathrm{d}\lambda}{\mathrm{d}t} = -\frac{3}{2}\frac{n_c}{a_c}(a - a_c) \tag{4.26}$$

and the longitude drift acceleration satisfies

$$\frac{\mathrm{d}^2\lambda}{\mathrm{d}t^2} = \frac{d}{\mathrm{d}t}\left(-\frac{3}{2}\frac{n_c}{a_c}(a - a_c)\right) = -\frac{3}{2}\frac{n_c}{a_c}\frac{\mathrm{d}a}{\mathrm{d}t} = -\frac{3}{2}\frac{n_c}{a_c}\cdot\left(-\frac{2}{3}\frac{a_c}{n_c}\right)\Gamma_\lambda = \Gamma_\lambda \tag{4.27}$$

Recall the definition of Γ_λ which satisfies

$$\Gamma_\lambda = -3n_c^2\left\{\begin{array}{l} -6J_{22}\left(\frac{R_e}{a_c}\right)^2 \sin 2(\lambda - \lambda_{22}) \\ +\frac{3}{2}J_{31}\left(\frac{R_e}{a_c}\right)^3 \sin(\lambda - \lambda_{31}) \\ -45J_{33}\left(\frac{R_e}{a_c}\right)^3 \sin 3(\lambda - \lambda_{33}) \end{array}\right\} \tag{4.28}$$

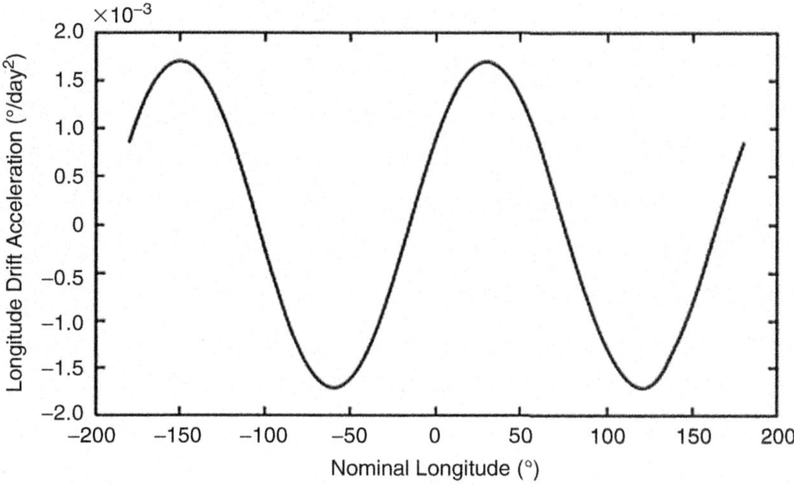

Fig. 4.13 The drifting acceleration via the nominal longitude

Therefore, the perturbation acceleration of mean longitude is a constant that only interrelated with the satellite's nominal position. The relation between the constant and the longitude is illustrated in Fig. 4.13 and the acceleration is listed in Table 4.5.

In the vicinity of the nominal position, the perturbation of mean longitude can be considered as the motion with a constant acceleration. This kind of motion draws a parabola curve. The mean longitude acceleration is a constant; the mean longitude variation rate (mean longitude drift rate) changes in linearity; the mean longitude changes in parabola. Suppose the mean longitude drifting acceleration as $\ddot{\lambda}_n$ in the vicinity of nominal longitude λ_n, the longitude drift equation satisfies the differential equation

$$\begin{cases} \dfrac{\mathrm{d}\lambda}{\mathrm{d}t} = D \\ \dfrac{\mathrm{d}^2\lambda}{\mathrm{d}t^2} = \dfrac{d}{\mathrm{d}t}(D) = \ddot{\lambda}_n \\ \lambda|_{t=t_0} = \lambda_0,\ \dfrac{\mathrm{d}\lambda}{\mathrm{d}t}|_{t=t_0} = D_0 \end{cases} \tag{4.29}$$

The solution of the above equation with time is

$$\lambda = \lambda_0 + D_0 t + \frac{1}{2}\ddot{\lambda}_n t^2 \tag{4.30}$$

$$D = D_0 + \ddot{\lambda}_n t \tag{4.31}$$

Table 4.5 The magnitude of tangential acceleration and longitude drift acceleration

Nominal longitude (°)	Tangential acceleration (m/s²)	Longitude drift acceleration (°/day²)	Nominal longitude (°)	Tangential acceleration (m/s²)	Longitude drift acceleration (°/day²)
−180	−3.42E-08	0.001038388	0	−2.13E-08	0.000646755
−179	−3.57E-08	0.001084008	1	−2.31E-08	0.000701686
−178	−3.72E-08	0.001128052	2	−2.49E-08	0.000756088
−177	−3.86E-08	0.001170479	3	−2.67E-08	0.000809885
−176	−3.99E-08	0.001211252	4	−2.84E-08	0.000862999
−175	−4.12E-08	0.001250334	5	−3.02E-08	0.000915354
−174	−4.24E-08	0.00128769	6	−3.19E-08	0.000966875
−173	−4.36E-08	0.001323291	7	−3.35E-08	0.001017485
−172	−4.47E-08	0.001357107	8	−3.52E-08	0.001067109
−171	−4.58E-08	0.001389112	9	−3.68E-08	0.001115672
−170	−4.68E-08	0.001419282	10	−3.83E-08	0.001163099
−169	−4.77E-08	0.001447595	11	−3.98E-08	0.001209318
−168	−4.86E-08	0.001474033	12	−4.13E-08	0.001254256
−167	−4.94E-08	0.001498579	13	−4.28E-08	0.001297841
−166	−5.01E-08	0.001521218	14	−4.42E-08	0.001340003
−165	−5.08E-08	0.00154194	15	−4.55E-08	0.001380674
−164	−5.14E-08	0.001560734	16	−4.68E-08	0.001419785
−163	−5.20E-08	0.001577593	17	−4.80E-08	0.00145727
−162	−5.25E-08	0.001592513	18	−4.92E-08	0.001493066
−161	−5.29E-08	0.001605492	19	−5.03E-08	0.001527109
−160	−5.33E-08	0.001616529	20	−5.14E-08	0.001559339
−159	−5.36E-08	0.001625626	21	−5.24E-08	0.001589697
−158	−5.38E-08	0.001632788	22	−5.33E-08	0.001618126
−157	−5.40E-08	0.001638022	23	−5.42E-08	0.001644573
−156	−5.41E-08	0.001641336	24	−5.50E-08	0.001668984
−155	−5.41E-08	0.001642741	25	−5.57E-08	0.00169131
−154	−5.41E-08	0.00164225	26	−5.64E-08	0.001711504
−153	−5.40E-08	0.001639879	27	−5.70E-08	0.001729522
−152	−5.39E-08	0.001635645	28	−5.75E-08	0.001745321
−151	−5.37E-08	0.001629566	29	−5.80E-08	0.001758863
−150	−5.34E-08	0.001621664	30	−5.83E-08	0.001770112
−149	−5.31E-08	0.001611961	31	−5.86E-08	0.001779036
−148	−5.27E-08	0.001600483	32	−5.88E-08	0.001785603
−147	−5.23E-08	0.001587257	33	−5.90E-08	0.001789788
−146	−5.18E-08	0.00157231	34	−5.90E-08	0.001791567
−145	−5.13E-08	0.001555673	35	−5.90E-08	0.00179092
−144	−5.07E-08	0.001537377	36	−5.89E-08	0.001787831
−143	−5.00E-08	0.001517456	37	−5.87E-08	0.001782286
−142	−4.93E-08	0.001495945	38	−5.85E-08	0.001774277
−141	−4.85E-08	0.00147288	39	−5.81E-08	0.001763796
−140	−4.77E-08	0.001448299	40	−5.77E-08	0.001750843
−139	−4.69E-08	0.00142224	41	−5.72E-08	0.001735417
−138	−4.60E-08	0.001394745	42	−5.66E-08	0.001717525

(continued)

Table 4.5 (continued)

Nominal longitude	Tangential acceleration	Longitude drift acceleration	Nominal longitude	Tangential acceleration	Longitude drift acceleration
(°)	(m/s^2)	(°/day^2)	(°)	(m/s^2)	(°/day^2)
−137	−4.50E-08	0.001365855	43	−5.59E-08	0.001697176
−136	−4.40E-08	0.001335613	44	−5.52E-08	0.001674382
−135	−4.30E-08	0.001304062	45	−5.43E-08	0.00164916
−134	−4.19E-08	0.001271248	46	−5.34E-08	0.001621531
−133	−4.08E-08	0.001237216	47	−5.24E-08	0.001591519
−132	−3.96E-08	0.001202013	48	−5.14E-08	0.001559152
−131	−3.84E-08	0.001165687	49	−5.02E-08	0.001524462
−130	−3.72E-08	0.001128285	50	−4.90E-08	0.001487487
−129	−3.59E-08	0.001089857	51	−4.77E-08	0.001448264
−128	−3.46E-08	0.001050452	52	−4.64E-08	0.001406839
−127	−3.33E-08	0.00101012	53	−4.49E-08	0.001363258
−126	−3.19E-08	0.000968912	54	−4.34E-08	0.001317574
−125	−3.05E-08	0.000926878	55	−4.18E-08	0.00126984
−124	−2.91E-08	0.00088407	56	−4.02E-08	0.001220116
−123	−2.77E-08	0.000840539	57	−3.85E-08	0.001168464
−122	−2.62E-08	0.000796336	58	−3.67E-08	0.001114949
−121	−2.48E-08	0.000751514	59	−3.49E-08	0.001059642
−120	−2.33E-08	0.000706123	60	−3.30E-08	0.001002614
−119	−2.18E-08	0.000660215	61	−3.11E-08	0.000943941
−118	−2.02E-08	0.000613842	62	−2.91E-08	0.000883702
−117	−1.87E-08	0.000567056	63	−2.71E-08	0.00082198
−116	−1.71E-08	0.000519906	64	−2.50E-08	0.000758859
−115	−1.56E-08	0.000472445	65	−2.29E-08	0.000694427
−114	−1.40E-08	0.000424722	66	−2.07E-08	0.000628775
−113	−1.24E-08	0.000376787	67	−1.85E-08	0.000561996
−112	−1.08E-08	0.000328691	68	−1.63E-08	0.000494184
−111	−9.24E-09	0.000280482	69	−1.40E-08	0.000425438
−110	−7.65E-09	0.000232208	70	−1.17E-08	0.000355857
−109	−6.06E-09	0.000183918	71	−9.41E-09	0.000285543
−108	−4.47E-09	0.000135659	72	−7.07E-09	0.0002146
−107	−2.88E-09	8.75E-05	73	−4.72E-09	0.000143131
−106	−1.30E-09	3.94E-05	74	−2.35E-09	7.12E-05
−105	2.79E-10	−8.47E-06	75	3.15E-11	−9.55E-07
−104	1.85E-09	−5.61E-05	76	2.42E-09	−7.34E-05
−103	3.41E-09	−0.00010356	77	4.81E-09	−0.00014585
−102	4.96E-09	−0.00015068	78	7.19E-09	−0.00021833
−101	6.51E-09	−0.00019746	79	9.58E-09	−0.00029068
−100	8.03E-09	−0.00024385	80	1.20E-08	−0.0003628
−99	9.55E-09	−0.00028982	81	1.43E-08	−0.00043457
−98	1.10E-08	−0.00033533	82	1.67E-08	−0.00050588
−97	1.25E-08	−0.00038034	83	1.90E-08	−0.00057663
−96	1.40E-08	−0.00042481	84	2.13E-08	−0.0006467
−95	1.54E-08	−0.0004687	85	2.36E-08	−0.00071599

(continued)

Table 4.5 (continued)

Nominal longitude (°)	Tangential acceleration (m/s²)	Longitude drift acceleration (°/day²)	Nominal longitude (°)	Tangential acceleration (m/s²)	Longitude drift acceleration (°/day²)
−94	1.69E-08	−0.00051198	86	2.58E-08	−0.00078439
−93	1.83E-08	−0.00055461	87	2.81E-08	−0.00085179
−92	1.97E-08	−0.00059656	88	3.03E-08	−0.00091809
−91	2.10E-08	−0.0006378	89	3.24E-08	−0.00098319
−90	2.23E-08	−0.00067829	90	3.45E-08	−0.00104699
−89	2.37E-08	−0.000718	91	3.66E-08	−0.00110939
−88	2.49E-08	−0.00075689	92	3.86E-08	−0.00117028
−87	2.62E-08	−0.00079495	93	4.05E-08	−0.00122959
−86	2.74E-08	−0.00083214	94	4.24E-08	−0.00128721
−85	2.86E-08	−0.00086842	95	4.43E-08	−0.00134307
−84	2.98E-08	−0.00090378	96	4.60E-08	−0.00139707
−83	3.09E-08	−0.00093819	97	4.77E-08	−0.00144913
−82	3.20E-08	−0.00097161	98	4.94E-08	−0.00149917
−81	3.31E-08	−0.00100402	99	5.10E-08	−0.00154712
−80	3.41E-08	−0.0010354	100	5.25E-08	−0.00159291
−79	3.51E-08	−0.00106573	101	5.39E-08	−0.00163647
−78	3.61E-08	−0.00109496	102	5.53E-08	−0.00167774
−77	3.70E-08	−0.0011231	103	5.66E-08	−0.00171665
−76	3.79E-08	−0.0011501	104	5.78E-08	−0.00175315
−75	3.87E-08	−0.00117595	105	5.89E-08	−0.00178718
−74	3.96E-08	−0.00120062	106	5.99E-08	−0.00181871
−73	4.03E-08	−0.0012241	107	6.09E-08	−0.00184768
−72	4.11E-08	−0.00124636	108	6.17E-08	−0.00187406
−71	4.18E-08	−0.00126739	109	6.25E-08	−0.00189782
−70	4.24E-08	−0.00128715	110	6.32E-08	−0.00191892
−69	4.30E-08	−0.00130564	111	6.38E-08	−0.00193734
−68	4.36E-08	−0.00132283	112	6.44E-08	−0.00195306
−67	4.41E-08	−0.0013387	113	6.48E-08	−0.00196606
−66	4.46E-08	−0.00135324	114	6.51E-08	−0.00197634
−65	4.50E-08	−0.00136643	115	6.54E-08	−0.00198387
−64	4.54E-08	−0.00137825	116	6.55E-08	−0.00198867
−63	4.58E-08	−0.00138869	117	6.56E-08	−0.00199074
−62	4.61E-08	−0.00139772	118	6.56E-08	−0.00199007
−61	4.63E-08	−0.00140534	119	6.55E-08	−0.00198668
−60	4.65E-08	−0.00141153	120	6.53E-08	−0.0019806
−59	4.67E-08	−0.00141627	121	6.50E-08	−0.00197183
−58	4.68E-08	−0.00141956	122	6.46E-08	−0.00196039
−57	4.68E-08	−0.00142137	123	6.41E-08	−0.00194633
−56	4.68E-08	−0.00142171	124	6.36E-08	−0.00192967
−55	4.68E-08	−0.00142055	125	6.29E-08	−0.00191045
−54	4.67E-08	−0.00141789	126	6.22E-08	−0.0018887
−53	4.66E-08	−0.00141372	127	6.14E-08	−0.00186448
−52	4.64E-08	−0.00140803	128	6.06E-08	−0.00183782
−51	4.62E-08	−0.00140081	129	5.96E-08	−0.00180879

(continued)

Table 4.5 (continued)

Nominal longitude (°)	Tangential acceleration (m/s²)	Longitude drift acceleration (°/day²)	Nominal longitude (°)	Tangential acceleration (m/s²)	Longitude drift acceleration (°/day²)
−50	4.59E-08	−0.00139206	130	5.86E-08	−0.00177742
−49	4.55E-08	−0.00138178	131	5.75E-08	−0.00174379
−48	4.51E-08	−0.00136996	132	5.63E-08	−0.00170795
−47	4.47E-08	−0.0013566	133	5.50E-08	−0.00166997
−46	4.42E-08	−0.00134169	134	5.37E-08	−0.00162991
−45	4.37E-08	−0.00132525	135	5.23E-08	−0.00158784
−44	4.31E-08	−0.00130726	136	5.09E-08	−0.00154383
−43	4.24E-08	−0.00128774	137	4.94E-08	−0.00149796
−42	4.17E-08	−0.00126669	138	4.78E-08	−0.00145031
−41	4.10E-08	−0.00124412	139	4.62E-08	−0.00140094
−40	4.02E-08	−0.00122003	140	4.45E-08	−0.00134995
−39	3.94E-08	−0.00119444	141	4.27E-08	−0.00129741
−38	3.85E-08	−0.00116736	142	4.10E-08	−0.00124341
−37	3.75E-08	−0.0011388	143	3.91E-08	−0.00118803
−36	3.65E-08	−0.00110878	144	3.73E-08	−0.00113135
−35	3.55E-08	−0.00107731	145	3.54E-08	−0.00107347
−34	3.44E-08	−0.00104442	146	3.34E-08	−0.00101448
−33	3.33E-08	−0.00101013	147	3.14E-08	−0.00095445
−32	3.21E-08	−0.00097446	148	2.94E-08	−0.00089349
−31	3.09E-08	−0.00093744	149	2.74E-08	−0.00083168
−30	2.96E-08	−0.00089909	150	2.53E-08	−0.0007691
−29	2.83E-08	−0.00085945	151	2.33E-08	−0.00070586
−28	2.70E-08	−0.00081854	152	2.12E-08	−0.00064204
−27	2.56E-08	−0.0007764	153	1.90E-08	−0.00057774
−26	2.42E-08	−0.00073307	154	1.69E-08	−0.00051303
−25	2.27E-08	−0.00068859	155	1.48E-08	−0.00044801
−24	2.12E-08	−0.000643	156	1.26E-08	−0.00038277
−23	1.96E-08	−0.00059633	157	1.05E-08	−0.0003174
−22	1.81E-08	−0.00054863	158	8.30E-09	−0.00025199
−21	1.65E-08	−0.00049996	159	6.15E-09	−0.00018662
−20	1.48E-08	−0.00045035	160	4.00E-09	−0.00012137
−19	1.32E-08	−0.00039986	161	1.86E-09	−5.63E-05
−18	1.15E-08	−0.00034855	162	−2.77E-10	8.40E-06
−17	9.77E-09	−0.00029646	163	−2.40E-09	7.28E-05
−16	8.03E-09	−0.00024365	164	−4.50E-09	0.000136677
−15	6.27E-09	−0.00019019	165	−6.59E-09	0.000200049
−14	4.49E-09	−0.00013612	166	−8.66E-09	0.00026281
−13	2.69E-09	−8.15E-05	167	−1.07E-08	0.000324882
−12	8.71E-10	−2.64E-05	168	−1.27E-08	0.000386193
−11	−9.57E-10	2.91E-05	169	−1.47E-08	0.000446671
−10	−2.80E-09	8.49E-05	170	−1.67E-08	0.000506245
−9	−4.65E-09	0.000140996	171	−1.86E-08	0.000564848
−8	−6.50E-09	0.000197315	172	−2.05E-08	0.000622414
−7	−8.36E-09	0.000253772	173	−2.24E-08	0.000678878

(continued)

Table 4.5 (continued)

Nominal longitude (°)	Tangential acceleration (m/s²)	Longitude drift acceleration (°/day²)	Nominal longitude (°)	Tangential acceleration (m/s²)	Longitude drift acceleration (°/day²)
−6	−1.02E-08	0.000310296	174	−2.42E-08	0.00073418
−5	−1.21E-08	0.000366815	175	−2.60E-08	0.000788259
−4	−1.39E-08	0.000423256	176	−2.77E-08	0.000841058
−3	−1.58E-08	0.000479546	177	−2.94E-08	0.000892522
−2	−1.76E-08	0.000535609	178	−3.11E-08	0.000942598
−1	−1.95E-08	0.00059137	179	−3.27E-08	0.000991236

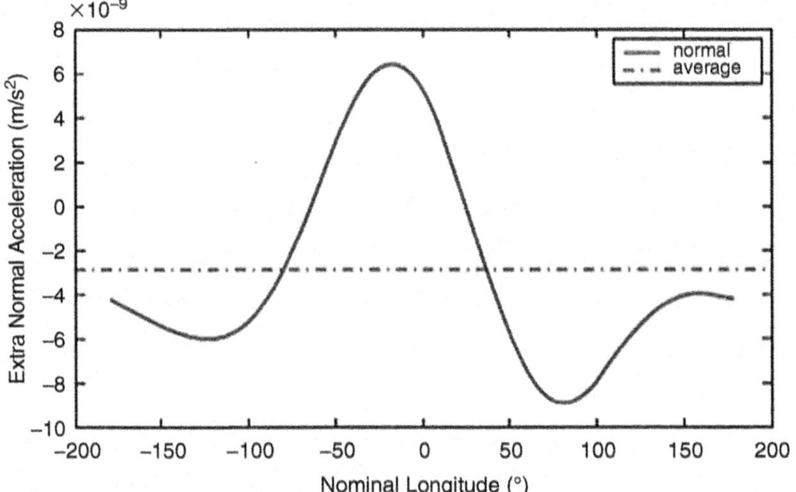

Fig. 4.14 Normal acceleration via nominal longitude

On the phase plane of (λ, D), the longitude drift motion which draws a left parabola or a right parabola relies on the sign of the drift acceleration. If the mean longitude drift acceleration satisfies $\ddot{\lambda}_n > 0$, it draws a left parabola. If the drift acceleration satisfies $\ddot{\lambda}_n < 0$, it draws a right parabola. If the drift acceleration satisfies $\ddot{\lambda}_n = 0$, it draws a beeline.

4.4.6 Inclination Vector Evolution

Because of the tangential perturbation from the zonal terms of the Earth's gravity, the semi-major axis of a real geostationary orbit under perturbation condition increases about 2 km to that under two-body condition. As shown in Fig. 4.14, at the same time, the zonal term of the Earth's gravity as a dominated factor induces normal perturbation acceleration to the geostationary orbit too, with an average value of approximately $-2.95 \times 10^{-9}(\mathrm{m/s^2})$. The normal direction acceleration creates the procession motion of the orbit plane.

The dominated zonal term of the Earth's gravity is J_2. For simplification, we omit the high-order terms and then the perturbation function of the non-spherical Earth becomes

$$R = \left(\frac{\mu}{r}\right)\left\{-\frac{1}{2}J_2\left(\frac{R_e}{r}\right)^2(3\sin^2\varphi - 1)\right\} \tag{4.32}$$

The Lagrange perturbation equation of the inclination vector for geostationary orbit is

$$\begin{cases} \dfrac{di_x}{dt} = -\dfrac{1}{na^2}\dfrac{\partial R}{\partial i_y} \\ \dfrac{di_y}{dt} = \dfrac{1}{na^2}\dfrac{\partial R}{\partial i_x} \end{cases} \tag{4.33}$$

Differentiating perturbation function (4.32) with the inclination vector of (i_x, i_y) yields

$$\frac{\partial R}{\partial i_x} = \frac{\partial R}{\partial r}\frac{\partial r}{\partial i_x} + \frac{\partial R}{\partial \varphi}\frac{\partial \varphi}{\partial i_x},\ \frac{\partial R}{\partial i_y} = \frac{\partial R}{\partial r}\frac{\partial r}{\partial i_y} + \frac{\partial R}{\partial \varphi}\frac{\partial \varphi}{\partial i_y} \tag{4.34}$$

The radius r only depends on the elements on orbit plane and is independent of the inclination, so

$$\frac{\partial r}{\partial i_x} = 0,\ \frac{\partial r}{\partial i_y} = 0$$

Because of the geostationary orbit with a small inclination, using approximate expression $\sin(i) \approx i$, then

$$\sin\varphi = i\sin(\omega + f) = i\sin(l - \Omega) = i_x \sin l - i_y \cos l \tag{4.35}$$

so that

$$\frac{\partial R}{\partial \varphi} = -3\mu J_2\left(\frac{R_e^2}{r^3}\right)\sin\varphi\cos\varphi$$

$$\frac{\partial \varphi}{\partial i_x} = \frac{1}{\cos\varphi}\cdot\sin l,\quad \frac{\partial \varphi}{\partial i_y} = -\frac{1}{\cos\varphi}\cdot\cos l$$

Now perform differential variable of the inclination vector (i_x, i_y) to the perturbation function of the non-spherical Earth:

$$\begin{aligned}\frac{\partial R}{\partial i_x} = \frac{\partial R}{\partial \varphi}\frac{\partial \varphi}{\partial i_x} &= -3\mu J_2\left(\frac{R_e^2}{r^3}\right)\sin\varphi\sin l \\ &= -3\mu J_2\left(\frac{R_e^2}{r^3}\right)\left(i_x\sin^2 l - i_y\sin l\cos l\right)\end{aligned} \tag{4.36}$$

$$\begin{aligned}\frac{\partial R}{\partial i_y} = \frac{\partial R}{\partial \varphi}\frac{\partial \varphi}{\partial i_y} &= 3\mu J_2\left(\frac{R_e^2}{r^3}\right)\sin\varphi\cos l \\ &= 3\mu J_2\left(\frac{R_e^2}{r^3}\right)\left(i_x\sin l\cos l - i_y\cos^2 l\right)\end{aligned} \tag{4.37}$$

Replacing the Lagrange perturbation equation with the expressions above, we get

$$\frac{\mathrm{d}i_x}{\mathrm{d}t} = -\frac{1}{na^2}\frac{\partial R}{\partial i_y} = -3n_e J_2\left(\frac{R_e^2}{a_c^2}\right)\left(i_x\sin l\cos l - i_y\cos^2 l\right) \tag{4.38}$$

$$\frac{\mathrm{d}i_y}{\mathrm{d}t} = \frac{1}{na^2}\frac{\partial R}{\partial i_x} = -3n_e J_2\left(\frac{R_e^2}{a_c^2}\right)\left(i_x\sin^2 l - i_y\sin l\cos l\right) \tag{4.39}$$

Performing integral to the above equation, we can calculate the average daily variation of inclination for geostationary orbit by

$$\frac{\delta i_x}{\mathrm{d}t} = \frac{3}{2}n_e J_2\left(\frac{R_e^2}{a_c^2}\right)i_y \tag{4.40}$$

$$\frac{\delta i_y}{\mathrm{d}t} = -\frac{3}{2}n_e J_2\left(\frac{R_e^2}{a_c^2}\right)i_x \tag{4.41}$$

Replacing the constant coefficients, we get

$$\kappa = \frac{3}{2}n_e J_2\left(\frac{R_e^2}{a_c^2}\right) = 0.0134\left({}^\circ/_{\text{day}}\right) = 4.9\left({}^\circ/_{\text{year}}\right) \tag{4.42}$$

The normal perturbation acceleration from the zonal J2 term of the Earth's gravity changes the inclination vector, which perturbation motion can be expressed by the following periodical expression:

$$\begin{aligned} i_x &= i_0\cos(\kappa t - \Omega_0) \\ i_y &= i_0\sin(\kappa t - \Omega_0)\end{aligned} \tag{4.43}$$

In the expression, the magnitude and the phase of the periodical motion caused by the dominated zonal terms of the Earth's gravitation are

$$i_0 = \sqrt{i_x^2 + i_y^2}, \Omega_0 = \arctan\left(\frac{i_y}{i_x}\right) \tag{4.44}$$

The frequency of the periodical solution is 4.9 (°/year) and its period is 73.64 years. That is the retrogressive procession motion of the orbit plane induced by the zonal terms of the Earth's gravitation. The right ascension of the ascending node of geostationary orbit withdraws 4.9° westward every year, and it turns a round circle around the equator plane in every 73.64 years.

4.4.7 Eccentricity Vector Evolution

We can image that the non-spherical Earth's perturbation takes very small effect on the eccentricity vector, since the geostationary satellite located at the nominal longitude suffers the same and continuous perturbation forces from the Earth's gravitation.

To simplification, we still take the main J2 term of the Earth's gravitation as the dominated perturbation, so we omit the high-order terms and the perturbation function of the Earth becomes

$$R = \left(\frac{\mu}{r}\right)\left\{-\frac{1}{2}J_2\left(\frac{R_e}{r}\right)^2(3\sin^2\varphi - 1)\right\} \tag{4.45}$$

The Lagrange perturbation equation of the inclination vector for geostationary orbit is

$$\begin{cases} \dfrac{\mathrm{d}e_x}{\mathrm{d}t} = -\dfrac{1}{na^2}\dfrac{\partial R}{\partial e_y} \\ \dfrac{\mathrm{d}e_y}{\mathrm{d}t} = \dfrac{1}{na^2}\dfrac{\partial R}{\partial e_x} \end{cases} \tag{4.46}$$

Differentiating perturbation function (4.45) with the eccentricity vector, we have

$$\frac{\partial R}{\partial e_x} = \frac{\partial R}{\partial r}\frac{\partial r}{\partial e_x} + \frac{\partial R}{\partial \varphi}\frac{\partial \varphi}{\partial e_x}, \quad \frac{\partial R}{\partial e_y} = \frac{\partial R}{\partial r}\frac{\partial r}{\partial e_y} + \frac{\partial R}{\partial \varphi}\frac{\partial \varphi}{\partial e_y}$$

The latitude only depends on the inclination and is independent of the elements in orbit plane, so

$$\frac{\partial \varphi}{\partial e_x} = 0, \frac{\partial \varphi}{\partial e_y} = 0$$

Because of the geostationary orbit with a small eccentricity, using approximate expression $f \approx E \approx M$, the radius and its derivative partial differential can be expressed as the functions of the mean longitude and eccentricity vector:

$$r = a(1 - e\cos E) = a\big(1 - (e_x \cos l + e_y \sin l)\big) \tag{4.47}$$

$$\frac{\partial r}{\partial e_x} = -a\cos l, \quad \frac{\partial r}{\partial e_y} = -a\sin l \tag{4.48}$$

Now perform differential variable of the eccentricity vector (e_x, e_y) to the perturbation function of the non-spherical Earth:

$$\frac{\partial R}{\partial e_x} = \frac{\partial R}{\partial r}\frac{\partial r}{\partial e_x} = -\frac{3}{2}J_2\mu\left(\frac{R_e}{r}\right)^2\left(\frac{1}{r}\right)^2 \cdot (-a\cos l) \tag{4.49}$$

$$\frac{\partial R}{\partial e_y} = \frac{\partial R}{\partial r}\frac{\partial r}{\partial e_y} = -\frac{3}{2}J_2\mu\left(\frac{R_e}{r}\right)^2\left(\frac{1}{r}\right)^2 \cdot (-a\sin l) \tag{4.50}$$

Replacing the Lagrange perturbation equation with the above expressions, we get

$$\begin{cases} \dfrac{de_x}{dt} = -\dfrac{1}{na^2}\dfrac{\partial R}{\partial e_y} = -\dfrac{3}{2}J_2 n_e \left(\dfrac{R_e}{a_c}\right)^2 \sin l \\ \dfrac{de_y}{dt} = \dfrac{1}{na^2}\dfrac{\partial R}{\partial e_x} = -\dfrac{3}{2}J_2 n_e \left(\dfrac{R_e}{a_c}\right)^2 \cos l \end{cases} \tag{4.51}$$

Performing integral to the above equation, we can calculate that the average daily variation rate of eccentricity satisfies

$$\begin{cases} \dfrac{de_x}{dl} = -\dfrac{3}{2}J_2 \left(\dfrac{R_e}{a_c}\right)^2 \sin l = -3.72 \times 10^{-5} \cdot \sin l \\ \dfrac{de_y}{dl} = -\dfrac{3}{2}J_2 \left(\dfrac{R_e}{a_c}\right)^2 \cos l = -3.72 \times 10^{-5} \cdot \cos l \end{cases} \tag{4.52}$$

It means that the zonal terms of the Earth's gravitation are of no long-term effect on the eccentricity vector. There is only short-periodical daily oscillation motion, and the amplitude of the short-periodical motion is 3.72×10^{-5}.

4.5 The Solar and Lunar Perturbation

The distances from the geostationary orbit to the Sun and Moon are much longer than the distance to the Earth. So we only consider the solar and lunar attraction as particle centric attraction. The solar and lunar attractive effect on the geostationary orbit can be expressed as

$$\mathbf{a} = \mu_s \left(\frac{\mathbf{r_s} - \mathbf{r}}{|\mathbf{r_s} - \mathbf{r}|^3 - \frac{\mathbf{r_s}}{r_s^3}} \right) + \mu_m \left(\frac{\mathbf{r_m} - \mathbf{r}}{|\mathbf{r_m} - \mathbf{r}|^3 - \frac{\mathbf{r_m}}{r_m^3}} \right), \tag{4.53}$$

The right of the expression is the composition of the solar and lunar attractions. The geometrical relationship among the Sun, Moon, and Earth is illustrated in Fig. 4.15.

Define the mean longitude of a satellite at a particular epoch as l and the mean longitudes of the Sun and Moon at the epoch as α_s, α_m. In the ECI reference frame, the angles between the axial plane of Earth-pointing-Sun or Earth-pointing-Moon and the axial plane of Earth-pointing-Satellite are defined as dihedral angles λ_S, λ_M. Figure 4.16 illustrates the motion of perturbation body in the inertial reference frame:

$$\lambda_S = l - \alpha_S, \lambda_M = l - \alpha_m \tag{4.54}$$

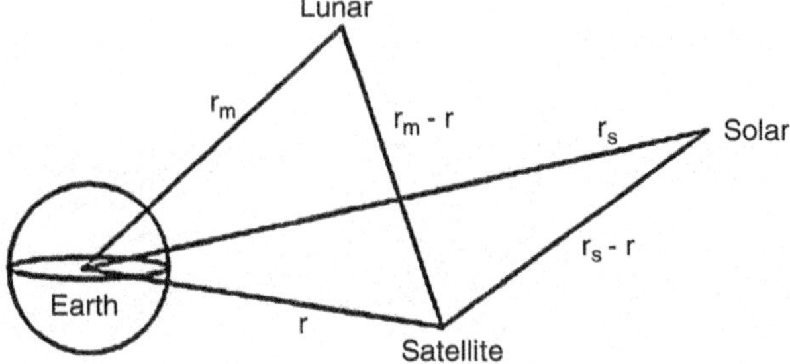

Fig. 4.15 Geometrical relationship among the Sun, Moon, and Earth

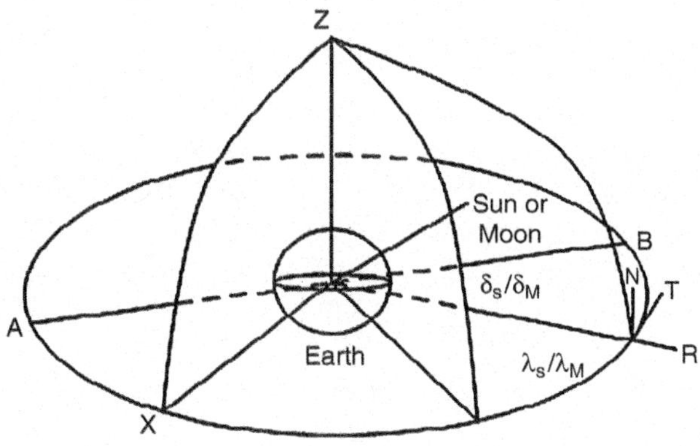

Fig. 4.16 Perturbation body in the inertial reference frame

When the dihedral angle equals zero, the satellite and the Sun or Moon are in the same celestial meridian plane. For the Sun, the time when the satellite gets across this plane is defined as the noon of local time; the time when the satellite turns 90° on equatorial plane, where the dihedral angle equals 90°, is defined as 18 o'clock of local time; the time when the dihedral angle equals 180° is defined as the midnight of local time; and the time when the dihedral angle equals 270° is defined as 6 o'clock of local time. For the Moon, there are similar definitions. Therefore, for the geostationary orbit, when a satellite moves a circle around the Earth in inertial space, the dihedral angle also almost rotates 360°. Because the dihedral angles not only are the function of time but also clarify the relative motion among the satellite, the Sun, and Moon, we choose these angles as the independent variables to survey how the lunisolar attractions take effects on the geostationary satellite.

In the geostationary orbit, the gravitational acceleration of the Sun is as the same magnitude as the perturbation acceleration from the zonal term J2 of the Earth's gravitation. So we cannot ignore the solar gravitational perturbation. Figure 4.17a, b shows the gravitational acceleration from the Sun projected in the radial, tangential, and normal direction, respectively, when the Sun lies in the northern hemisphere in a half year and lies in the southern hemisphere in the other half year.

The Solar Gravitational Acceleration Always Creates Angular Momentum. As Fig. 4.17a shows, the solar gravitation creates the radial, tangential, and normal attraction accelerations to the geostationary satellite. The radial and tangential accelerations are oscillation function with the dihedral angle in a period of half a day and the frequency is $2\omega_e$. The normal acceleration reverses its direction between day and night. If the Sun lies in the northern hemisphere of the Earth, the normal acceleration is positive from 6 a.m. to 18 p.m. of local spacecraft time, while the geostationary satellite travels along arc $\overset{\frown}{\mathbf{AB}}$ from point A to point B as illustrated in Fig. 4.18. On the contrary, the southward normal acceleration is negative from 18 p.m. to 6 a.m. of local time, when the geostationary satellite travels along arc $\overset{\frown}{\mathbf{BA}}$ from point B to point A as illustrated in Fig. 4.18.

As Fig. 4.17b shows, if the Sun lies in the southern hemisphere of the Earth, the normal acceleration is negative from 6 a.m. to 18 p.m., while the geostationary satellite travels along arc $\overset{\frown}{\mathbf{BA}}$ from point B to point A as illustrated in Fig. 4.18. On the contrary, the normal acceleration is positive from 18 p.m. to 6 a.m., while the geostationary satellite travels along arc $\overset{\frown}{\mathbf{AB}}$ from point A to point B as illustrated in Fig. 4.18.

Therefore, no matter where the Sun lies in a year, the solar gravitational acceleration always induces angular momentum to the geostationary orbit around axis AB, which changes the orbit plane of geostationary orbit. In the geostationary orbit, the gravitational acceleration of the Moon is also as the same magnitude as the perturbation acceleration from the zonal term J2 of the Earth's gravitation. We cannot ignore lunar gravitation perturbation for the same reason. As Fig. 4.19 shows, the Moon lies in the northern hemisphere in a half month and lies in the

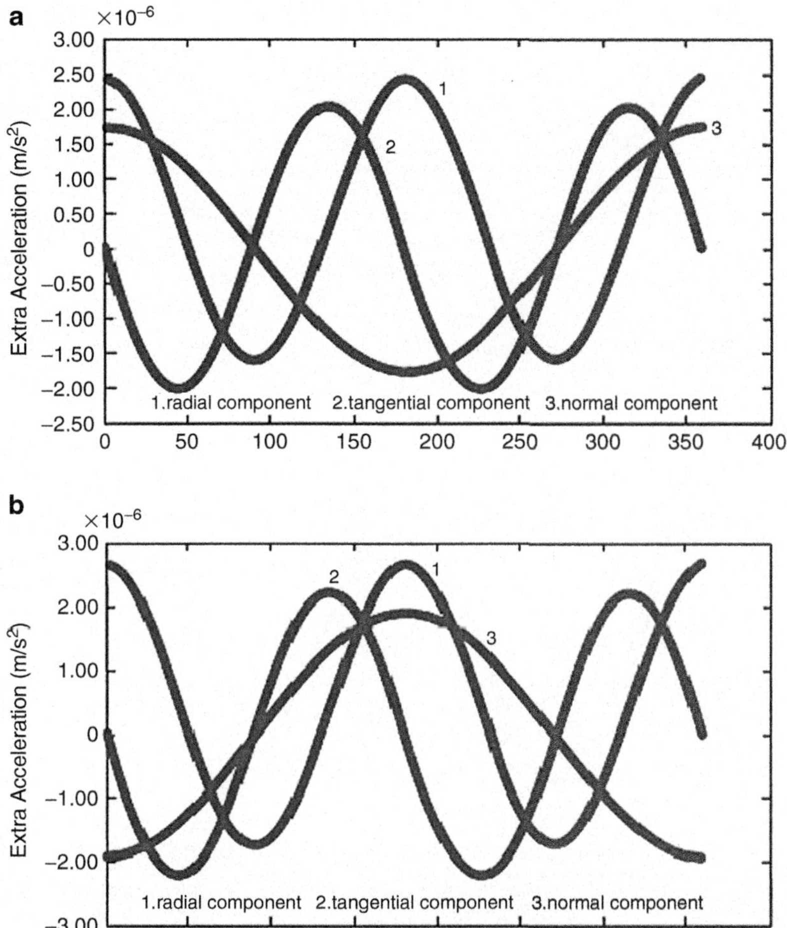

Fig. 4.17 The acceleration due to solar attraction. (**a**) The acceleration due to solar attraction in case if the Sun is above the north hemispheres. (**b**) The acceleration due to solar attraction in case if the Sun is above the south hemispheres

southern hemisphere in the other half month. The lunar gravitation also creates a radial, tangential, and normal acceleration to the geostationary satellite. The radial and tangential accelerations are oscillation function with the dihedral angle in a period of half a day and the frequency is $2\omega_e$. The normal acceleration almost takes the same effect as the solar normal gravitational acceleration. No matter where the Moon lies in a month, the lunar gravitational acceleration always creates angular momentum to the geostationary orbit plane, which changes the inclination vector of geostationary orbit too.

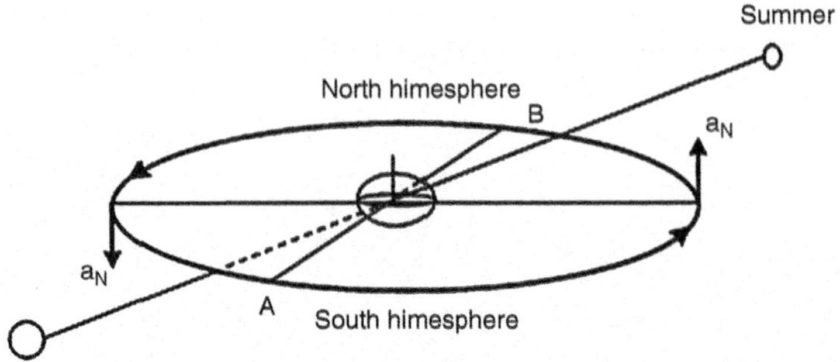

Fig. 4.18 Solar gravitational acceleration

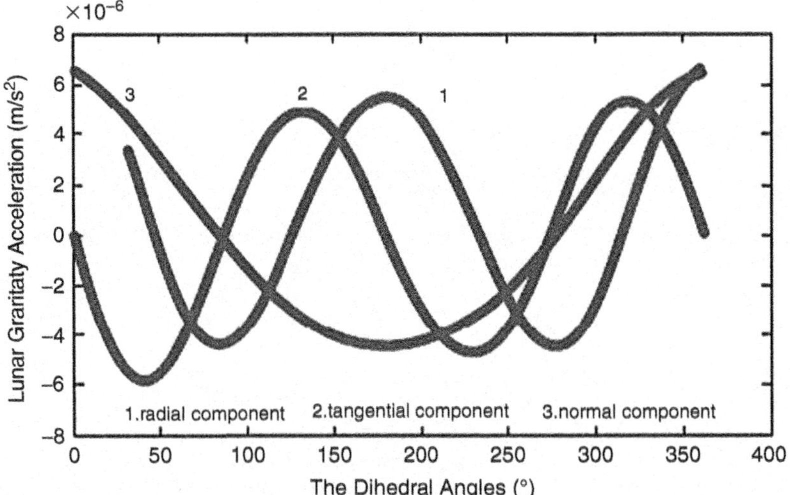

Fig. 4.19 The normal acceleration due to lunar attraction

4.5.1 The Lunar and Solar Potential Function

The potential function of lunisolar perturbation can be expressed as

$$R_k = \mu_k \left(\frac{1}{|\mathbf{r}_k - \mathbf{r}|} - \frac{\mathbf{r}_k \cdot \mathbf{r}}{|\mathbf{r}_k|^3} \right) = \mu_k \left(\frac{1}{|\mathbf{r}_k - \mathbf{r}|} - \frac{r}{r_k^2} \cos\theta \right)$$
$$\cos\theta_k = \frac{1}{r_k r} (\mathbf{r}_k \cdot \mathbf{r}) \tag{4.55}$$

In the expression,

$k = s$ is the solar perturbation; $k = m$ is the lunar perturbation.

Because the solar and lunar perturbations are the same in expression, the subscript k is adopted to stand for each of them. If there is a need to differentiate the two expressions, $k = s$ is used to stand for the former and $k = m$ is used to stand for the latter.

From the following equation,

$$|\mathbf{r}_k - \mathbf{r}|^2 = r_k^2 + r^2 - 2r_k r\cos\theta_k, \tag{4.56}$$

And according to the function of reciprocal distance of any two particles $\mathbf{r}_k$ and $\mathbf{r}$, perform Legendre expansion to obtain the expression below:

$$\frac{1}{\|\mathbf{r}_k - \mathbf{r}\|} = \frac{1}{r_k}\sum_{n=0}^{\infty}\left(\frac{r}{r_k}\right)^n P_n(\cos\theta_k), \tag{4.57}$$

For the geostationary orbit of the Earth, only keep zero- to second-order items of the expansion form and perform zero- to second-order Legendre polynomial expansion:

$$P_0(\cos\theta_k) = 1, P_1(\cos\theta_k) = \cos\theta_k, P_2(\cos\theta_k) = \frac{1}{2}(3\cos^2\theta_k - 1)$$

Replace it to the expression

$$\frac{1}{\|\mathbf{r}_k - \mathbf{r}\|} = \frac{1}{r_k}\sum_{n=0}^{\infty}\left(\frac{r}{r_k}\right)^n P_n(\cos\theta_k) = \frac{1}{r_k}\left(1 + \left(\frac{r}{r_k}\right)\cos\theta_k + \frac{1}{2}\left(\frac{r}{r_k}\right)^2(3\cos^2\theta_k - 1)\right)$$

So the potential expression of lunisolar perturbation is approximately

$$\begin{aligned} R_k &= \mu_k\left(\frac{1}{|\mathbf{r}_k - \mathbf{r}|} - \frac{r}{r_k^2}\cos\theta_k\right) = \frac{\mu_k}{r_k}\left(1 - \frac{1}{2}\left(\frac{r}{r_k}\right)^2 + \frac{3}{2}\left(\frac{r}{r_k}\right)^2\cos^2\theta_k\right) \\ \cos\theta_k &= \frac{\mathbf{r}_k}{r_k}\cdot\frac{\mathbf{r}}{r} \end{aligned} \tag{4.58}$$

For exp.ediently analyzing solar and lunar perturbation functions, some basic coefficients and auxiliary parameters of solar and lunar motion are given in Table 4.6.

Table 4.6 Perturbation body parameters

Perturbation body	Sun	Moon
Period (day)	365	**27.3**
Inclination relative to the equatorial plane	23.4°	**18.3°–28.6°**
Inclination relative to the ecliptic plane	0°	**5.15°**
Gravity constant $\mu_k(\mathrm{m}^3/\mathrm{s}^2)$	1.327124×10^{20}	4.90280×10^{12}
Mean geocentric distance $r_k(\mathrm{km})$	149.6×10^6	385.0×10^3
Geocentric radio $\left(\frac{r}{r_k}\right)$	2.8185×10^{-4}	**0.1095**
Mean motion $n_k = \sqrt{\frac{\mu_k}{r_k^3}}$	0.0172	**0.025**
Auxiliary parameter $\left(\frac{n_k}{n_e}\right)$	2.7375×10^{-3}	3.9789×10^{-3}
Auxiliary parameter $\left(\frac{n_k}{n_e}\right)^2$	7.49×10^{-6}	1.62×10^{-5}
Auxiliary parameter $P_k = \frac{\mu_k}{n_e r_k^3}$	5.44×10^{-10} 2.69×10^{-3}	1.18×10^{-9} 5.69×10^{-3}

4.5.2 Semi-major Axis Evolution

Because of the gravitational attractions from the Sun and Moon, the geostationary orbit radius and mean longitude experience the perturbation evolution motion. The effects induced by the radial and tangential extra acceleration from the lunisolar gravitational perturbations are almost the same as from the non-spherical Earth. When analyzing the perturbation motion of geostationary orbit radius and mean longitude, we ignore the effects of small inclination and eccentricity.

Because of the geostationary orbit with a small inclination, by using approximate expression,

$$\omega + f \approx \omega + M, \ \cos i \approx 1 \ \sin i \approx 0 \, \text{and} \ r \approx a$$

Defining the mean longitude as $l = \omega + \Omega + M$, the satellite's position vector in the ECI reference frame can be expressed approximately as

$$\mathbf{r} = r \begin{pmatrix} \cos(\omega + f)\cos\Omega - \sin(\omega + f)\sin\Omega \\ \cos(\omega + f)\sin\Omega + \sin(\omega + f)\cos\Omega \\ 0 \end{pmatrix} \approx r \begin{pmatrix} \cos l \\ \sin l \\ 0 \end{pmatrix} \tag{4.59}$$

The position vector of perturbation bodies of the Sun or Moon in the ECI reference frame can be expressed with its orbit elements

$$\mathbf{r}_k = r_k \begin{pmatrix} \cos(\omega_k + M_k)\cos\Omega_k - \sin(\omega_k + M_k)\sin\Omega_k \cos i_k \\ \cos(\omega_k + M_k)\sin\Omega_k + \sin(\omega_k + M_k)\cos\Omega_k \cos i_k \\ \sin i_k \sin(\omega_k + M_k) \end{pmatrix} \tag{4.60}$$

or with the celestial right ascension and declination (α_k, δ_k)

$$\mathbf{r}_k = r_k \begin{pmatrix} \cos\delta_k \cos\alpha_k \\ \cos\delta_k \sin\alpha_k \\ \sin\delta_k \end{pmatrix} \tag{4.61}$$

Lunisolar Perturbation Decreases Geostationary Orbit Radius. Lunisolar attraction is similar to the perturbation from the zonal terms of the Earth's gravitation, which increases the orbit radius about 2 km to the ideal geostationary orbit. The lunisolar attraction decreases the orbit radius for geostationary satellite to counterpart the extra attractions from the Sun and Moon.

Defining the orbit radius of geostationary orbit with the consideration of lunisolar attraction as a_c, and the ideal geostationary orbit radius as a_s, in order to balance the extra attraction from the Sun and Moon, the perturbation orbit radius a_c should satisfy

$$\left(\frac{d\lambda}{dt}\right)\Big|_{a=a_c} = \left((n_c - \omega_e) - \frac{2}{na_c}\frac{\partial R}{\partial a}\right)\Big|_{a=a_c} = 0 \tag{4.62}$$

According to Sect. 4.4, some relations are reviewed

$$(n_c - \omega_e) = \sqrt{\frac{\mu}{a_c^3}} - \sqrt{\frac{\mu}{a_s^3}} \approx -\frac{3}{2}\sqrt{\frac{\mu}{a_c^3}}\left(\frac{a_c - a_s}{a_s}\right)$$

$$\frac{2}{na_c}\frac{\partial R_k}{\partial a}\Big|_{a=a_c} = \frac{2}{na_c}\left\{\left(\frac{\mu_k}{r_k}\right)\left(-\frac{r}{r_k^2} + 3\frac{r}{r_k^2}\cos^2\theta_k\right)\right\} = 2\frac{n_k^2}{n_e}(3\cos^2\theta_k - 1)$$

so that the perturbation orbit radius a_c should satisfy

$$-\frac{3}{2}\sqrt{\frac{\mu}{a_c^3}}\left(\frac{a_c - a_s}{a_s}\right) = 2\frac{n_k^2}{n_e}(3\cos^2\theta_k - 1) \tag{4.63}$$

$$a_c = a_s\left(1 - \frac{4}{3}\left(\frac{n_k}{n_e}\right)^2 (3\cos^2\theta_k - 1)\right) , \tag{4.64}$$

Using approximate expression

$$\overline{(3\cos^2\theta_k - 1)} = \frac{1}{2}$$

and replacing the coefficients in Table 4.6 to the expression (4.64), the decrements of orbit radius for geostationary satellite with lunisolar perturbation are

$$\Delta a_s = -\frac{2}{3}a_s\left(\frac{n_s}{n_e}\right)^2 = -209.0(\text{m})$$

$$\Delta a_m = -\frac{2}{3}a_s\left(\frac{n_m}{n_e}\right)^2 = -455.1(\mathrm{m})$$

Lunisolar Attraction Induces Short-Periodical Perturbation of Semi-Major Axis. Perform the differential to the lunisolar potential expression with respect to the mean longitude:

$$\begin{aligned}\frac{\partial R_k}{\partial l} &= \frac{\partial}{\partial l}\left\{\frac{\mu_k}{r_k}\left(1-\frac{1}{2}\left(\frac{r}{r_k}\right)^2+\frac{3}{2}\left(\frac{r}{r_k}\right)^2\cos^2\theta_k\right)\right\}\\ &= \frac{3}{2}\left(\frac{r}{r_k}\right)^2\frac{\mu_k}{r_k}\frac{\partial}{\partial l}(\cos^2\theta_k)\\ &= \frac{3}{2}r^2n_k^2\left(2\cos\theta_k\frac{\partial}{\partial l}(\cos\theta_k)\right)\end{aligned} \tag{4.65}$$

According to Lagrange evolution equation of the semi-major axis for geostationary orbit, we get

$$\begin{aligned}\frac{\mathrm{d}a}{\mathrm{d}t} &= \frac{2}{na}\cdot\frac{\partial R_k}{\partial l}\\ &= 3a_s\frac{n_k^2}{n_e}\left((y_k^2-x_k^2)\sin 2l+2x_ky_k\cos 2l\right)\\ &= 3a_s\frac{n_k^2}{n_e}\cos^2\delta_k(-\sin 2l\cos 2\alpha_k+\cos 2l\sin 2\alpha_k)\\ &= -3a_s\frac{n_k^2}{n_e}\cos^2\delta_k\sin 2(l-\alpha_k)\end{aligned} \tag{4.66}$$

Performing integral to the above equation, we can calculate that the average daily variation of the semi-major axis for geostationary orbit is

$$\frac{\delta a}{\delta t} = \frac{1}{2\pi}\int_0^{2\pi}\left(\frac{\mathrm{d}a}{\mathrm{d}t}\right)\mathrm{d}l = 0 \tag{4.67}$$

The average variation of the semi-major axis caused by the lunisolar attraction equals zero in a day, which means that the lunisolar attraction has no long-periodical effects on the semi-major axis of geostationary orbit. But it induces short-periodical oscillation for the semi-major axis of geostationary orbit. The period is a half solar day and the amplitude correlates to solar and lunar celestial declination and phase. The short-periodical libration of the semi-major axis can be expressed as

$$\delta a = -3a_s \left(\frac{n_s}{n_e}\right)^2 \cos^2\delta_s \sin 2(l-\lambda_s) - 3a_s \left(\frac{n_m}{n_e}\right)^2 \cos^2\delta_m \sin 2(l-\lambda_m)$$
$$= -3a_s \left(\left(\frac{n_s}{n_e}\right)^2 \cos^2\delta_s \sin 2(l-\lambda_s) + \left(\frac{n_m}{n_e}\right)^2 \cos^2\delta_m \sin 2(l-\lambda_m)\right) \tag{4.68}$$

For the geostationary orbit, when a satellite moves a circle around the Earth in a day, the Sun and Moon can be considered as fixed in inertial space constantly, and the dihedral angle between the Sun or Moon and the satellite nearly rotates 360°. So we select the dihedral angle as an independent variable to study how the lunisolar attractions take effect on the geostationary satellite for the reason that the angle is the function of time, and more importantly, it clarifies not only the relative motion among the satellite, the Sun, and Moon but also the relation between the perturbation of the semi-major axis and the lunisolar attraction.

Under the conditions of full moon and new moon, the Sun, Moon, and Earth are closely aligned, and it is called the astronomic spring tide of the ocean surface on the Earth. The same effect is noticeable on the geostationary satellite at the spring tide too. At the spring tide, the lunisolar perturbation effect on the orbit semi-major axis is superposed and the amplitude reaches its maximum.

As for full moon as illustrated in Fig. 4.20a, we have

$$(l-\lambda_m) - (l-\lambda_s) = \pi$$

and as for new moon as illustrated in Fig. 4.20b, we get

$$(l-\lambda_m) - (l-\lambda_s) = 0$$

then

$$\delta a = -3a_s \left(\left(\frac{n_s}{n_e}\right)^2 \cos^2\delta_s + \left(\frac{n_m}{n_e}\right)^2 \cos^2\delta_m\right) \sin 2(l-\lambda_m) \tag{4.69}$$

As Fig. 4.21 shows, the amplitude of geostationary orbit semi-major axis from lunisolar perturbation is superposed. Especially when at the vernal equinox or autumnal equinox of spring tide, the amplitude reaches its maximum of approximately 3 km.

Under the condition of half moon, the Sun and Moon are seen at right angles from the Earth, and the corresponding ocean tide is called a neap tide. The geostationary satellite also experiences the neap tide. At the neap tide, lunisolar perturbation effect on the orbit semi-major axis is counteracted and the amplitude

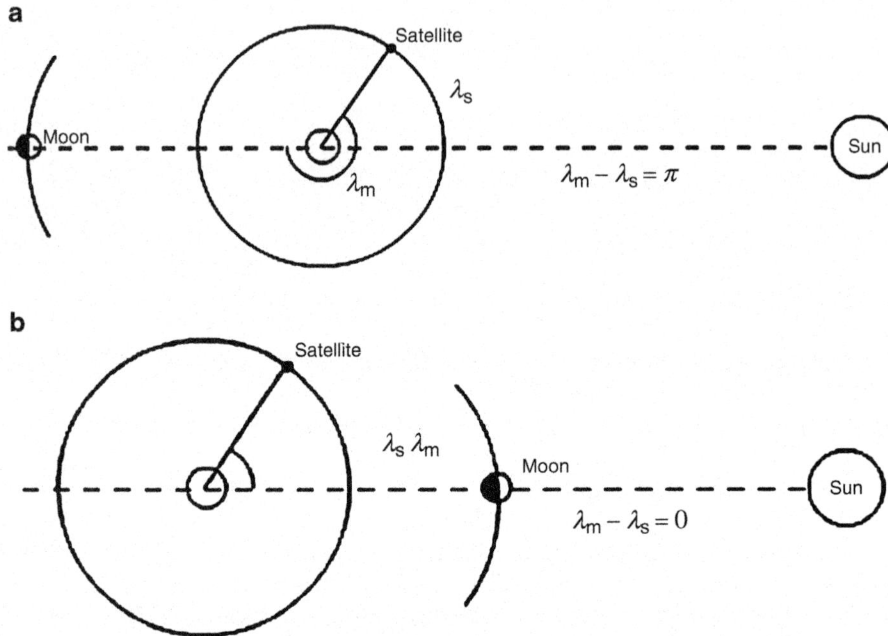

Fig. 4.20 Full moon and new moon. (**a**) Full moon. (**b**) New moon

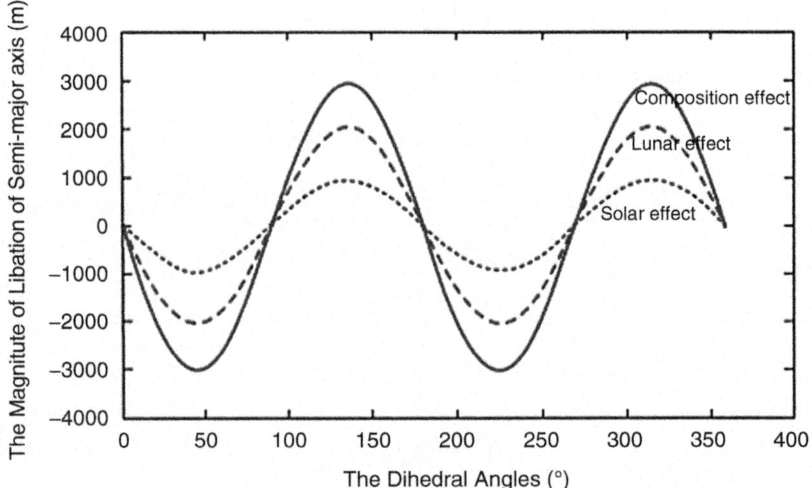

Fig. 4.21 Oscillation of semi-major axis during the full moon

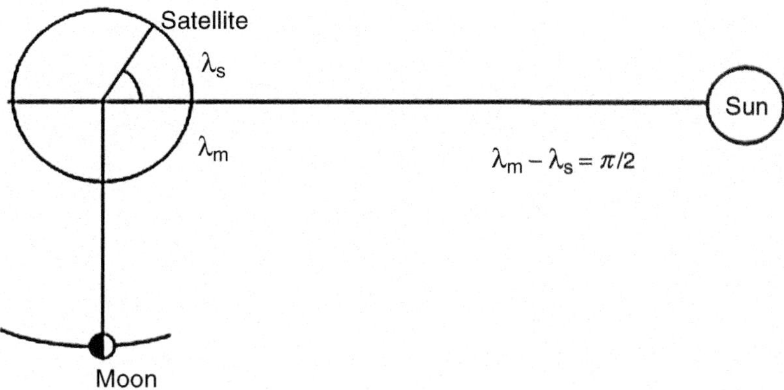

Fig. 4.22 Geometry in astronomical neap

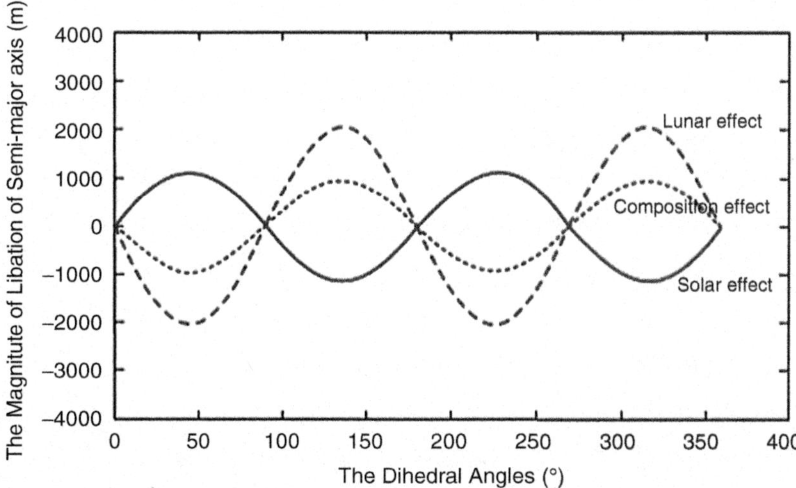

Fig. 4.23 Semi-major axis at astronomical neap

reaches its minimum. Figure 4.22 illustrates the geometry in astronomical neap tide at the half moon, and then

$$(l - \lambda_m) - (l - \lambda_s) = \frac{\pi}{2}$$

and

$$\delta a = -3a_s \left(\left(\frac{n_s}{n_e} \right)^2 \cos^2 \delta_s - \left(\frac{n_m}{n_e} \right)^2 \cos^2 \delta_m \right) \sin 2(l - \lambda_m) \tag{4.70}$$

The amplitude of geostationary orbit semi-major axis from solar and lunar perturbations is counteracted. The amplitude reaches its minimum of approximately 1 km as illustrated in Fig. 4.23.

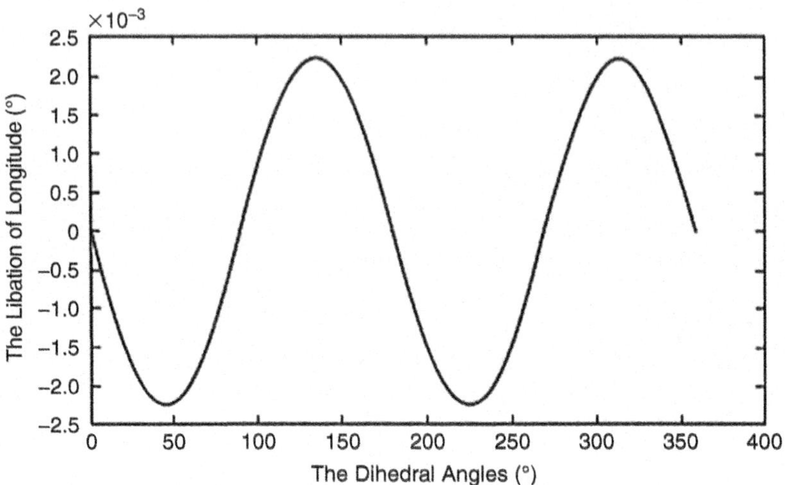

Fig. 4.24 Longitude libration due to the lunisolar attractions

4.5.3 Longitude Evolution

According to Lagrange evolution equation of mean longitude drift rate, the mean longitude variation rate of geostationary satellite changes linearly with the deviation of semi-major axis caused by the lunisolar perturbation:

$$\begin{aligned}\frac{d\lambda}{dt} &= -\frac{3}{2}\frac{n_e}{a_c}\delta a \\ &= \frac{9}{2}n_e\left(\left(\frac{n_s}{n_e}\right)^2 \cos^2\delta_s \sin 2(l-\lambda_s) + \left(\frac{n_m}{n_e}\right)^2 \cos^2\delta_m \sin 2(l-\lambda_m)\right)\end{aligned} \tag{4.71}$$

So the lunisolar perturbation induces the geostationary satellite with a periodical perturbation motion along the tangential direction, and the amplitude of periodical perturbation is

$$\delta\lambda = \frac{9}{2}\left(\left(\frac{n_s}{n_e}\right)^2 \cos^2\delta_s \sin 2(l-\lambda_s) + \left(\frac{n_m}{n_e}\right)^2 \cos^2\delta_m \sin 2(l-\lambda_m)\right) \tag{4.72}$$

As Fig. 4.24 shows, the lunisolar attractions induce a half-day periodical oscillation to the geostationary satellite's longitude. The maximum amplitude is 0.0025°, which does not include the daily longitude libration caused by the eccentricity perturbation induced by the lunisolar attractions.

4.5.4 Eccentricity Evolution

According to Lagrange perturbation equation of the eccentricity vector,

$$\begin{cases} \dfrac{de_x}{dt} = -\dfrac{1}{na^2}\dfrac{\partial R_k}{\partial e_y} \\ \dfrac{de_y}{dt} = \dfrac{1}{na^2}\dfrac{\partial R_k}{\partial e_x} \end{cases} \tag{4.73}$$

and the lunisolar potential function is

$$R_k = \frac{\mu_k}{r_k}\left(1 - \frac{1}{2}\left(\frac{r}{r_k}\right)^2 + \frac{3}{2}\left(\frac{r}{r_k}\right)^2 \cos^2\theta_k\right), \cos\theta_k = \frac{\mathbf{r}_k}{r_k}\cdot\frac{\mathbf{r}}{r} \tag{4.74}$$

Performing partial differentiation to the potential function with respect to the eccentricity vector, and introducing total differential formula with multivariable potential function, we get

$$\frac{\partial R_k}{\partial e_x} = \frac{\partial R_k}{\partial r}\frac{\partial r}{\partial e_x} + \frac{\partial R_k}{\partial \theta_k}\frac{\partial \theta_k}{\partial e_x}, \frac{\partial R_k}{\partial e_y} = \frac{\partial R_k}{\partial r}\frac{\partial r}{\partial e_y} + \frac{\partial R_k}{\partial \theta_k}\frac{\partial \theta_k}{\partial e_y} \tag{4.75}$$

In the function,

$$\begin{aligned} \frac{\partial R_k}{\partial r} &= \frac{\mu_k}{r_k}\frac{\partial}{\partial r}\left(1 - \frac{1}{2}\left(\frac{r}{r_k}\right)^2 + \frac{3}{2}\left(\frac{r}{r_k}\right)^2 \cos^2\theta_k\right) \\ &= \frac{\mu_k}{r_k}\left(\frac{1}{r_k^2}(3\cos^2\theta_k - 1)r\right) = n_k^2(3\cos^2\theta_k - 1)r \end{aligned} \tag{4.76}$$

$$\begin{aligned} \frac{\partial R_k}{\partial \theta_k} &= \frac{\mu_k}{r_k}\frac{\partial}{\partial \theta_k}\left(1 - \frac{1}{2}\left(\frac{r}{r_k}\right)^2 + \frac{3}{2}\left(\frac{r}{r_k}\right)^2 \cos^2\theta_k\right) \\ &= \frac{\mu_k}{r_k}\left(-3\left(\frac{r}{r_k}\right)^2 \sin\theta_k\cos\theta_k\right) = -3n_k^2 r^2 \sin\theta_k\cos\theta_k \end{aligned} \tag{4.77}$$

Before we derive the partial derivative expression of r and θ_k to the eccentricity vector (e_x, e_y), the function of r and θ_k to the eccentricity vector (e_x, e_y) should be established in advance by the following relations

$$r = a(1 - e\cos E) \approx a(1 - e\cos f) \tag{4.78}$$

$$f \approx M + 2e\sin M$$

$$l = \Omega + \omega + M$$

and the following approximate expression

$$\sin(A + x) \approx \sin(A) + \cos(A)x$$

$$\cos(A + x) \approx \cos(A) - \sin(A)x$$

Only keeping the first-order terms of eccentricity in expression (4.78), obtain

$$\begin{aligned} r &\approx a(1 - e\cos(M + 2e\sin M)) \approx a(1 - e(\cos M - 2e\sin M\cos M)) \\ &\approx a(1 - e\cos M) = a(1 - e_x\cos l - e_y\sin l) \end{aligned} \tag{4.79}$$

so that

$$\frac{\partial r}{\partial e_x} = -a\cos l, \quad \frac{\partial r}{\partial e_y} = -a\sin l \tag{4.80}$$

The radius vector $\mathbf{r}$ from the satellite to the Earth and the direction of line of sight from the Sun or Moon to the satellite $\left(\frac{\mathbf{r}_k}{r_k}\right)$ are

$$\begin{aligned} \mathbf{r} = \begin{pmatrix} x \\ y \\ z \end{pmatrix}^{\mathrm{T}} &= r\begin{pmatrix} \cos(\Omega + \omega + f) \\ \sin(\Omega + \omega + f) \\ 0 \end{pmatrix} \approx r\begin{pmatrix} \cos(\Omega + \omega + M + 2e\sin M) \\ \sin(\Omega + \omega + M + 2e\sin M) \\ 0 \end{pmatrix} \\ &= r\begin{pmatrix} \cos(\Omega + \omega + M) - 2e\sin M\sin(\Omega + \omega + M) \\ \sin(\Omega + \omega + M) + 2e\sin M\cos(\Omega + \omega + M) \\ 0 \end{pmatrix} \\ &= r\begin{pmatrix} \cos l - 2e_x\sin^2 l + e_y\sin 2l \\ \sin l + e_x\sin 2l - 2e_y\cos^2 l \\ 0 \end{pmatrix} \end{aligned} \tag{4.81}$$

Transform the expression and only keep the first-order terms of the eccentricity vector

$$\mathbf{r} \approx a\begin{pmatrix} \cos l - \frac{3}{2}e_x + \frac{1}{2}e_x\cos 2l + \frac{1}{2}e_y\sin 2l \\ \sin l - \frac{3}{2}e_y + \frac{1}{2}e_x\sin 2l - \frac{1}{2}e_y\cos 2l \\ 0 \end{pmatrix} \tag{4.82}$$

$$\frac{\mathbf{r}_k}{r_k} = \begin{pmatrix} x_k \\ y_k \\ z_k \end{pmatrix}^T$$

because

$$\begin{aligned}
\cos\theta_k &= \frac{\mathbf{r}_k}{r_k} \cdot \frac{\mathbf{r}}{r} \\
&= x_k\left(\cos l - 2e_x \sin^2 l + e_y \sin 2l\right) + y_k\left(\sin l + e_x \sin 2l - 2e_y \cos^2 l\right) \\
&= \frac{a}{r}\left(\begin{array}{c} x_k\left(\cos l - \frac{3}{2}e_x + \frac{1}{2}e_x \cos 2l + \frac{1}{2}e_y \sin 2l\right) \\ +y_k\left(\sin l - \frac{3}{2}e_y + \frac{1}{2}e_x \sin 2l - \frac{1}{2}e_y \cos 2l\right) \end{array}\right)
\end{aligned} \tag{4.83}$$

so that

$$\frac{\partial\theta_k}{\partial e_x} = -\frac{1}{\sin\theta_k} \cdot \frac{\partial}{\partial e_x}\left(\cos\theta_k\right) = -\frac{1}{\sin\theta_k} \cdot \left(-2x_k \sin^2 l + y_k \sin 2l\right) \tag{4.84}$$

$$\frac{\partial\theta_k}{\partial e_y} = -\frac{1}{\sin\theta_k} \cdot \frac{\partial}{\partial e_y}\left(\cos\theta_k\right) = -\frac{1}{\sin\theta_k} \cdot \left(x_k \sin 2l - 2y_k \cos^2 l\right) \tag{4.85}$$

Replacing the total differential formula with the partial derivative above, we obtain

$$\begin{aligned}
\frac{\partial R_k}{\partial e_x} = \frac{\partial R_k}{\partial r}\frac{\partial r}{\partial e_x} + \frac{\partial R_k}{\partial\theta_k}\frac{\partial\theta_k}{\partial e_x} &= \left(n_k^2\left(3\cos^2\theta_k - 1\right)r\right) \cdot \left(-a\cos l\right) \\
&+ 3n_k^2 r^2 \cos\theta_k \cdot \left(-2x_k \sin^2 l + y_k \sin 2l\right)
\end{aligned} \tag{4.86}$$

$$\begin{aligned}
\frac{\partial R_k}{\partial e_y} = \frac{\partial R_k}{\partial r}\frac{\partial r}{\partial e_y} + \frac{\partial R_k}{\partial\theta_k}\frac{\partial\theta_k}{\partial e_y} &= \left(n_k^2\left(3\cos^2\theta_k - 1\right)r\right) \cdot \left(-a\sin l\right) \\
&+ 3n_k^2 r^2 \cos\theta_k \cdot \left(x_k \sin 2l - 2y_k \cos^2 l\right)
\end{aligned} \tag{4.87}$$

4.5.5 *Inclination Evolution*

No matter where the Sun lies in a year, the solar gravitational acceleration always induces an angular momentum to the geostationary orbit, as well as the gravitational acceleration of the Moon, which change the orbit plane of geostationary orbit. The Lagrange perturbation equation for the geostationary orbit inclination vector as

$$\begin{cases} \dfrac{di_x}{dt} = -\dfrac{1}{na^2}\dfrac{\partial R_k}{\partial i_y} \\ \dfrac{di_y}{dt} = \dfrac{1}{na^2}\dfrac{\partial R_k}{\partial i_x} \end{cases} \tag{4.88}$$

and the lunisolar potential expression is

$$R_k = \frac{\mu_k}{r_k}\left(1 - \frac{1}{2}\left(\frac{r}{r_k}\right)^2 + \frac{3}{2}\left(\frac{r}{r_k}\right)^2 \cos^2\theta_k\right) \tag{4.89}$$

where

$$\cos\theta_k = \frac{\vec{r}_k}{r_k} \cdot \frac{\vec{r}}{r}$$

For analyzing how the lunisolar attractions affect the inclination vector, we assume the eccentricity is very small. So we use the following approximate expression:

$$r \approx a, f \approx M \approx E,\ \sin i \approx i,\ \cos i \approx 1$$

Then the radius vector from the satellite to the Earth and the direction of line of sight from the Sun or Moon to the satellite can be expressed as

$$\mathbf{r} = r\begin{pmatrix} \cos(\omega + f)\cos\Omega - \sin(\omega + f)\sin\Omega \\ \cos(\omega + f)\sin\Omega + \sin(\omega + f)\cos\Omega \\ i\sin(\omega + f) \end{pmatrix} = r\begin{pmatrix} \cos l \\ \sin l \\ i_x \sin l - i_y \cos l \end{pmatrix} \tag{4.90}$$

$$\mathbf{r_k} = r_k\begin{pmatrix} x_k \\ y_k \\ z_k \end{pmatrix} = r_k\begin{pmatrix} \cos(\omega_k + M_k)\cos\Omega_k - \sin(\omega_k + M_k)\sin\Omega_k\cos i_k \\ \cos(\omega_k + M_k)\sin\Omega_k + \sin(\omega_k + M_k)\cos\Omega_k\cos i_k \\ \sin i_k \sin(\omega_k + M_k) \end{pmatrix} \tag{4.91}$$

also

$$\cos\theta_k = \frac{\mathbf{r_k}}{r_k} \cdot \frac{\mathbf{r}}{r} = x_k \cos l + y_k \sin l + z_k(i_x \sin l - i_y \cos l) \tag{4.92}$$

Perform partial differentiation to the lunisolar potential expression with respect to the inclination vector and with these approximate expressions listed above:

$$\frac{\partial R_k}{\partial i_x}=\frac{\partial R_k}{\partial r}\frac{\partial r}{\partial i_x}+\frac{\partial R_k}{\partial \theta_k}\frac{\partial \theta_k}{\partial i_x}=\frac{\mu_k}{r_k}\left(-3\left(\frac{r}{r_k}\right)^2\cos\theta_k\sin\theta_k\cdot\frac{\partial \theta_k}{\partial i_x}\right) \tag{4.93}$$

$$\frac{\partial R_k}{\partial i_y}=\frac{\partial R_k}{\partial r}\frac{\partial r}{\partial i_y}+\frac{\partial R_k}{\partial \theta_k}\frac{\partial \theta_k}{\partial i_y}=\frac{\mu_k}{r_k}\left(-3\left(\frac{r}{r_k}\right)^2\cos\theta_k\sin\theta_k\cdot\frac{\partial \theta_k}{\partial i_y}\right) \tag{4.94}$$

$$\frac{\partial \theta_k}{\partial i_x}=-\frac{z_k}{\sin\theta_k}\sin l \tag{4.95}$$

$$\frac{\partial \theta_k}{\partial i_y}=\frac{z_k}{\sin\theta_k}\cos l \tag{4.96}$$

Clear up the expression above.

$$\begin{aligned}\frac{\partial R_k}{\partial i_x}&=\frac{\mu_k}{r_k}\left(3\left(\frac{r}{r_k}\right)^2\cos\theta_k z_k\sin l\right)\\&=3n_k^2a^2\left(x_k\cos l+y_k\sin l+z_k\left(i_x\sin l-i_y\cos l\right)\right)z_k\sin l\\&=\frac{3}{2}n_k^2a^2\left(y_kz_k+x_kz_k\sin 2l-y_kz_k\cos 2l+i_xz_k^2-i_xz_k^2\cos 2l-i_yz_k^2\sin 2l\right)\end{aligned} \tag{4.97}$$

$$\begin{aligned}\frac{\partial R_k}{\partial i_y}&=\frac{\mu_k}{r_k}\left(-3\left(\frac{r}{r_k}\right)^2\cos\theta_k z_k\cos l\right)\\&=-3n_k^2a^2\left(x_k\cos l+y_k\sin l+z_k\left(i_x\sin l-i_y\cos l\right)\right)z_k\cos l\\&=-\frac{3}{2}n_k^2a^2\left(x_kz_k+y_kz_k\sin 2l+x_kz_k\cos 2l-i_yz_k^2-i_yz_k^2\cos 2l+i_xz_k^2\sin 2l\right)\end{aligned} \tag{4.98}$$

In order to conclude the secular and long-periodical perturbations of the inclination vector, we ignore the short-period terms which contain the trigonometric functions of the right longitude of geostationary satellite, and get inclination perturbation equations which contain the secular and long-periodical perturbations below:

$$\begin{cases}\dfrac{\mathrm{d}i_x}{\mathrm{d}t}=-\dfrac{1}{na^2}\dfrac{\partial R_k}{\partial i_y}=-\dfrac{1}{na^2}\left(-\dfrac{3}{2}n_k^2a^2x_kz_k\right)=\dfrac{3}{2}\dfrac{n_k^2}{n}x_kz_k\\[2ex]\dfrac{\mathrm{d}i_y}{\mathrm{d}t}=\dfrac{1}{na^2}\dfrac{\partial R_k}{\partial i_x}=\dfrac{1}{na^2}\left(\dfrac{3}{2}n_k^2a^2y_kz_k\right)=\dfrac{3}{2}\dfrac{n_k^2}{n}y_kz_k\end{cases} \tag{4.99}$$

From expression (4.91), the direction cosine of the Sun or Moon in the ECI reference frame is

$$\frac{\mathbf{r_k}}{r_k} = \begin{pmatrix} x_k \\ y_k \\ z_k \end{pmatrix} = \begin{pmatrix} \cos\lambda_k \cos\Omega_k - \sin\lambda_k \sin\Omega_k \cos i_k \\ \cos\lambda_k \sin\Omega_k + \sin\lambda_k \cos\Omega_k \cos i_k \\ \sin i_k \sin\lambda_k \end{pmatrix} \tag{4.100}$$

Here

$$\lambda_k = \omega_k + f_k$$

Replacing the involved parameters with expression (4.100), we get the secular and long-periodical perturbations of inclination equations:

$$\frac{di_x}{dt} = \frac{3}{8}\frac{n_k^2}{n}(-\sin\Omega_k \sin 2i_k + 2\sin i_k \cos\Omega_k \sin 2\lambda_k + \sin 2i_k \sin\Omega_k \cos 2\lambda_k) \tag{4.101}$$

$$\frac{di_y}{dt} = \frac{3}{8}\frac{n_k^2}{n}(\cos\Omega_k \sin 2i_k + 2\sin i_k \sin\Omega_k \sin 2\lambda_k - \sin 2i_k \cos\Omega_k \cos 2\lambda_k) \tag{4.102}$$

There are secular terms (only include terms containing the inclination and the right ascension of the Sun or Moon) and long-period terms (include terms containing the right longitude of the Sun or Moon) in the perturbation equations. So the inclination vector has secular and long-period terms.

4.5.5.1 Secular Perturbation Motion of Inclination Vector

According to expressions (4.101 and 4.102), the secular term perturbation equation is

$$\begin{cases} \dfrac{di_x}{dt} = -\dfrac{3}{8}\dfrac{n_k^2}{n}(\sin\Omega_k \sin 2i_k) \\ \dfrac{di_y}{dt} = \dfrac{3}{8}\dfrac{n_k^2}{n}(\cos\Omega_k \sin 2i_k) \end{cases} \tag{4.103}$$

Since the solar and lunar perturbations are the same in expression forms, according to the symbolic assumption above, the lunisolar secular perturbation satisfies the equation

$$\begin{cases} \dfrac{di_x}{dt} = -\dfrac{3}{8}\left(\dfrac{n_s^2}{n_e}\sin\Omega_s \sin 2i_s + \dfrac{n_m^2}{n_e}\sin\Omega_m \sin 2i_m\right) \\ \dfrac{di_y}{dt} = \dfrac{3}{8}\left(\dfrac{n_s^2}{n_e}\cos\Omega_s \sin 2i_s + \dfrac{n_m^2}{n_e}\cos\Omega_m \sin 2i_m\right) \end{cases} \tag{4.104}$$

In the equation:

n_s: the mean angular velocity of the Sun's apparent motion (0.9856°/day)
n_m: the mean angular velocity of the Moon's apparent motion
Ω_s: the right ascension of the ascending node of the solar orbit ($\Omega_s = 0$)
Ω_m: the right ascension of the ascending node of the lunar orbit
i_s: the inclination of the Sun's orbit ($i_s = 23.4437\,°$)
i_m: the inclination of Moon's orbit (relative to the Earth's true equatorial plane)

Apply the coefficients in Table (4.6) to expression (4.104) and denote some auxiliary variables

$$P_s = \frac{\mu_s}{n_e r_s^3} = \frac{n_s^2}{n_e} = 2.69 \times 10^{-3} \text{ (Unit : degrees per day)}$$

$$P_m = \frac{\mu_m}{n_e r_m^3} = \frac{n_m^2}{n_e} = 5.69 \times 10^{-3} \text{ (Unit : degrees per day)}$$

$$\sin \Omega_s = 0, \quad \cos \Omega_s = 1$$

By replacing the perturbation equation with the above coefficients and variables, the variation of inclination in a day is

$$\begin{cases} \Delta i_x = -\dfrac{3}{8}(P_m \sin \Omega_m \sin 2i_m) \\ \Delta i_y = \dfrac{3}{8}(P_s \sin 2i_s + P_m \cos \Omega_m \sin 2i_m) \end{cases} \tag{4.105}$$

Because the relation between the ecliptic plane and lunar orbit is already known, the inclination of lunar orbit relative to the ecliptic plane is $i_{sm} = 5.15°$, as illustrated in Fig. 4.25. The right ascension of the ascending node of the Moon's orbit can be calculated by Gregorian calendar $\Omega_{sm} = 12.111° - 0.052954T$, where T means Julian day relative to 1/1, 1950.

In the Earth-centered sphere, the spherical triangle is composed of the Earth's equator plane, the ecliptic plane, and the Moon's orbit plane, which satisfy the following equations:

$$\cos i_{sm} = \cos i_m \cos i_s + \sin i_m \sin i_s \cos \Omega_m$$

$$\cos i_m = \cos i_s \cos i_{sm} - \sin i_s \sin i_{sm} \cos \Omega_{sm}$$

$$\sin i_m \sin \Omega_m = \sin i_{sm} \sin \Omega_{sm}$$

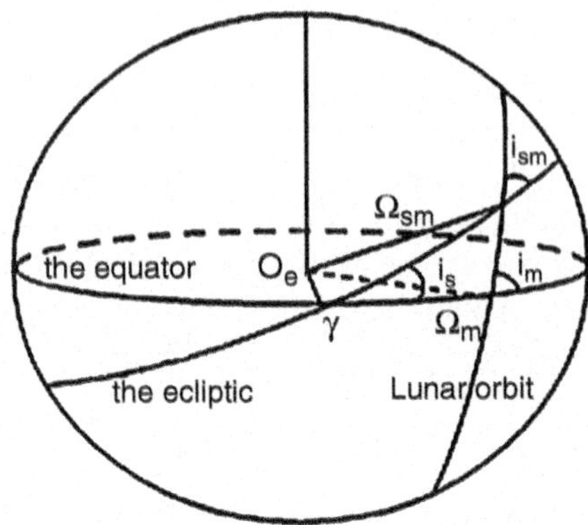

Fig. 4.25 The ecliptic and lunar orbit in the Earth-centered frame

Replacing the variables with some astronomical constants listed in Table 4.6, we get

$$\cos i_m = 0.9137 - 0.0357 \cos \Omega_{sm}$$

$$\sin i_m \sin \Omega_m = 0.089 \sin \Omega_{sm}$$

$$\sin i_m \cos \Omega_m = (\cos i_{sm} - \cos i_m \cos i_s)/\sin i_s = 0.396 + 0.082 \cos \Omega_{sm}$$

Replacing the terms of function (4.105) with above relations, and simplifying to

$$\begin{cases} \Delta i_x = -3.5 \sin \Omega_{sm} \times 10^{-4} (^\circ/\text{day}) \\ \Delta i_y = (22.79 + 2.59 \cos \Omega_{sm}) \times 10^{-4} (^\circ/\text{day}) \end{cases} \tag{4.106}$$

The secular perturbation of the inclination from the solar and lunar attractions is mainly correlated to the right ascension of the ascending node of the lunar orbit. Since the period of the procession motion of the Moon is about 18.6 years, the secular perturbation of the geostationary orbit inclination can be considered as a constant in a pretty short time:

$$i_x(t) = i_x(t_0) + \Delta i_x (t - t_0), i_y(t) = i_y(t_0) + \Delta i_y (t - t_0)$$

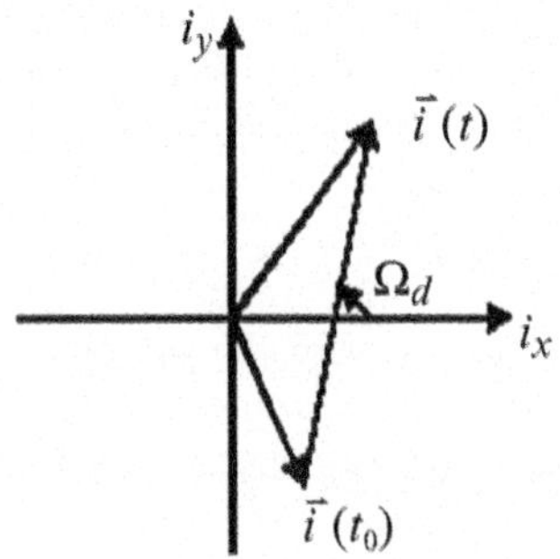

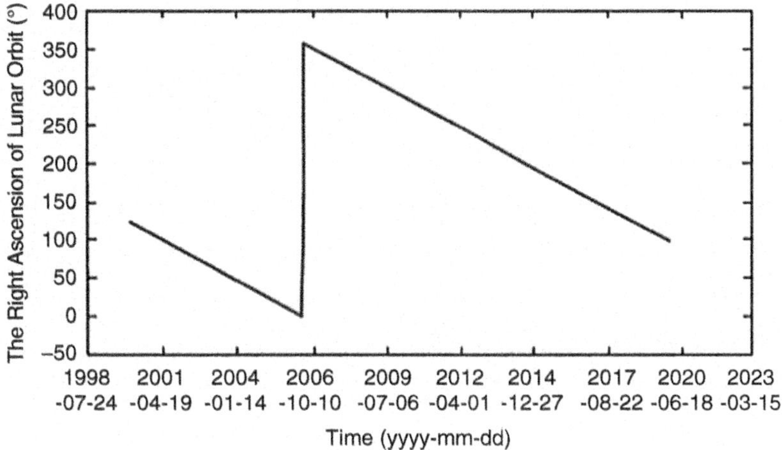

Fig. 4.26 Right ascension of the lunar orbit

The inclination vector moves in linearity with time, with a slope of Ω_d, and an included angle is Δi, which are denoted as

$$\Omega_d = \arctan\left(\frac{\Delta i_y}{\Delta i_x}\right)$$

$$\Delta i = \sqrt{(\Delta i_y)^2 + (\Delta i_x)^2}$$

In every year, the included angle and the slope of the inclination's perturbation motion change a little with the procession motion of the lunar orbit. The closer the mean longitude of lunar orbit to the vernal equinox (e.g., in June, 2006, the mean longitude of lunar orbit almost overlaps the vernal equinox) as illustrated in Fig. 4.26, the higher the perturbation velocity of the inclination vector.

When the mean longitude of the lunar orbit is close to the vernal equinox (e.g., in June, 2006), the secular drift rate reaches the maximum velocity, of about 0.95°/year. When the mean longitude of lunar orbit is 180° away from the vernal equinox, the perturbation velocity of inclination vector reaches the minimum value of about 0.75°/year as illustrated in Fig. 4.27.

The perturbation direction of the inclination vector is defined as the angle between the perturbation direction and the vernal equinox; its magnitude varies from 80° to 100° with the procession motion of the lunar orbit (Fig. 4.28), which means that the inclination vector drifts nearly perpendicular to the vernal equinox direction.

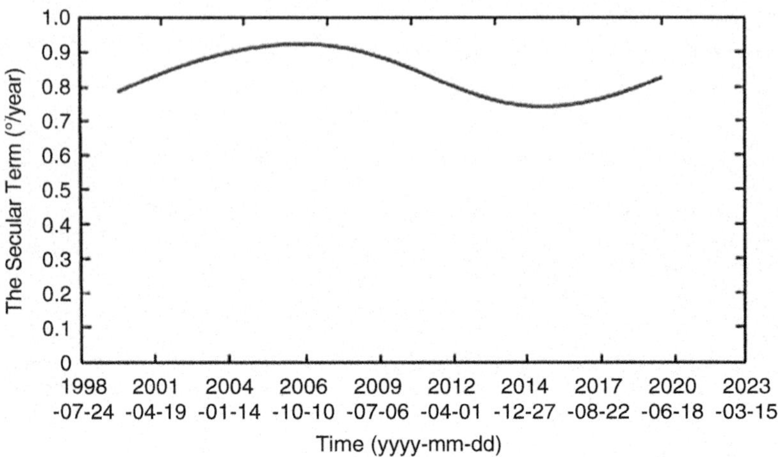

Fig. 4.27 The magnitude of inclination secular term

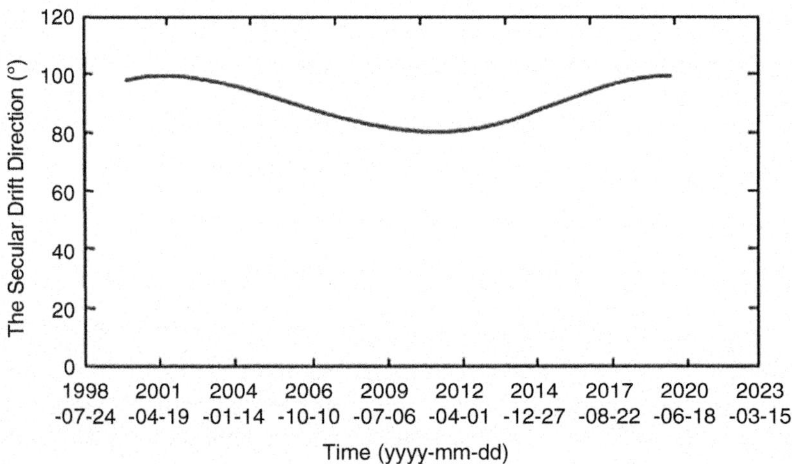

Fig. 4.28 Secular perturbation direction of inclination

4.5.5.2 Long-Periodical Perturbation of Inclination Vector

The long-periodical perturbation equation is

$$\begin{cases} \dfrac{\mathrm{d}i_x}{\mathrm{d}t} = \dfrac{3}{8}\dfrac{n_k^2}{n}(2\sin i_k \cos\Omega_k \sin 2\lambda_k + \sin 2i_k \sin\Omega_k \cos 2\lambda_k) \\ \dfrac{\mathrm{d}i_y}{\mathrm{d}t} = \dfrac{3}{8}\dfrac{n_k^2}{n}(2\sin i_k \sin\Omega_k \sin 2\lambda_k - \sin 2i_k \cos\Omega_k \cos 2\lambda_k) \end{cases} \tag{4.107}$$

1. Semiannual periodical term

The semiannual periodical perturbation motion of the inclination vector is induced by the solar attraction. Suppose the motion of the Sun satisfies the following approximate expressions:

$$\Omega_s = 0,\ \sin\Omega_s = 0,\ \cos\Omega_s = 1$$

Then the long-periodical perturbation equation of the inclination vector of geostationary orbit from the solar attraction satisfies

$$\begin{cases} \dfrac{di_x}{dt} = \dfrac{3}{8}\dfrac{n_s^2}{n}(2\sin i_s \sin 2\lambda_s) \\ \dfrac{di_y}{dt} = \dfrac{3}{8}\dfrac{n_s^2}{n}(-\sin 2i_s \cos 2\lambda_s) \end{cases} \tag{4.108}$$

Since $\lambda_s = n_s t$, we obtain

$$\begin{cases} \dfrac{di_x}{d\lambda_s} = \dfrac{di_x}{dt}\cdot\dfrac{dt}{d\lambda_s} = \dfrac{3}{8}\left(\dfrac{n_s}{n}\right)\sin i_s(\sin 2\lambda_s) \\ \dfrac{di_y}{d\lambda_s} = \dfrac{di_y}{dt}\cdot\dfrac{dt}{d\lambda_s} = -\dfrac{3}{16}\left(\dfrac{n_s}{n}\right)\sin 2i_s(\cos 2\lambda_s) \end{cases} \tag{4.109}$$

There is a periodical term which contains the mean motion of the Sun in the above equation, so the average variation of the inclination vector in a year equals zero. But there is a semiannual periodical perturbation; the period is half a year, or 182.63 days as shown in Fig. 4.29.

The amplitude of the semiannual periodical term is

$$\begin{aligned} i_x &: \frac{3}{8}\left(\frac{n_s}{n_e}\right)\sin i_s = 0.0235(^\circ) \\ i_y &: \frac{3}{16}\left(\frac{n_s}{n_e}\right)\sin 2i_s = 0.0215(^\circ) \end{aligned} \tag{4.110}$$

2. Semimonthly periodical term

The perturbation equation of the inclination vector from the lunar attraction is

$$\begin{cases} \dfrac{di_x}{dt} = \dfrac{3}{8}P_m(2\sin i_m \cos\Omega_m \sin 2\lambda_m + \sin 2i_m \sin\Omega_m \cos 2\lambda_m) \\ \dfrac{di_y}{dt} = \dfrac{3}{8}P_m(2\sin i_m \sin\Omega_m \sin 2\lambda_m - \sin 2i_m \cos\Omega_m \cos 2\lambda_m) \end{cases} \tag{4.111}$$

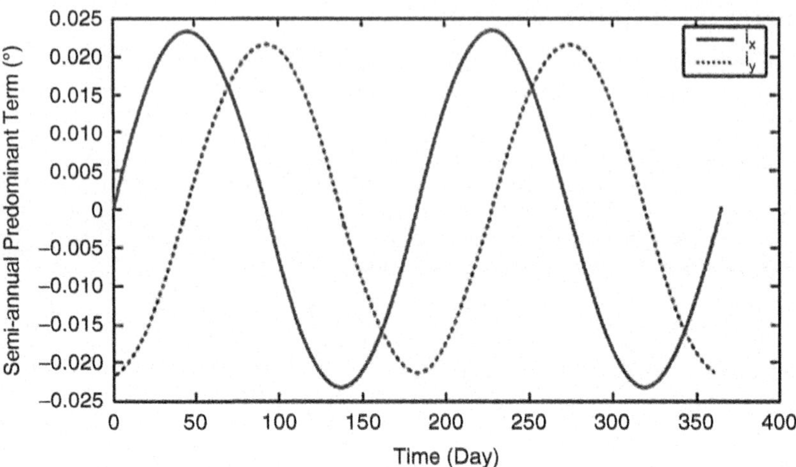

Fig 4.29 Predominant long-period term

Because the variations of the lunar orbit elements relative to ecliptic plane are relatively certain, by making use of the spherical geometrical relations of the spherical triangle composed of the Earth's equator plane, the ecliptic plane and the Moon's orbit plane are

$$\begin{aligned}\cos i_m &= 0.9137 - 0.0357\cos\Omega_{sm}\\ \sin i_m \sin\Omega_m &= 0.089\sin\Omega_{sm}\\ \sin i_m\cos\Omega_m &= (\cos i_{sm} - \cos i_m\cos i_s)/\sin i_s = 0.396 + 0.082\cos\Omega_{sm}\end{aligned}$$

Replacing the expression above to perturbation Eq. (4.111), we get

$$\begin{cases}\dfrac{di_x}{dt} = \dfrac{3}{8}P_m\begin{pmatrix}2(0.396+0.082\cos\Omega_{sm})\sin 2\lambda_m + \\ 2\cdot 0.089\sin\Omega_{sm}(0.9137-0.0357\cos\Omega_{sm})\cos 2\lambda_m\end{pmatrix}\\ \dfrac{di_y}{dt} = \dfrac{3}{8}P_m\begin{pmatrix}2\cdot 0.089\sin\Omega_{sm}\sin 2\lambda_m - \\ 2\cdot(0.396+0.082\cos\Omega_{sm})(0.9137-0.0357\cos\Omega_{sm})\cos 2\lambda_m\end{pmatrix}\end{cases} \tag{4.112}$$

If the mean ecliptic longitude of the lunar orbit Ω_{sm} is assigned, the right composition of perturbation equation above is a periodical function of the mean lunar motion. Therefore, the lunar attraction not only induces the secular perturbation of inclination vector but also induces semimonthly periodical perturbation. By taking main terms of the above equation, we get

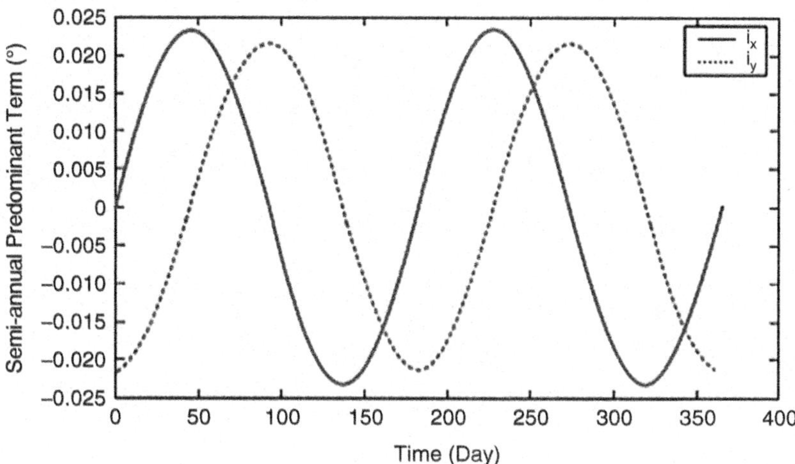

Fig. 4.30 Predominant medium-period term

$$\begin{cases} \dfrac{\mathrm{d}i_x}{\mathrm{d}\lambda_m} = \dfrac{3}{8}\left(\dfrac{P_m}{n_m}\right)((0.396)\sin 2\lambda_m) \\ \dfrac{\mathrm{d}i_y}{\mathrm{d}\lambda_m} = -\dfrac{3}{8}\left(\dfrac{P_m}{n_m}\right)((0.396)(0.9137)\cos 2\lambda_m) \end{cases} \tag{4.113}$$

There is a periodical term in the equation. The average variation of the inclination vector in a month equals zero. But there is a semimonthly periodical perturbation as shown in Fig. 4.30, whose period is half a month, or 13.7 days, and whose amplitude of semiannual periodical term satisfies

$$\begin{aligned} i_x &: \frac{3}{8}\left(\frac{P_m}{n_m}\right)0.396 = 0.0037(°) \\ i_y &: \frac{3}{8}\left(\frac{P_m}{n_m}\right)(0.396)(0.9137) = 0.0034(°) \end{aligned} \tag{4.114}$$

4.5.6 Solar-Lunar Ephemeris

There are two methods to calculate the solar-lunar ephemeris: analytical method and numerical interpolation method. If high precision is not required, for example, the calculation of the lunar and solar attraction perturbations of satellite around the

Earth, the former will be adopted. Because the lunar and solar attractions are far less than the Earth-centric gravity, the accuracy of analytical method has 0.1–1 % errors. It's enough for most cases in calculation of solar-lunar ephemeris. For more detailed analysis and calculation, please consult reference books [6]. The comparison results of the accuracy are listed in Tables 4.7 and 4.8 for solar and lunar ephemeris, respectively.

4.6 The Solar Radiation Perturbation

A simplified scenario may be helpful to illustrate the perturbation of geostationary orbit due to the solar radiation pressure. As shown in Fig. 4.31, the decomposition of the solar radiation force into the radial and tangential components reveals that the solar radiation pressure deforms the shape of orbit, the effect of which will be revealed in this section by deploying some perturbation equations about the solar radiation pressure to the geostationary orbit.

The acceleration expression of the solar radiation pressure to the Earth round satellite can be simplified as

$$\mathbf{a} = -\varepsilon C_R\left(\frac{S}{m}\right)P_0\mathbf{u} \tag{4.115}$$

In the equation:

$\varepsilon = 0, 1$: switch to reflect whether the satellite experience ecliptic or not
C_R: the solar radiation pressure coefficient which correlates to the surface material of satellite surface (often has a value of 1.5)
P_0: the solar radiation pressure per meter square (constant, 4.56×10^{-6}(N/m^2))
S: the surface area of a satellite facing to the Sun
M: satellite mass
$\mathbf{u}$: the direction cosine from a satellite to the Sun

Therefore, the acceleration of solar radiation pressure depends on the ratio of the satellite area to satellite mass. In general, the satellite's solar panels face to the Sun and keep the direction all the time. The area of the solar panels is about 30–70 m^2. The following analysis assumes that the satellite area to the Sun is 50 m^2 and the satellite mass is 1,000 kg.

Now we give the perturbation acceleration due to the solar radiation pressure to the geostationary satellite within a solar day when the Sun is located at different right ascension. As illustrated in Figs. 4.32 and 4.33, when the Sun is located at the vernal equinox and autumnal equinox, the normal component due to the solar radiation pressure equals zero; the radial and tangential components reach the maximum value of about 3.4×10^{-7}(m/s^2).

Table 4.7 The solar ephemeris in 2007

Epoch (0 h UTC)	JPL ephemeris (DE405)			Analytical method (Oliver2000)			Error (JPL/De405- analytical method)		
	Geocentric distance	Right ascension	Declination	Geocentric distance	Right ascension	Declination	Geocentric distance	Right ascension	Declination
	(km)	(°)	(°)	(km)	(°)	(°)	(km)	(°)	(°)
2007-1-1	1.470980E+8	280.599	−23.0806	1.471030E+8	280.574	−23.0833	−4352.12	0.024736	0.002697
2007-2-1	1.473840E+8	313.757	−17.387	1.473890E+8	313.734	−17.394	−4867.91	0.022935	0.007062
2007-3-1	1.481900E+8	341.147	−7.97474	1.481940E+8	341.125	−7.98392	−4094.12	0.021816	0.009178
2007-4-1	1.494420E+8	9.61727	4.14255	1.494480E+8	9.59587	4.13371	−5678.55	0.0214	0.008843
2007-5-1	1.506880E+8	37.4328	14.7625	1.506950E+8	37.409	14.7557	−6588.15	0.023794	0.00689
2007-6-1	1.516700E+8	68.0795	21.9094	1.516760E+8	68.0527	21.9067	−5963.77	0.026748	0.002681
2007-7-1	1.520850E+8	99.141	23.1722	1.520890E+8	99.1137	23.1748	−3606.93	0.02727	−0.00262
2007-8-1	1.518540E+8	130.393	18.2726	1.518550E+8	130.369	18.2794	−1047.22	0.024067	−0.00683
2007-9-1	1.510110E+8	159.447	8.65439	1.510110E+8	159.426	8.6628	52.4216	0.020771	−0.00841
2007-10-1	1.498150E+8	186.435	−2.78149	1.498160E+8	186.415	−2.77341	−1315.98	0.019832	−0.00808
2007-11-1	1.485130E+8	215.379	−14.0905	1.485160E+8	215.359	−14.0844	−2841.76	0.020893	−0.00605
2007-12-1	1.475320E+8	246.181	−21.6335	1.475370E+8	246.157	−21.6309	−5187.39	0.023912	−0.00257

Table 4.8 The lunar ephemeris in Jan. 2007

	JPL ephemeris (DE405)			Analytical method (Oliver2000)			Error (JPL/De405- analytical method)		
Epoch (0 h UTC)	Geocentric distance (km)	Right ascension (°)	Declination (°)	Geocentric distance (km)	Right ascension (°)	Declination (°)	Geocentric distance (km)	Right ascension (°)	Declination (°)
2007-1-1	373715	59.5575	25.4375	373741	59.5285	25.433	−26.051	0.028968	0.004434
2007-1-2	376115	74.8679	27.7706	376130	74.8448	27.7698	−14.7495	0.023148	0.000805
2007-1-3	379192	90.3851	28.3685	379217	90.374	28.3705	−24.7486	0.011081	−0.00208
2007-1-4	382857	105.564	27.2445	382909	105.566	27.2472	−51.4984	−0.00261	−0.00278
2007-1-5	386935	119.944	24.6013	387018	119.957	24.6031	−83.4574	−0.01276	−0.00182
2007-1-6	391174	133.297	20.7573	391281	133.313	20.7582	−106.954	−0.01638	−0.00089
2007-1-7	395276	145.63	16.055	395387	145.643	16.0563	−111.581	−0.01362	−0.00126
2007-1-8	398919	157.108	10.8011	399013	157.115	10.8039	−94.0594	−0.00689	−0.00276
2007-1-9	401803	167.976	5.2444	401862	167.975	5.24842	−59.0098	0.000505	−0.00403
2007-1-10	403670	178.501	−0.41852	403686	178.495	−0.41478	−16.2525	0.00575	−0.00375
2007-1-11	404334	188.958	−6.02538	404310	188.951	−6.02378	24.1041	0.007346	−0.0016
2007-1-12	403700	199.62	−11.4258	403643	199.615	−11.4273	56.3603	0.005489	0.001469
2007-1-13	401769	210.754	−16.4583	401687	210.752	−16.4622	81.3017	0.001855	0.003944

2007-1-14	398650	222.604	−20.929	398545	222.606	−20.9338	104.635	−0.0011	0.004816
2007-1-15	394552	235.365	−24.598	394419	235.366	−24.6023	132.794	−0.00115	0.004288
2007-1-16	389776	249.111	−27.1818	389607	249.109	−27.1854	168.61	0.002504	0.003649
2007-1-17	384688	263.727	−28.3875	384479	263.719	−28.3918	209.265	0.008535	0.00432
2007-1-18	379691	278.876	−27.9817	379443	278.862	−27.9883	247.384	0.013699	0.0066
2007-1-19	375174	294.077	−25.8716	374900	294.063	−25.8806	274.087	0.01452	0.009001
2007-1-20	371473	308.884	−22.1502	371191	308.875	−22.1591	281.858	0.00932	0.008904
2007-1-21	368818	323.037	−17.0769	368552	323.038	−17.0812	265.99	−0.00098	0.00432
2007-1-22	367315	336.511	−11.0132	367090	336.524	−11.0088	225.039	−0.01347	−0.0044
2007-1-23	366937	349.46	−4.35646	366775	349.485	−4.34225	161.493	−0.02439	−0.0142
2007-1-24	367551	2.14665	2.50182	367468	2.1767	2.52258	82.762	−0.03005	−0.02075
2007-1-25	368962	14.8709	9.19134	368961	14.8986	9.21232	1.00509	−0.02773	−0.02098
2007-1-26	370962	27.9262	15.3607	371031	27.9428	15.3758	−69.6755	−0.01661	−0.01512
2007-1-27	373364	41.5477	20.6709	373483	41.5464	20.6776	−118.257	0.001278	−0.00673
2007-1-28	376037	55.847	24.7987	376178	55.8264	24.7992	−141.425	0.020631	−0.00048
2007-1-29	378901	70.7415	27.465	379046	70.7073	27.464	−144.853	0.034145	0.001001
2007-1-30	381922	85.9261	28.487	382062	85.89	28.4882	−140.04	0.03614	−0.0012
2007-1-31	385084	100.946	27.8321	385222	100.92	27.8358	−138.271	0.026561	−0.00365

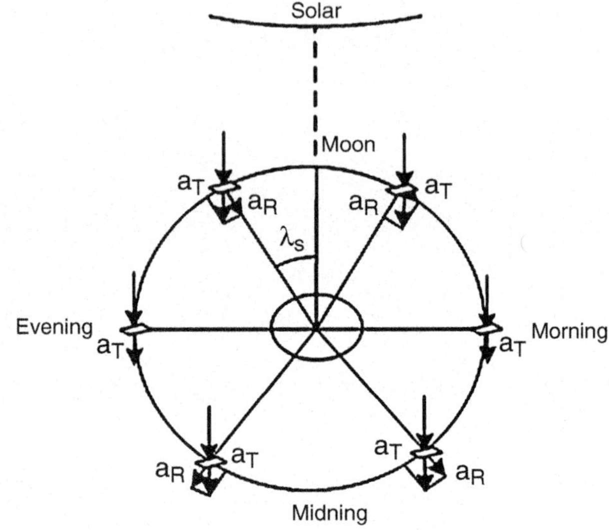

Fig. 4.31 Solar radiation pressure

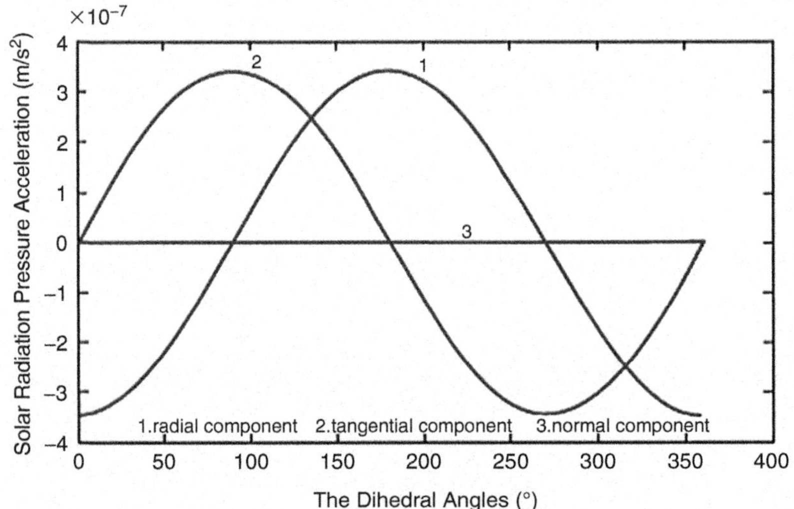

Fig. 4.32 Solar radiation pressure acceleration (spring)

When the Sun is located at the summer solstice and winter solstice, the normal component due to the solar radiation pressure reaches the maximum value of about 1.4×10^{-7}(m/s^2), as illustrated in Figs. 4.34 and 4.35.

Though the perturbation acceleration due to the solar radiation pressure is much smaller than the lunisolar attraction or the zonal term J2 of the Earth's gravity, the continuous effect of solar radiation pressure cannot be neglected. Especially the tangential perturbation acceleration due to the solar radiation pressure is positive in

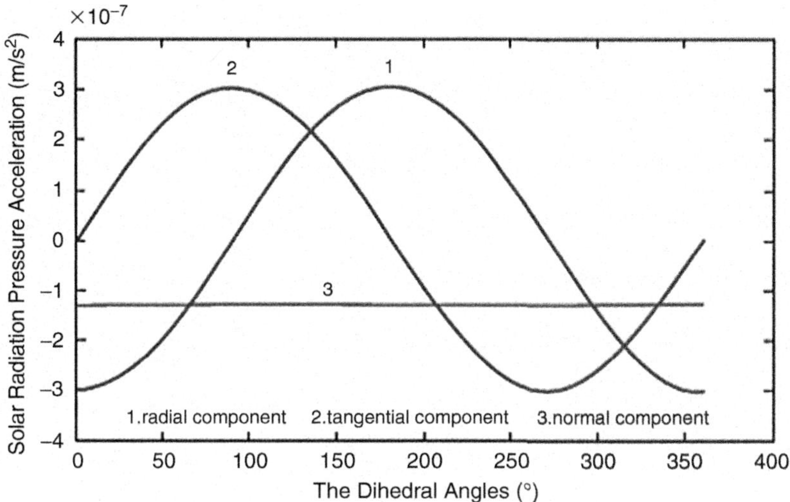

Fig. 4.33 Solar radiation pressure acceleration (autumn)

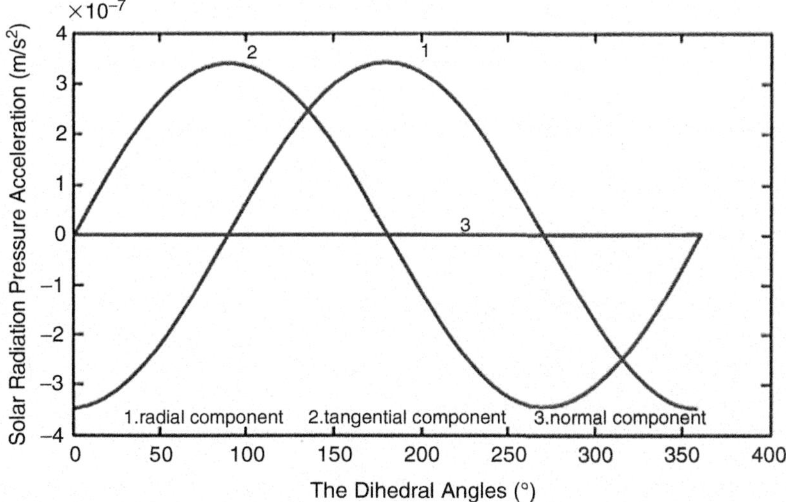

Fig. 4.34 Solar radiation pressure acceleration (summer)

half a circle and negative in other half circle for geostationary orbit, which is a periodical perturbation for semi-major axis, but this is a superimposed effect to the eccentricity of geostationary orbit too. It is cognizable that the solar radiation pressure will cause the eccentricity with some long-periodical perturbation motion, whose magnitude varies with the position of the Sun.

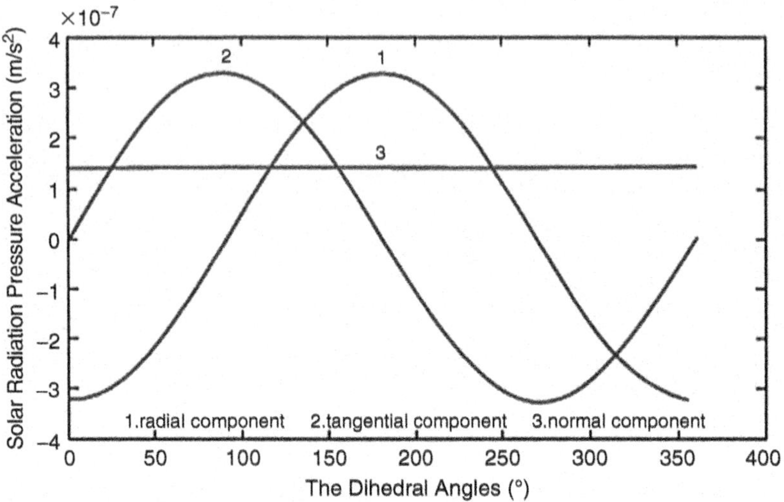

Fig. 4.35 Solar radiation pressure acceleration (winter)

4.6.1 Solar Radiation Pressure Potential Function

For simplification, on the condition of, firstly, not considering the ecliptic of the satellite and, secondly, assuming the satellite pointing to the Sun is identical to the Earth pointing to the Sun, given the vector from the satellite to the Earth is $\mathbf{r} = (x, y, z)^T$, the direction cosine from the Sun to the Earth centric $\left(\frac{\mathbf{r}_s}{r_s}\right) = (x_s, y_s, z_s)^T$, then the virtual potential function of solar radiation pressure is

$$R = -C_R\left(\frac{S}{m}\right)P_0(x_s x + y_s y + z_s z) \tag{4.116}$$

4.6.2 Longitude Drift Evolution

To analyze the perturbation motion of the orbit radius and the mean longitude of geostationary satellite, we omit the effect of small inclination and eccentricity, and then

$$\omega + f \approx \omega + M, \ \cos i \approx 1, \ \sin i \approx 0, r \approx a$$

If the satellite mean longitude at a particular epoch is

$$l = \omega + \Omega + M$$

the position vector in ECI can be expressed as

$$\mathbf{r} = (x, y, z)^T \approx r\begin{pmatrix} \cos l \\ \sin l \\ 0 \end{pmatrix} \tag{4.117}$$

The direction cosine from the Earth to the Sun can be expressed with the solar orbit elements by

$$\left(\frac{\mathbf{r}_s}{r_s}\right) = (x_s, y_s, z_s)^T = \begin{pmatrix} \cos(\omega_s + M_s)\cos\Omega_s - \sin(\omega_s + M_s)\sin\Omega_s\cos i_s \\ \cos(\omega_s + M_s)\sin\Omega_s + \sin(\omega_s + M_s)\cos\Omega_s\cos i_s \\ \sin i_s \sin(\omega_s + M_s) \end{pmatrix} \tag{4.118}$$

Because $\Omega_s \approx 0, \sin\Omega_s \approx 0, \cos\Omega_s \approx 1$, the direction cosine from the Sun to the Earth centric can be expressed in ECI as

$$\left(\frac{\mathbf{r}_s}{r_s}\right) = (x_s, y_s, z_s)^T \cong \begin{pmatrix} \cos(\omega_s + M_s) \\ \sin(\omega_s + M_s)\cos i_s \\ \sin(\omega_s + M_s)\sin i_s \end{pmatrix} \tag{4.119}$$

Or with the celestial right ascension and declination parameters (α_s, δ_s), we obtain

$$\left(\frac{\mathbf{r}_s}{r_s}\right) = (x_s, y_s, z_s)^T = \begin{pmatrix} \cos\delta_s\cos\alpha_s \\ \cos\delta_s\sin\alpha_s \\ \sin\delta_s \end{pmatrix} \tag{4.120}$$

Therefore, the virtual potential function of solar radiation pressure is

$$R = -C_R\left(\frac{S}{m}\right)P_0(x_s x + y_s y + z_s z) = -C_R\left(\frac{S}{m}\right)P_0 r\cos\delta_s\cos(l - \alpha_s) \tag{4.121}$$

According to Lagrange evolution equation of the mean longitude drift motion due to the solar radiation pressure, we get

$$\begin{cases} \dfrac{\mathrm{d}a}{\mathrm{d}t} = \dfrac{2}{na}\dfrac{\partial R}{\partial \lambda} = \dfrac{2}{na}\dfrac{\partial R}{\partial l} \\ \dfrac{\mathrm{d}\lambda}{\mathrm{d}t} = (n - \omega_e) - \dfrac{2}{na}\dfrac{\partial R}{\partial a} = (n - \omega_e) - \dfrac{2}{na}\dfrac{\partial R}{\partial r} \end{cases} \tag{4.122}$$

The Short-Periodical Oscillation of Semi-major Axis. This is due to the solar radiation pressure which is defined by the potential function of solar radiation pressure and can be obtained with some derivations below:

$$\frac{\partial R}{\partial l} = C_R\left(\frac{S}{m}\right)P_0 r\cos\delta_s(\sin(l-\alpha_s)) \tag{4.123}$$

Then the perturbation equation for semi-major axis is

$$\frac{\mathrm{d}a}{\mathrm{d}t} = \frac{2}{na}\frac{\partial R}{\partial l} = \frac{2}{n}C_R\left(\frac{S}{m}\right)P_0\cos\delta_s\sin(l-\alpha_s) \tag{4.124}$$

The solar mean longitude in a day can be considered as a constant. Therefore, by performing integration to the above sine function along the orbit within a solar day, the average value of semi-major axis perturbation variation equals zero. But there is a daily periodical term whose amplitude is

$$\delta a = \frac{2}{n_e^2}C_R\left(\frac{S}{m}\right)P_0\cos\delta_s \tag{4.125}$$

The oscillation of the semi-major axis for geostationary orbit due to the solar radiation pressure reaches its maximum value of 129 m when the Sun is located at the vernal equinox or the autumnal equinox, while it reaches its minimum value of 118 m when the Sun is located at the summer solstice or the winter solstice. Because this oscillation is much smaller than that due to the solar and lunar attraction, it is often ignored.

Daily Periodical Libration of Mean Longitude. Due to solar radiation pressure, the relation between the variations of semi-major axis and mean longitude drift rate is

$$\frac{\mathrm{d}\lambda}{\mathrm{d}t} = -\frac{3}{2}\frac{n_e}{a_s}\delta a = -\frac{3}{2}\frac{n_e}{a_s}\frac{2}{n_e^2}C_R\left(\frac{S}{m}\right)P_0\cos\delta_s\sin(l-\alpha_s) \tag{4.126}$$

The average value of the perturbation of mean longitude drift rate due to the solar radiation pressure in a day equals zero and the daily periodical amplitude is

$$\delta\lambda = \frac{3}{2}\frac{1}{a_s}\frac{2}{n_e^2}C_R\left(\frac{S}{m}\right)P_0\cos\delta_s \tag{4.127}$$

The maximum amplitude of value 0.0016° occurs when the Sun is located at the vernal equinox or autumnal equinox, and the minimum amplitude of value 0.0015° occurs when the Sun is located at the summer solstice or winter solstice.

4.6.3 Eccentricity Evolution

The eccentricity perturbation equation for geostationary orbit is given as:

$$\begin{cases} \dfrac{\mathrm{d}e_x}{\mathrm{d}t} = -\dfrac{1}{na^2}\dfrac{\partial R}{\partial e_y} \\ \dfrac{\mathrm{d}e_y}{\mathrm{d}t} = \dfrac{1}{na^2}\dfrac{\partial R}{\partial e_x} \end{cases} \tag{4.128}$$

where the potential function of the solar radiation pressure is

$$R = -C_R\left(\frac{S}{m}\right)P_0(x_s x + y_s y + z_s z) \cong -C_R\left(\frac{S}{m}\right)P_0(x_s x + y_s y) \tag{4.129}$$

In the expression

$$\mathbf{r} = \begin{pmatrix} x \\ y \\ z \end{pmatrix} \approx a\begin{pmatrix} \cos l - \frac{3}{2}e_x + \frac{1}{2}e_x\cos 2l + \frac{1}{2}e_y\sin 2l \\ \sin l - \frac{3}{2}e_y + \frac{1}{2}e_x\sin 2l - \frac{1}{2}e_y\cos 2l \\ 0 \end{pmatrix} \tag{4.130}$$

so that

$$\frac{\partial R}{\partial e_x} = -C_R\left(\frac{S}{m}\right)P_0\cdot a\left(-\frac{3}{2}x_s + \frac{1}{2}x_s\cos 2l + \frac{1}{2}y_s\sin 2l\right) \tag{4.131}$$

$$\frac{\partial R}{\partial e_y} = -C_R\left(\frac{S}{m}\right)P_0\cdot a\left(-\frac{3}{2}y_s + \frac{1}{2}x_s\sin 2l - \frac{1}{2}y_s\cos 2l\right) \tag{4.132}$$

Therefore, the perturbation motion of the eccentricity vector due to the solar radiation pressure follows the equations below:

$$\begin{cases} \dfrac{\mathrm{d}e_x}{\mathrm{d}t} = -\dfrac{1}{na^2}\dfrac{\partial R}{\partial e_y} = \dfrac{1}{na}C_R\left(\dfrac{S}{m}\right)P_0\left(-\dfrac{3}{2}y_s + \dfrac{1}{2}x_s\sin 2l - \dfrac{1}{2}y_s\cos 2l\right) \\ \dfrac{\mathrm{d}e_y}{\mathrm{d}t} = \dfrac{1}{na^2}\dfrac{\partial R}{\partial e_x} = -\dfrac{1}{na}C_R\left(\dfrac{S}{m}\right)P_0\left(-\dfrac{3}{2}x_s + \dfrac{1}{2}x_s\cos 2l + \dfrac{1}{2}y_s\sin 2l\right) \end{cases} \tag{4.133}$$

The right parts of the above equations are composed of two components. One is the long-period term that does not cover the mean motion of geostationary satellite; the other is the short-period term which is governed by the triangle function about the mean motion of geostationary satellite.

The Long-Period Term. In consideration of the first part in the right side of the above perturbation equation,

$$\begin{cases} \dfrac{de_x}{dt} = -\dfrac{3}{2}\dfrac{1}{na}C_R\left(\dfrac{S}{m}\right)P_0 y_s \\ \dfrac{de_y}{dt} = \dfrac{3}{2}\dfrac{1}{na}C_R\left(\dfrac{S}{m}\right)P_0 x_s \end{cases} \tag{4.134}$$

Replacing the equation with the direction cosine of the solar mean motion, we have

$$x_s = \cos(\omega_s + M_s) = \cos\lambda_s, y_s = \sin(\omega_s + M_s)\cos i_s = \sin\lambda_s \cos i_s$$

The perturbation motion equation for the mean eccentricity of geostationary orbit becomes

$$\begin{cases} \dfrac{de_x}{dt} = -\dfrac{3}{2}\dfrac{1}{na}C_R\left(\dfrac{S}{m}\right)P_0 \cos i_s \sin\lambda_s \\ \dfrac{de_y}{dt} = \dfrac{3}{2}\dfrac{1}{na}C_R\left(\dfrac{S}{m}\right)P_0 \cos\lambda_s \end{cases} \tag{4.135}$$

Assuming the original eccentricity vector $\mathbf{e}_0 = (e_x(t_0), e_y(t_0))$ at a given epoch t_0, by performing integration to the above equation along the solar mean motion, the equation (4.135) becomes

$$\begin{cases} \dfrac{de_x}{d\lambda_s} = -R_e \cos i_s \sin\lambda_s \\ \dfrac{de_y}{d\lambda_s} = R_e \cos\lambda_s \end{cases} \tag{4.136}$$

Then the eccentricity vector at any moment $\mathbf{e_t} = (e_x(t), e_y(t))$ satisfies

$$\begin{cases} e_x(t) = e_x(t_0) + R_e \cos i_s(\cos\lambda(t) - \cos\lambda(t_0)) \\ e_y(t) = e_y(t_0) + R_e(\sin\lambda(t) - \sin\lambda(t_0)) \end{cases} \tag{4.137}$$

with the mean motion of the Sun ($n_s = 0.9856(°/Day)$), in the equation

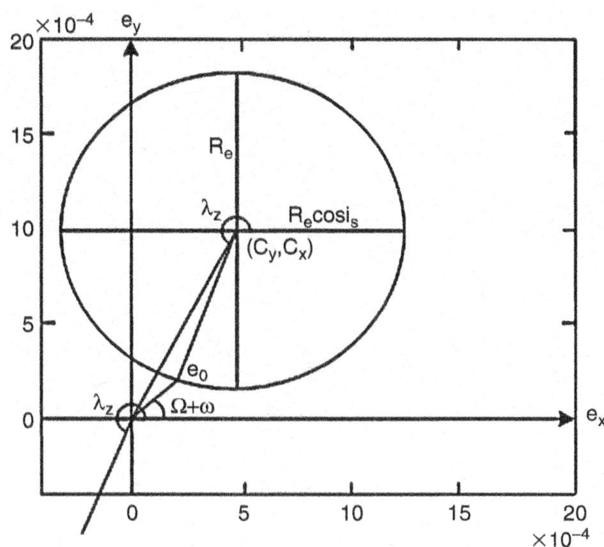

Fig. 4.36 Eccentricity perturbation circle

$$R_e = \frac{3}{2}\frac{1}{n_e a} C_R\left(\frac{S}{m}\right)P_0 \cdot \frac{1}{n_s} \approx 0.011 \cdot C_R\left(\frac{S}{m}\right) \tag{4.138}$$

In the above equation, the unit of area is meter square (m^2) and the unit of satellite mass is kilogram (kg). If the ratio of area to mass equals 0.05 and the coefficient of solar radiation pressure is 1.5, then $R_e = 8.36 \times 10^{-4}$.

Assume

$$C_x = e_x(t_0) - R_e \cos i_s \cos \lambda(t_0), \text{and}, C_y = e_y(t_0) - R_e \sin \lambda(t_0)$$

Then the motion equation of eccentricity is converted to

$$\left(\frac{e_x(t) - C_x}{R_e \cos i_s}\right)^2 + \left(\frac{e_y(t) - C_x}{R_e}\right)^2 = 1 \tag{4.139}$$

Therefore, the perturbation motion of eccentricity due to the solar radiation pressure is a kind of elliptic motion following the solar mean longitude, and the center of ellipse correlates with the original eccentricity vector and solar mean longitude at the moment, as illustrated in Fig. 4.36. The semi-minor axis of eccentricity drift motion points to the vernal equinox and equals $R_e \cos i_s$, and its semi-major axis is perpendicular to the vernal equinox at right angle and equals R_e. Since the long-period perturbation of eccentricity caused by the solar radiation pressure experiences a nearly round shape on the eccentricity vector phase plane, with the radius of circle of Re, and the magnitude relying on the satellite itself, we always call this circle as eccentricity perturbation circle, and sometimes we just consider the perturbation motion as a perfect circle to design some strategies to maintain the geostationary satellite.

The Short-Period Term. In consideration of the second part in the right side of the perturbation Eq. (4.133), we obtain

$$\begin{cases} \dfrac{de_x}{dt} = \dfrac{1}{2}\dfrac{1}{na}C_R\left(\dfrac{S}{m}\right)P_0(x_s \sin 2l - y_s \cos 2l) = \dfrac{1}{2}\dfrac{1}{na}C_R\left(\dfrac{S}{m}\right)P_0 \cos\delta_s \sin 2\left(l - \dfrac{\alpha_s}{2}\right) \\ \dfrac{de_y}{dt} = -\dfrac{1}{2}\dfrac{1}{na}C_R\left(\dfrac{S}{m}\right)P_0(x_s \cos 2l + y_s \sin 2l) = -\dfrac{1}{2}\dfrac{1}{na}C_R\left(\dfrac{S}{m}\right)P_0 \cos\delta_s \cos 2\left(l - \dfrac{\alpha_s}{2}\right) \end{cases} \tag{4.140}$$

There is the short-periodical perturbation term of eccentricity due to the solar radiation pressure. Its period is equal to a solar day and its amplitude is correlated with the declination of the Sun. The short-periodical amplitude is given by

$$\delta e : \frac{1}{2}\frac{1}{n_e^2 a}C_R\left(\frac{S}{m}\right)P_0 \cos\delta_s \tag{4.141}$$

In this example, the amplitude reaches its maximum value of 0.000015 at the vernal equinox or autumnal equinox, and it reaches its minimum value of 0.000014 at the summer solstice or winter solstice. The phase angle of short-periodical libration correlates to present solar mean longitude. From the above analysis, because the daily periodical perturbation due to the solar radiation pressure is much smaller than the effect due to the zonal term J2 of the Earth's gravity, this short-periodical perturbation can be ignored.

4.6.4 Inclination Evolution

According to Lagrange perturbation equation, the inclination vector perturbation motion of geostationary orbit is

$$\begin{cases} \dfrac{di_x}{dt} = -\dfrac{1}{na^2}\dfrac{\partial R}{\partial i_y} \\ \dfrac{di_y}{dt} = \dfrac{1}{na^2}\dfrac{\partial R}{\partial i_x} \end{cases} \tag{4.142}$$

where the potential function of solar radiation pressure

$$\begin{aligned} R &= -C_R\left(\frac{S}{m}\right)P_0(x_s x + y_s y + z_s z) \\ &= -C_R\left(\frac{S}{m}\right)P_0\left(x_s x + y_s y + r z_s\left(i_x \sin l - i_y \cos l\right)\right) \end{aligned} \tag{4.143}$$

Then,

$$\frac{\partial R}{\partial i_x} = -C_R\left(\frac{S}{m}\right)P_0 r z_s \sin l,\ \frac{\partial R}{\partial i_y} = C_R\left(\frac{S}{m}\right)P_0 r z_s \cos l$$

And then the motion equation of inclination due to the solar radiation equation is

$$\begin{cases} \dfrac{di_x}{dt} = -\dfrac{1}{na^2}\dfrac{\partial R}{\partial i_y} = -\dfrac{1}{na}C_R\left(\dfrac{S}{m}\right)P_0 \sin i_s \sin \lambda_s \cos l \\ \dfrac{di_y}{dt} = \dfrac{1}{na^2}\dfrac{\partial R}{\partial i_x} = -\dfrac{1}{na}C_R\left(\dfrac{S}{m}\right)P_0 \sin i_s \sin \lambda_s \sin l \end{cases} \tag{4.144}$$

There is a periodical term which contains the mean longitude of the geostationary orbit in the right part of equation. Performing integration to the above equation, the average variation of inclination is equal to zero. But there is a daily short-period term whose amplitude changes with the decline angle of solar motion. When the Sun intersects the Earth's equator plane at the vernal equinox, the right ascension node of the Sun is $\lambda_s = 0\,°$, while at the autumnal equinox, the right ascension node of the Sun is $\lambda_s = 180\,°$. At these moments there is no normal component of solar radiation pressure, and the above perturbation equation of inclination also indicates that the variation of inclination due to the solar radiation pressure is equal to zero too. When the Sun reaches at the summer solstice, the right ascension node of the Sun is $\lambda_s = 90\,°$, while at the winter solstice, the right ascension node of the Sun is $\lambda_s = 270\,°$. At these moments the normal component of solar radiation pressure reaches its maximum, and the daily variation of the inclination reaches the maximum too. The maximum amplitude is

$$\delta i = \frac{1}{n^2 a}C_R\left(\frac{S}{m}\right)P_0 \sin i_s \approx 3.5° \times 10^{-5} \tag{4.145}$$

4.6.5 Eclipses of the Solar by the Earth and Moon

The solar radiation pressure only exists when the satellite is located at sunlight area. At the vernal equinox and autumnal equinox, the Sun intersects the Earth's equator plane and is on the same orbit plane of the satellite. Like people on the Earth, the geostationary satellite also experiences day and night as shown in Fig. 4.37. Therefore, the eclipses of the Sun by the Earth and Moon must be considered when precisely predicting the motion of geostationary satellite.

Figure 4.38 indicates the occurrence of eclipse season. The vernal eclipse starts on February 26, reaches the longest of 71.5 min at the vernal equinox, and ends on April 13; the autumnal eclipse starts on August 31, reaches the longest at the autumnal equinox, and ends on October 16. Every eclipse season lasts nearly for 46 days.

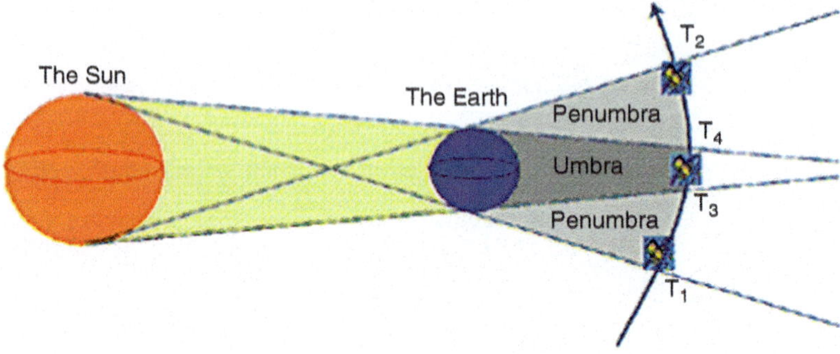

Fig. 4.37 Eclipses by the Earth

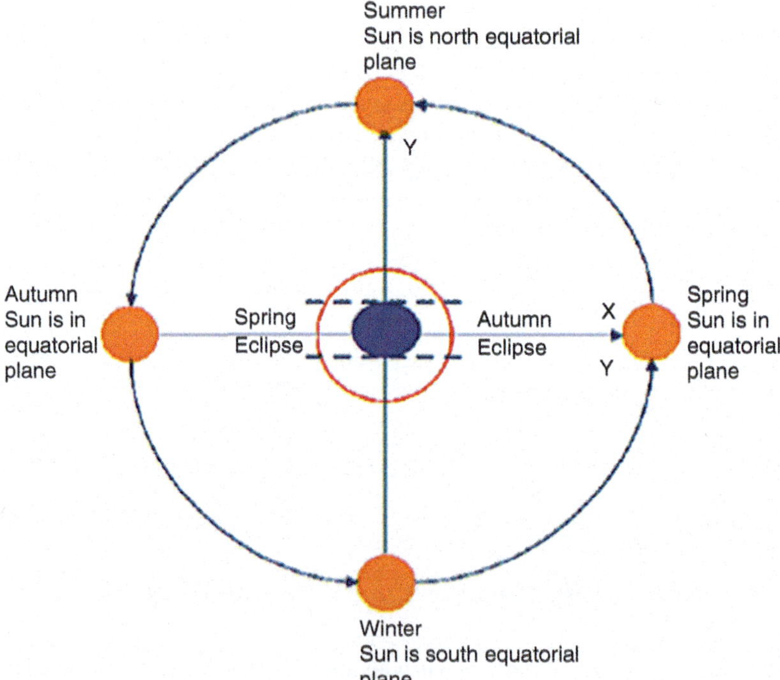

Fig. 4.38 Spring and autumn eclipse season

The spring is from February 26 to April 13, and the autumn is from August 31 to October 16. The maximum eclipse duration is approximate 72 min, during which the first 3 min and 3 min in the end are in the penumbra, as illustrated Fig. 4.39.

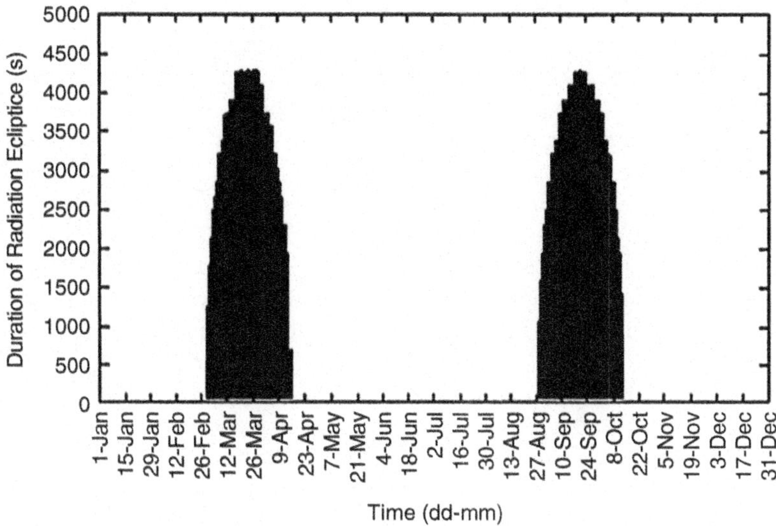

Fig. 4.39 The length of the eclipse by the Sun

4.7 Perturbation Summaries

1. The tangential perturbation acceleration from the zonal terms of the Earth's gravitation increases the geostationary orbit semi-major axis about 2 km greater than Kepler semi-major axis.
2. The elliptic equator plane of the Earth (J22) has an extra gravitational acceleration toward the tangential direction to the geostationary satellite located at nominal position, which consequently causes inconsistency between the orbit plane motion and Earth's rotation angular velocity and finally makes the satellite deviate from its nominal position.
3. The perturbation of solar and lunar attractions is similar to the zonal terms of the Earth's gravity. The perturbation of solar and lunar attractions decreases the radius of geostationary orbit, while the zonal terms increase the radius.
4. The perturbation of solar and lunar attractions does not induce long-periodical perturbation motion to the semi-major axis. The variation rate of semi-major axis equals zero in a round. But it does induce short-periodical perturbation to the semi-major axis and its period is half a solar day. The amplitude of short-periodical variation rate correlates to solar and lunar celestial declination and phase.
5. The perturbation of solar and lunar attractions induces short-periodical half-daily libration to the mean longitude of geostationary satellite. The maximum amplitude is 0.0025°; it is noticeable that the amplitude does not include the daily oscillation caused by the eccentricity perturbation from solar and lunar attraction.

6. The inclination perturbation induced by the solar and lunar attraction varies a little bit every year. The closer the mean longitude of lunar orbit to the vernal equinox, the higher the perturbation drift rate, and the maximum drift rate is 0.95°/year. When the mean longitude of lunar orbit is 180° away from the vernal equinox, the perturbation velocity of inclination vector reaches 0.75°/year of the minimum value.
7. The average variation of inclination from the solar attraction in a year equals zero. But there is semiannual periodical perturbation. The period is half a year and the amplitude is 0.025°. Besides the secular perturbation of inclination being induced from the lunar attraction, there is semimonthly periodical perturbation caused by the lunar attraction. The period is half a month and the amplitude is 0.0035°.
8. The magnitude of perturbation due to the solar radiation pressure is tenth of the perturbation due to the lunisolar attraction and the zonal term J2 of the Earth's gravity. But the continuous effect due to the solar radiation pressure cannot be ignored. Especially the tangential perturbation due to the solar radiation pressure is positive in half a circle and negative in other half circle. This is a periodical perturbation for semi-major axis. But for the eccentricity, this is a superimposed effect and causes long-periodical perturbation. The perturbing magnitude changes with the season, the solar longitude, and the ratio of satellite area to mass.

References

1. Chao CC, Baker JM (1983) On the propagation and control of geosynchronous satellites. J Astronaut Sci 4(1):99–115
2. Liu L (1992.8) Orbital dynamics for earth satellite. High Education Press, Beijing [In Chinese]
3. Li JS (1995.8) The precision orbit determination for earth satellite. PLA Press, Beijing [In Chinese]
4. Soop EM (1994.10) Handbook of geostationary orbits. Kluwer Academic Publishers, Dordrecht
5. Soop EM (1987) Coordinated station keeping at longitude 19 degrees west. Dordrecht, OAD paper No. 342
6. Oliver M, Eberhard G (2000) Satellite orbits- models, methods, and application. Springer, Berlin/Heidelberg

Chapter 5
Harmonic Analysis Geostationary Orbit

Abstract The characteristics of the perturbation period of geostationary satellite are analyzed. The spectral decomposing algorithm is established to identify periodical motions from high-precise oscillation ephemeris, and an identification algorithm of periodical motions based on singular value decomposition is presented.

5.1 Introduction

In the previous chapter, we have discussed the main perturbations of geostationary orbit by Lagrange equation. We have known that there are secular, long-periodical, middle long-period, and short-period terms of perturbation motion. We have also known the magnitude and period of these perturbations. The orbit maneuver for maintaining the geostationary satellite in a particular slot is named as station keeping maneuver of geostationary satellite, which utilizes free perturbation motion rules and propellant on board to conquer the secular and long-periodical perturbations. It is necessary to identify and analyze these periodical motions. To maneuver the geostationary satellite, especially more restrictive collocated geostationary satellites, we need to separate the short-period term from the precise ephemeris to eliminate the superimposed effect of short-period term. To improve the accuracy and reduce the intenseness of calculation, we need to compress the momentary ephemeris but keep its precision. Introducing mean orbit elements and imitable mean orbit elements is an important way to separate the short-period term from the periodical perturbation motion. Kozai [1, 2] 1959 borrowed the idea of mean from linear mechanics and put forward the method of mean orbit element to analyze the perturbation due to the non-spherical Earth's gravity field. The method of mean orbit element can well construct the solution with power form of minimal error of perturbation motion equation. This method can be well applied in early orbit determination and quantity analysis of satellite motion, but for high-order solution, the power form grows very complicated, causing difficulties to identify and analyze

H. Li, *Geostationary Satellites Collocation*, DOI 10.1007/978-3-642-40799-4_5,

the periodical motions. The short-period terms due to the three-body's gravity and solar radiation pressure are difficult to identify and analyze too. Cook, Blitzer, Kamel et al. [3–7] have established the spectral decomposing resolute function of perturbation motion considering the eccentricity and inclination as zero strictly. He has also analyzed the periodic perturbed motion of satellite due to the zonal terms of Earth's gravity field and lunisolar attraction. Although the geostationary orbit requires zero eccentricity and zero inclination, there is no strict "synchronized" orbit. With the development of computer, the numerical integral of orbit dynamic model can achieve centimeter's level precision. Therefore, can we use numerical analysis to identify and analyze periodical perturbation from all periodical perturbative signal of the precise ephemeris? This chapter introduces the harmonic analysis and mean orbit element calculation which are applicable to practical engineering. The characteristics of the perturbation period of geostationary satellite are analyzed. The spectral decomposing algorithm is established to identify periodical motions from high-precise osculating ephemeris, and an identification algorithm of periodical motions based on singular value decomposition is presented.

5.2 Harmonic Analysis

The geostationary satellite in orbit suffers a lot of additional perturbation forces besides the symmetric spherical Earth's gravitational attraction. The perturbation forces include the nonhomogeneous and non-spherical part of the Earth's gravitational attraction, the attractions from other planets such as the Sun and Moon, the solar radiation pressure, etc. Though these additional forces are only 10^{-5} of the Earth's central gravitational attraction, they will result in that the satellite motion does not follow the strict Kepler orbit. Considering the precise perturbation model, suppose the high-precise numerical ephemeris in the true equator and equinox of the epoch (TOD) coordinate is

$$f(t) : (a(t), e(t), i(t), \Omega(t), \omega(t), M(t)), t \in [t_0, t_f]$$

where t_0 means the precise orbit determination time; derivation time t_f depends on the choice of the harmonic analysis periodical term.

Because the numerical calculation of perturbation force model includes the models for the Earth's gravity of non-spherical part, the lunisolar attraction, and the solar radiation pressure and the ephemeris includes the characteristics of the perturbed orbit elements induced by every term of perturbations, from the analysis in Chap. 4, the characteristics are indicated by the secular, long-period, middle short-period, and short-period terms. The purpose of this chapter is to decompose these secular, long-period, middle short-period, and short-period terms from high-precise numerical ephemeris, which contains the signatures of each of these perturbation forces. It is possible to identify these terms numerically by using some parameter estimation techniques.

5.3 Basic Functions and Periodic Expansion

The signatures of the periodical perturbation term hidden in high-fidelity ephemeris are the projections of the ephemeris data on certain basic functions which characterize the perturbation effects. If only considering two-body's motion, then every orbit element keeps constant. Therefore, the basic function of the secular term is given by

$$P(t, t_0, k) = \frac{(t - t_0)^k}{k!}, k = 0, 1, 2 \tag{5.1}$$

Then the periodical basics function is given by

$$Q(t, t_0, \omega_k, \varphi_k) = \cos(\omega_k(t - t_0) + \varphi_k) \tag{5.2}$$

Therefore, any periodical function of the secular, long-period, medium-period, and short-period terms can be expressed with proper precision as

$$f(t) = \sum_{k=0}^{2} a_k P(t, t_0, k) + \sum_{k=3} a_k Q(t, t_0, \omega_k, \varphi_k) = \sum_{k=0}^{m} a_k \Phi_k(t) \tag{5.3}$$

If the power and frequency are known, the determination of the coefficients of the above expression is a classical mathematical problem. We will introduce a stable algorithm that is applicable to engineering.

5.4 Determining the Coefficients with SVD Method

Define

$$\boldsymbol{\Phi}(t) = \begin{pmatrix} \Phi_0(t) \\ \vdots \\ \Phi_m(t) \end{pmatrix} \in R^{m+1}, t \in [t_0, t_f] \tag{5.4}$$

as the column vector of the basic function, including the secular and periodical basic functions for a particular station keeping element, and denote

$$\mathbf{P} = \begin{pmatrix} a_0 \\ \vdots \\ a_m \end{pmatrix} \in R^{m+1}$$

which is the corresponding coefficient vector of the basic function. For any element of precise ephemeris, we have

$$f(t) \approx \sum_{k=0}^{m} a_k \Phi_k(t) = \mathbf{\Phi}^T(t)\mathbf{P}, t \in [t_0, t_f] \tag{5.5}$$

At any sample time $t_i \in [t_0, t_f], i = 1, 2, \ldots, n$, there is

$$\begin{aligned} f(t_i) &\approx \sum_{k=0}^{m} a_k \Phi_k(t_i) = \Phi^T(t_i)P \\ i &= 1, 2, \ldots, n \end{aligned} \tag{5.6}$$

Therefore, the coefficient vector satisfies the following linear equations

$$\begin{pmatrix} \Phi^T(t_1) \\ \vdots \\ \Phi^T(t_n) \end{pmatrix} \mathbf{P} = \begin{pmatrix} f(t_1) \\ \vdots \\ f(t_n) \end{pmatrix} \tag{5.7}$$

Denote

$$\mathbf{f} = \begin{pmatrix} f(t_1) \\ \vdots \\ f(t_n) \end{pmatrix} \in R^n, \mathbf{\Phi} = \begin{pmatrix} \Phi^T(t_1) \\ \vdots \\ \Phi^T(t_n) \end{pmatrix} \in R^{n \times (m+1)}$$

Normally the above equations are overdetermined equations. The least square solution of the overdetermined equations is

$$\hat{\mathbf{P}} = (\mathbf{\Phi}^T\mathbf{\Phi})^{-1}\mathbf{\Phi}^T\mathbf{f} \tag{5.8}$$

For using the overdetermined equations regular inverse matrix to calculate the least square solution, the regular matrix must be nonsingular, which means that every line of the coefficient matrix must be linear independent. If the ephemeris of short time to decompose the long-period term is used, the condition number of the regular matrix will be great and the matrix is close to the singular matrix. Therefore, a more stable singular value decomposition (SVD) algorithm of the coefficient matrix is recommended to handle this problem.

Assume the coefficient vector satisfies the following linear equation:

$$\mathbf{\Phi}\mathbf{P} = \mathbf{f} \tag{5.9}$$

Applying SVD (singular value decomposition) to the coefficient matrix,

$$\mathbf{\Phi}_{n\times(m+1)} = \mathbf{U}_{n\times n} \cdot \mathbf{D}_{n\times(m+1)} \cdot \mathbf{V}^T_{(m+1)\times(m+1)} \tag{5.10}$$

In the equation,

$\mathbf{U}_{n\times n}$: the orthogonal matrix with the same dimension of the condition equations
$\mathbf{V}_{(m+1)\times(m+1)}$: the orthogonal matrix with the same dimension of the coefficient vector

$\mathbf{D}_{n\times(m+1)} = \begin{pmatrix} \mathbf{S}_{(m+1)\times(m+1)} \\ 0 \end{pmatrix}$ is a block matrix. $\mathbf{S}_{(m+1)\times(m+1)}$ is the diagonal matrix with the same dimension of the coefficient vector. The diagonal elements are nonzero values of matrix $\mathbf{\Phi}_{n\times(m+1)}$ and then the least square solution of the overdetermined equations can be obtained by the expression below:

$$\hat{\mathbf{P}} = \mathbf{V}_{(m+1)\times(m+1)} \cdot \mathbf{S}^{-1}_{(m+1)\times(m+1)} \cdot \mathbf{U}^T_{n\times n} \cdot \mathbf{f} \tag{5.11}$$

For example, if the coefficient vector satisfies the following linear equations:

$$\begin{pmatrix} 0.01486433746352 & 0.81939293234217 \\ 0.28819334558908 & 0.62113870578822 \\ 0.81673121343671 & 0.56022204096293 \\ 0.98548350985117 & 0.24403153400252 \\ 0.01736269303774 & 0.82200758848706 \end{pmatrix} \cdot \begin{pmatrix} a_0 \\ a_1 \end{pmatrix} = \begin{pmatrix} 0.26321192795729 \\ 0.75363453438567 \\ 0.65964479880694 \\ 0.21406285585091 \\ 0.60211690829173 \end{pmatrix}$$

1. The least square solution of the overdetermined equations (regular equations) is

$$\hat{\mathbf{P}} = \left(\mathbf{\Phi}^T\mathbf{\Phi}\right)^{-1}\mathbf{\Phi}^T\mathbf{f} = \begin{pmatrix} 0.22089459275704 \\ 0.66511317439692 \end{pmatrix}$$

2. SVD of the overdetermined equations

Applying singular value decomposition to the coefficient vector, we get

$$\mathbf{U}_{5\times5} = \begin{pmatrix} -0.38359755335396 & -0.39422433505880 & -0.56354233344106 & -0.48069431921815 & -0.38573708740477 \\ -0.50649153651741 & -0.16766568265594 & 0.28364013185038 & 0.61536241025196 & -0.50619356174151 \\ -0.52512143898647 & 0.17388400856963 & 0.60940549533477 & -0.55045102185550 & 0.14014435655620 \\ -0.51936303313634 & 0.57271989349289 & -0.48013022826133 & 0.23221485834011 & 0.34322760216032 \\ -0.22545233337736 & -0.67692811115229 & 0.00825955139325 & 0.18259793981482 & 0.67640915864043 \end{pmatrix}$$

$$\mathbf{D}_{5\times2} = \begin{pmatrix} \mathbf{S}_{2\times2} \\ 0_{3\times2} \end{pmatrix} = \begin{pmatrix} 1.68457363702036 & 0 \\ 0 & 0.99515414405262 \\ 0 & 0 \\ 0 & 0 \\ 0 & 0 \end{pmatrix}$$

$$\mathbf{V}_{2\times2}^{T} = \begin{pmatrix} -0.62923407059612 & 0.77721585444524 \\ -0.77721585444524 & -0.62923407059612 \end{pmatrix}$$

Therefore, the least square solution (SVD) of the above equations is

$$\hat{\mathbf{P}} = \mathbf{V}_{2\times2}\mathbf{S}_{2\times2}^{-1}\mathbf{U}_{5\times2}^{T}\mathbf{f} = \begin{pmatrix} 0.22089459275704 \\ 0.66511317439692 \end{pmatrix}$$

5.5 Longitude and Drift Harmonics

The drift rate vector is defined as

$$l(t) = \begin{pmatrix} \lambda(t) \\ D(t) \end{pmatrix} \tag{5.12}$$

$\lambda(t)$: the osculation longitude, whose unit is the degree in the true equator and equinox of epoch coordinate, is related to the Kepler orbit elements by

$$\lambda(t) = \Omega(t) + \omega(t) + M(t) - \mathrm{GAST}(t) \tag{5.13}$$

In the equation: GAST(t) is the real sidereal time at the epoch.

$D(t)$: the longitude drift rate, whose unit is degree per day, is related to the Kepler orbit elements by

$$D(t) = -\frac{3}{2}\left(\frac{a(t) - a_c}{a_c}\right) \cdot 360.9856\,(^\circ/\mathrm{Day})$$

$$a_c = 42165760.0\,(\mathrm{m})$$

From the analysis in Chap. 4, the longitude and drift rate (λ, D) are indicated by the following secular, long-, medium-, and short-periodical perturbations listed in Table 5.1 with the frequencies from the lowest to the highest.

The longitude of geostationary satellite is well represented by an expansion of the secular terms plus the periodical sinusoids with the frequencies listed above.

$$\lambda(T) \approx A_{\lambda}^{0} + A_{\lambda}^{1}T + \frac{1}{2}A_{\lambda}^{2}T^{2} + \sum_{k=3}^{8} A_{\lambda}^{k}\cos(\omega_k T + \varphi_k) \tag{5.14}$$

Table 5.1 Main periodical terms of longitude

Terms	Expansion	Perturbation	Frequency (radian/day)	Period (day)
Secular terms	Constant	Centric gravity	$k=0$	
	Linear	Non-spherical gravity	$k=1$	
	Quadratic		$k=2$	
Long-period terms	Yearly	Solar attraction	n_s	365.25
	Half yearly		$2n_s$	182.63
Medium-period terms	Monthly	Lunar attraction	n_m	27.5
	Half monthly		$2n_m$	13.7
Short-period terms	Daily	Non-spherical gravity/solar radiation pressure	n_e	1
	Half daily		$2n_e$	0.5

Listing the above equation for every osculating longitude at every sample time within time span, which should be at least of 1 month in order to recover the lunar effects, the maximum duration should be limited to 2 months in case that the longitude drifts away from the nominal slot.

Define the basic function vector and the corresponding coefficient vector of the longitude as

$$\Phi_\lambda(T) = \left(1, T, \frac{1}{2}T^2, \cos(\omega_3 T + \varphi_3), \ldots, (\omega_8 T + \varphi_8)\right)^T \in R^9,$$

$$P_x = (A_\lambda^0, \ldots, A_\lambda^8) \in R^9$$

Then form the equation below

$$\mathbf{\Phi}_\lambda(t_i)\mathbf{P}_\lambda = \lambda(t_i), i = 1, 2, \ldots, n$$

Applying SVD (singular value decomposition) method to solve the equation above and neglecting the periodical term of formula (5.14), the mean motion of longitude is expressed below:

$$\bar{\lambda}(T) = A_\lambda^0 + A_\lambda^1 T + \frac{1}{2}A_\lambda^2 T^2 \tag{5.15}$$

Figure 5.1 illustrates the secular term of the longitude decomposed by SVD harmonic method, and Fig. 5.2 illustrates the short-period term of the longitude decomposed by harmonic method.

The main periodic terms due to the perturbation effect on the longitude drift rate are listed in Table 5.2.

The longitude drift rate of geostationary satellite is well represented by an expansion of the secular terms plus the periodical sinusoids with the frequencies listed above.

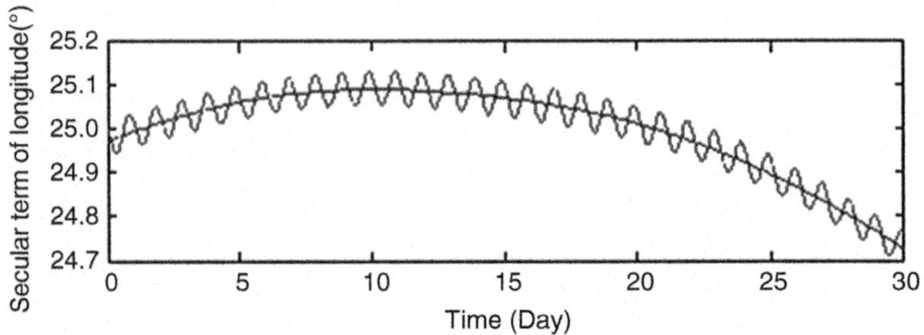

Fig. 5.1 The secular term of longitude

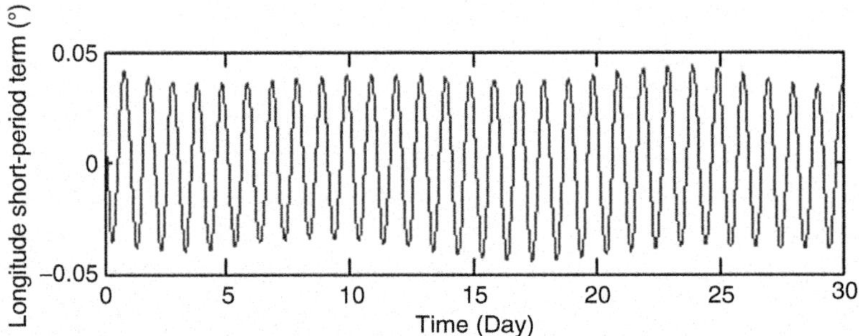

Fig. 5.2 The short-period term of longitude

Table 5.2 The main periodic terms of longitude drift rate

Terms	Expansion	Perturbation	Frequency (radian/day)	Period (day)
Secular terms	Constant	Centric gravity	$k=0$	
	Linear	Non-spherical gravity	$k=1$	
Short-period terms	Daily	Non-spherical gravity/solar radiation pressure	n_e	1
	Half daily		$2n_e$	0.5

Notes: $n_s=0.0172$, $n_m=0.23$, $n_e=6.283$

$$D(T) \approx A_D^0 + A_D^1 T + \sum_{k=2}^{3} A_D^k \sin(\omega_k T + \varphi_k) \tag{5.16}$$

Listing the above equation for every osculating longitude drift rate at every sample time within time span, which should be at least of 1 month in order to recover the lunar effects, the maximum duration should be limited to 2 months in case that the longitude drifts away from the nominal slot.

Define the basic function and the corresponding coefficient vector of longitude drift rate as

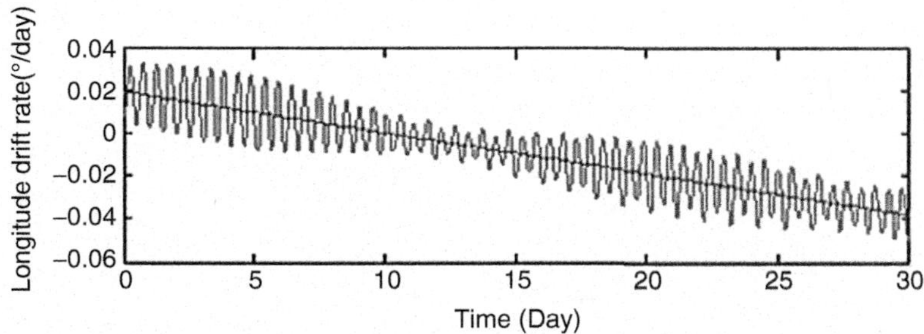

Fig. 5.3 The secular term of longitude drift decomposed by SVD harmonic analysis

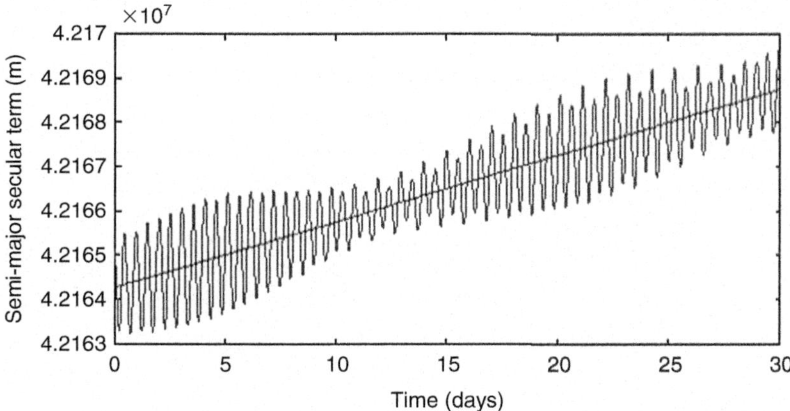

Fig. 5.4 The secular term of semi-major axis decomposed by SVD harmonic analysis

$$\mathbf{\Phi}_D(T) = (1, T, \sin(\omega_2 T + \varphi_2), \sin(\omega_3 T + \varphi_3))^T \in R^4$$
$$P_D = \left(A_D^0, A_D^1, A_D^2, A_D^3\right) \in R^4$$

Then form the equation below

$$\mathbf{\Phi}_D(t_i)\mathbf{P}_D = D(t_i), i = 1, 2, \ldots, n \tag{5.17}$$

Applying SVD (singular value decomposition) method to solve the above equation, and neglecting the periodical term of formula (5.16), the mean motion of longitude is

$$\overline{D}(T) = A_D^0 + A_D^1 T \tag{5.18}$$

In the equation, $A_D^1 = A_\lambda^2$ is the acceleration of longitude drift.

Figures 5.3 and 5.4 show the secular term of longitude drift rate and the semi-major axis of geostationary orbit by SVD decomposition method, respectively.

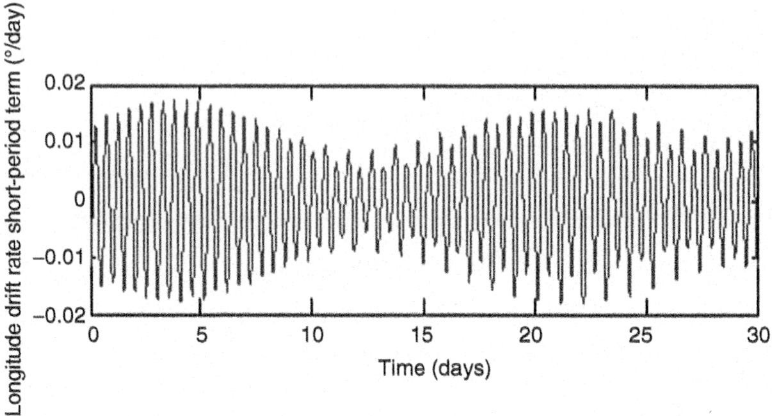

Fig. 5.5 The short-period term of longitude and drift decomposed by SVD harmonic analysis

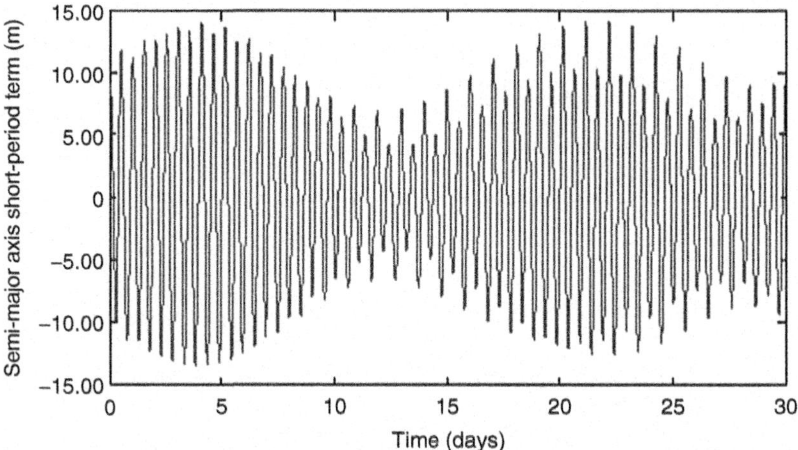

Fig. 5.6 The short-period term of semi-major axis decomposed by SVD harmonic analysis

Figures 5.5 and 5.6 show the short-period term of longitude drift rate and the semi-major axis of geostationary orbit by SVD decomposition method, respectively.

5.6 Eccentricity Vector Harmonics

The eccentricity vector is defined as

$$e(t) = \begin{pmatrix} e_x(t) \\ e_y(t) \end{pmatrix} = \begin{pmatrix} e(t)\cos(\Omega(t) + \omega(t)) \\ e(t)\sin(\Omega(t) + \omega(t)) \end{pmatrix}$$

Table 5.3 The main periodic perturbation terms for the eccentricity vector

Terms	Expansion	Perturbation	Frequency (radian/day)	Period (day)
Secular	Constant	Centric gravity	$k=0$	
Long period	Yearly	Solar radiation pressure	n_s	365.25
Medium period	Monthly	Lunar attraction	n_m	27.5
Short period	Daily	Non-spherical/solar radiation pressure	n_e	1
	Half daily		$2n_e$	0.5

Notes: $n_s=0.0172$, $n_m=0.23$, $n_e=6.283$

From the analysis in Chap. 4, the eccentricity vector (e_x, e_y) is indicated by the following secular, long-periodical, medium-periodical, and short-periodical perturbation terms. The eccentricity vector components are well represented by constant and purely sinusoidal expansions terms, whose frequencies are listed in Table 5.3.

Therefore, the eccentricity vector can be approximately expressed as

$$\begin{cases} e_x(T) = A_x^0 + \sum_{k=1}^{5} A_x^k \cos(\omega_k T + \varphi_k) \\ e_y(T) = A_y^0 + \sum_{k=1}^{5} A_y^k \sin(\omega_k T + \varphi_k) \end{cases} \tag{5.19}$$

In the equation, $\omega_k (k=1,\ldots,5)$ represents the different frequency terms listed above. The basic function and the corresponding coefficient vector of the eccentricity vector are given by the following:

For component e_x,

$$\mathbf{\Phi}_x(T) = (1, \sin(\omega_1 T + \varphi_1), \ldots, \sin(\omega_5 T + \varphi_5))^T \in R^6, T \in [t_0, t_f]$$

$$\mathbf{P}_x = (A_x^0, \ldots, A_x^5) \in R^6$$

For component e_y,

$$\mathbf{\Phi}_y(T) = (1, \sin(\omega_1 T + \varphi_1), \ldots, \sin(\omega_5 T + \varphi_5))^T \in R^6, T \in [t_0, t_f]$$

$$\mathbf{P}_y = \left(A_y^0, \ldots, A_y^5\right) \in R^6$$

Then form the equation below

$$\mathbf{\Phi}_X(t_i)\mathbf{P}_X = e_x(t_i), i = 1, 2, \ldots, n$$

$$\mathbf{\Phi}_Y(t_i)\mathbf{P}_Y = e_y(t_i), i = 1, 2, \ldots, n$$

Apply SVD (singular value decomposition) method to solve the equation above. Normally, there are different control strategies for eccentricity. If apply the control

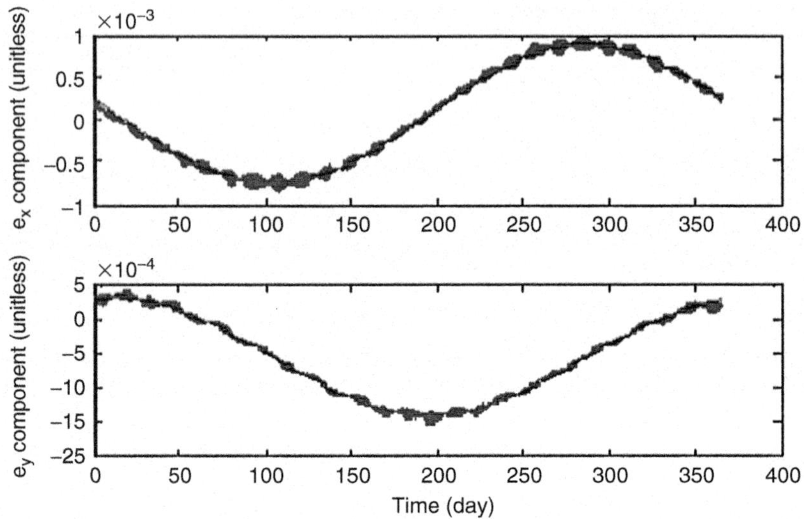

Fig. 5.7 The secular term and long-period term of the eccentricity vector

strategy of semimonthly period, the frequency term less than half a month can be eliminated from the orbit elements. Neglecting the relative short-period term of formula (5.19), the mean motion of eccentricity can be shown in Fig. 5.7.

$$\begin{aligned}\bar{e}_x(T) &= A_x^0 + A_x^1\cos(\omega_1 T + \varphi_1) + A_x^2\cos(\omega_2 T + \varphi_2)\\ \bar{e}_y(T) &= A_y^0 + A_y^1\sin(\omega_1 T + \varphi_1) + A_y^2\sin(\omega_2 T + \varphi_2)\end{aligned} \tag{5.20}$$

If leaving the eccentricity drifting freely within the confined circle, and only consider the annual periodical term, the mean motion of eccentricity can be expressed as

$$\begin{aligned}\bar{e}_x(T) &= A_x^0 + A_x^1\cos(\omega_1 T + \varphi_1)\\ \bar{e}_y(T) &= A_y^0 + A_y^1\sin(\omega_1 T + \varphi_1),\end{aligned} \tag{5.21}$$

the mean motion of eccentricity is shown in Fig. 5.8.

Figure 5.9 shows the daily period term of the eccentricity vector of geostationary orbit.

In this example, the ratio of satellite area to mass is 0.05. From the analysis in Chap. 4, the semi-major axis of eccentricity ecliptic perturbation is

$$R_e = 0.011 \cdot C_R\left(\frac{S}{m}\right) = 8.25 \times 10^{-4},$$

which is perpendicular to the direction of the vernal equinox as illustrated in Fig. 5.10. The semi-minor axis $R_e\cos(i_s) = 7.57 \times 10^{-4}$, which is the same with the harmonic analysis of momentary motion.

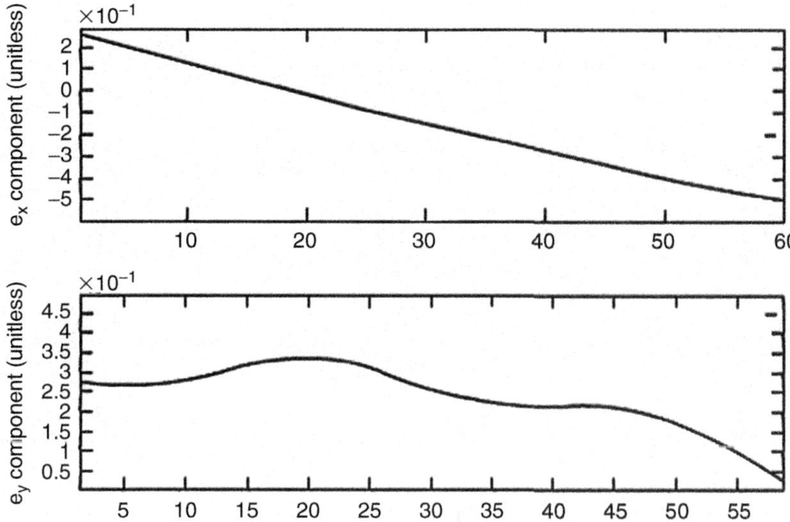

Fig. 5.8 The monthly periodical term of the eccentricity vector

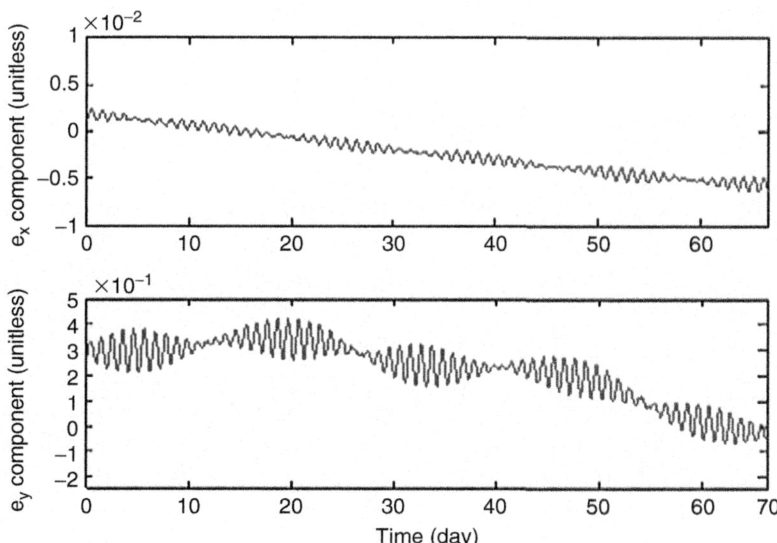

Fig. 5.9 The daily periodic term of the eccentricity vector

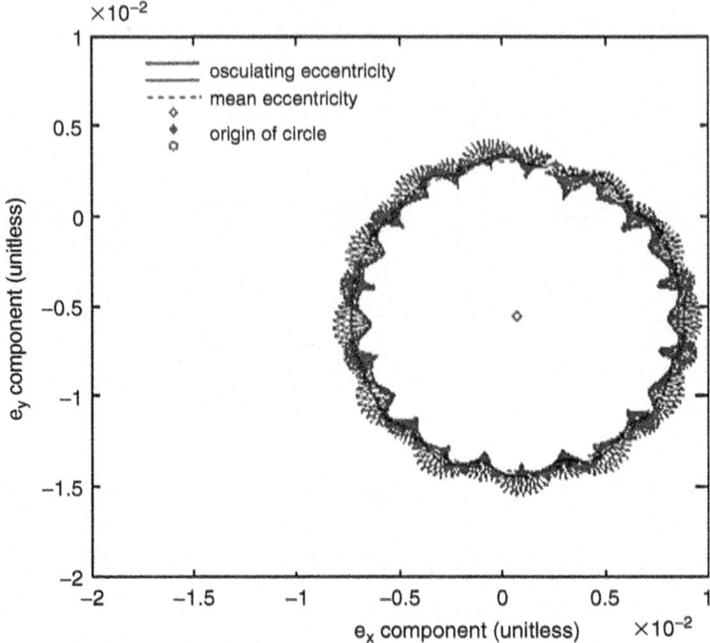

Fig. 5.10 The perturbation circle on the eccentricity phase plane

5.7 Inclination Vector Harmonics

The inclination vector is defined as

$$i(t) = \begin{pmatrix} i_x(t) \\ i_y(t) \end{pmatrix} = \begin{pmatrix} i(t)\cos(\Omega(t)) \\ i(t)\sin(\Omega(t)) \end{pmatrix}, \tag{5.22}$$

From the analysis in Chap. 4, the inclination vector (i_x, i_y) is indicated by the following secular, long-periodical, middle short-periodical, and short-periodical perturbations. The inclination vector components are well represented by constant, linear, and sinusoidal expansions terms, whose frequencies are listed in Table 5.4.

Therefore, the inclination vector can be approximately expressed as

$$\begin{cases} i_x(T) = \sum\limits_{k=0}^{1} A_x^k T^k + \sum\limits_{k=2}^{9} A_x^k \cos(\omega_k T + \varphi_k) \\ i_y(T) = \sum\limits_{k=0}^{1} A_y^k T^k + \sum\limits_{k=2}^{9} A_y^k \sin(\omega_k T + \varphi_k) \end{cases} \tag{5.23}$$

Table 5.4 The main periodic terms due to the perturbation effect on the inclination vector

Terms	Expansion	Perturbation	Frequency (radian/day)	Period (day)
Secular	Constant	Centric gravity	$k=0$	
	Linear	Lunisolar attraction	$k=1$	
Long period	Yearly	Solar attraction	n_s	365.25
	Half yearly		$2n_s$	182.25
	Seasonally		$3n_s$	121.75
Medium period	Monthly	Lunar attraction	n_m	27.5
	Half monthly		$2n_m$	13.77
	Ten days		$3n_m$	9.19
Short period	Daily	Non-spherical/solar radiation pressure	n_e	1
	Half daily		$2n_e$	0.5

Notes: $n_s=0.0172$, $n_m=0.23$, $n_e=6.283$

In the equation, $\omega_k(k=2,\ldots,9)$ represents the different frequency terms from long period to short period. The basic function and the corresponding coefficient vector of the inclination vector are given by the following:

For component i_x,

$$\mathbf{\Phi}_x(T) = (1, T, \cos(\omega_2 T + \varphi_2), \ldots, \cos(\omega_9 T + \varphi_9))^T \in R^{11}, T \in [t_0, t_f]$$
$$\mathbf{P}_x = \left(A_x^0, \ldots, A_x^{10}\right) \in R^{11}$$

For component i_y,

$$\mathbf{\Phi}_y(T) = (1, T, \sin(\omega_2 T + \varphi_2), \ldots, \sin(\omega_9 T + \varphi_9))^T \in R^{11}, T \in [t_0, t_f]$$
$$\mathbf{P}_y = \left(A_y^0, \ldots, A_y^{10}\right) \in R^{11}$$

Then form the equation below

$$\mathbf{\Phi}_X(t_i)\mathbf{P}_X = i_x(t_i), i = 1, 2, \ldots, n$$
$$\mathbf{\Phi}_Y(t_i)\mathbf{P}_Y = i_y(t_i), i = 1, 2, \ldots, n$$

In general, the period of inclination maneuver is usually a month, so the perturbation terms whose frequencies are less than a month can be eliminated from the station keeping orbit elements. Neglecting the relative short-period term of formula (5.23), the mean motion of inclination can be expressed below, which offers a rapid method for predicting the effects of inclination maneuver of given magnitude and epoch.

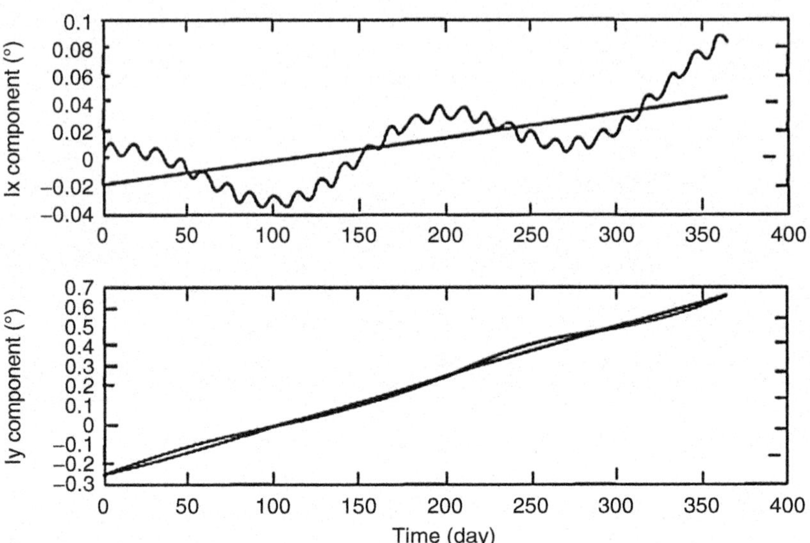

Fig. 5.11 The secular term of the inclination vector

$$\begin{cases} \bar{i}_x(T) = \sum_{k=0}^{1} A_x^k T^k + \sum_{k=2}^{4} A_x^k \cos(\omega_k T + \varphi_k) \\ \bar{i}_y(T) = \sum_{k=0}^{1} A_y^k T^k + \sum_{k=2}^{4} A_y^k \sin(\omega_k T + \varphi_k) \end{cases}, \tag{5.24}$$

The mean motion of inclination is shown in Figs. 5.11, 5.12, 5.13, and 5.14. Figure 5.11 shows the secular term on the inclination vector of geostationary orbit.

Figure 5.12 shows the secular and the yearly periodic terms on the inclination vector of geostationary orbit.

Figure 5.13 shows the secular, yearly periodic, and half-yearly periodic terms on the inclination vector of geostationary orbit.

Figure 5.14 shows the secular, yearly periodic, half-yearly periodic, and half-monthly periodic terms on the inclination vector of geostationary orbit.

Especially, the perturbation direction of inclination at a given epoch is

$$\overline{\Omega}_D = a\tan 2\left(\frac{\mathrm{d}\bar{i}_y}{\mathrm{d}T}, \frac{\mathrm{d}\bar{i}_x}{\mathrm{d}T}\right)$$

In the equation,

$$\frac{\mathrm{d}\bar{i}_x}{\mathrm{d}T} = A_x^1 - A_x^2\omega_2 \sin(\omega_2 T + \varphi_2) - A_x^3\omega_3 \sin(\omega_3 T + \varphi_3) \\ - A_x^4\omega_4 \sin(\omega_4 T + \varphi_4) \tag{5.25}$$

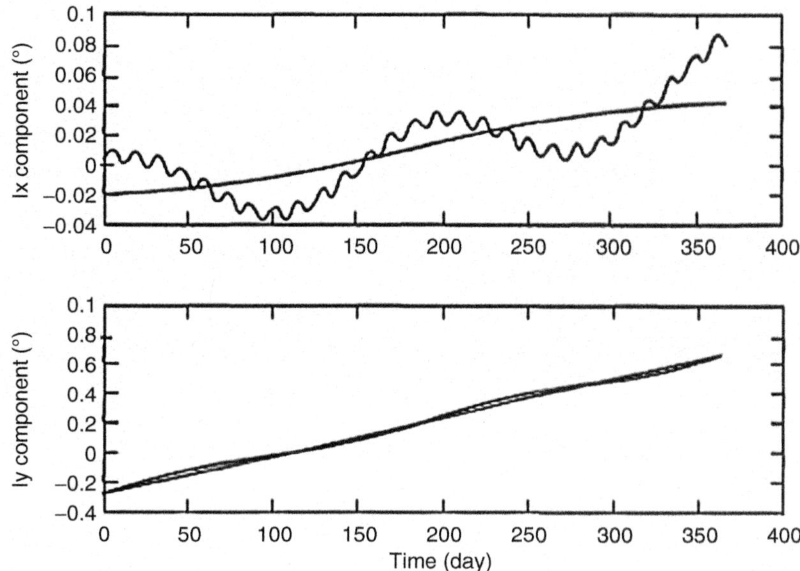

Fig. 5.12 The yearly periodic term of the inclination vector

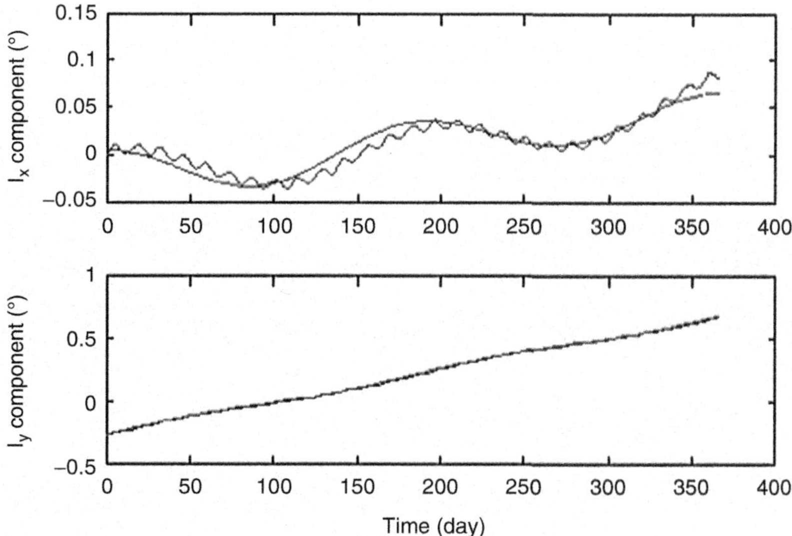

Fig. 5.13 The half-yearly periodic term of the inclination vector

$$
\begin{aligned}
\frac{\mathrm{d}\bar{i}_y}{\mathrm{d}T} = & A_y^1 + A_y^2\omega_2 \cos(\omega_2 T + \varphi_2) + A_y^3\omega_3 \cos(\omega_3 T + \varphi_3) \\
& + A_y^4\omega_4 \cos(\omega_4 T + \varphi_4)
\end{aligned} \tag{5.26}
$$

The inclination perturbation direction is also correlated to the perturbation terms we considered as illustrated in Fig. 5.15.

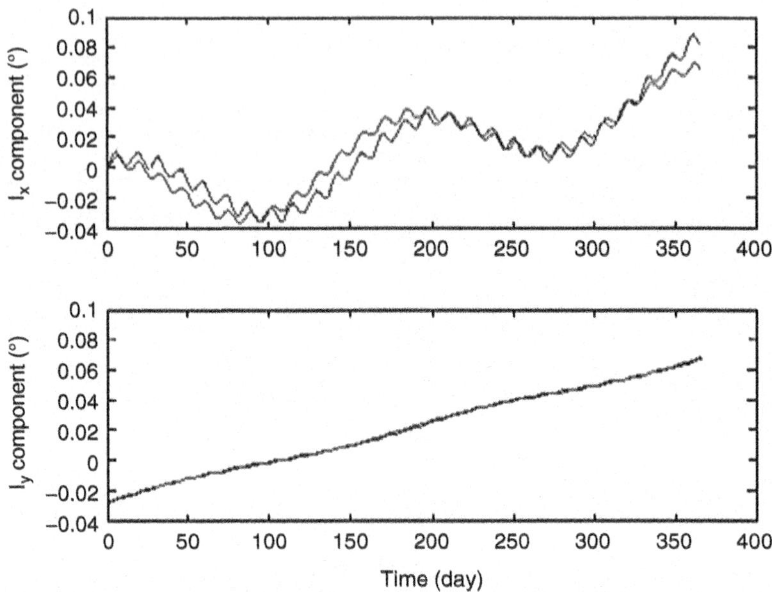

Fig. 5.14 The half-monthly periodic term of the inclination vector

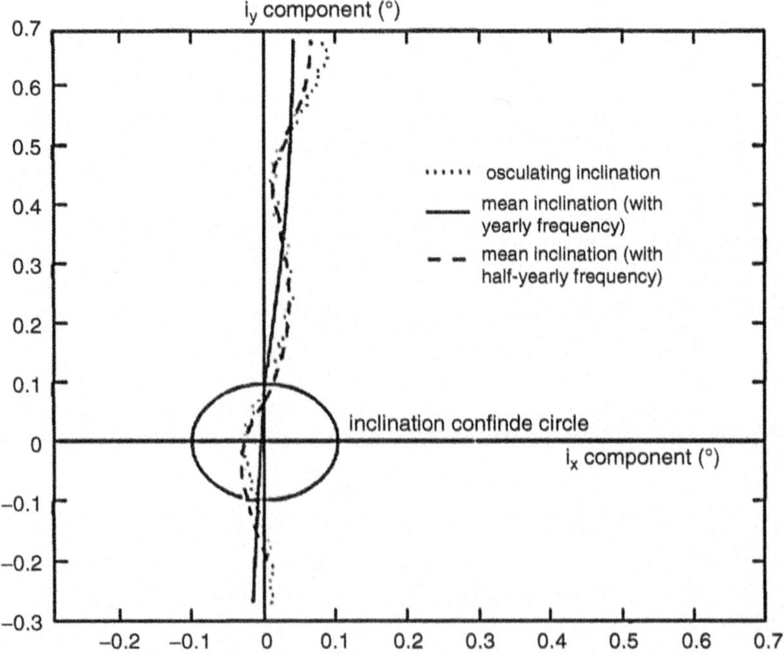

Fig. 5.15 Inclination drift direction

The experiment and numerical analysis indicates that the periodical perturbation acceleration of geostationary orbit can be accurately indentified by the spectral decomposition algorithm. The maneuver accuracy and strategy of east/west control is determined by the identification precision of longitude perturbation acceleration. For the collocated of two satellites that has a higher requirement on eccentricity control, this "out-of-control" would make the isolation of two collocated satellites failed. One of the advantages of spectral decomposing algorithm is that the short-periodical perturbations can be decomposed from precise ephemeris. Besides, the spectral decomposing algorithm can identify the direction of long-periodical perturbations. The direction of free perturbation should be known by using the control strategy combining initiative control and free control of long-period term. For example, the annual average perturbing direction of inclination is related to the mean longitude of lunar orbit, and because of the relative location change of the Sun and Moon, it also includes monthly average perturbing direction, bimonthly average perturbing direction, and season average perturbing direction. The inclination vector shows the polar coordinates of inclination perturbation in 2007. According to the requirement of inclination keeping period, by selecting different frequency combinations, the spectral decomposing algorithm can calculate annual average perturbing direction, season average perturbing direction, bimonthly average perturbing direction, and monthly average perturbing direction. This is very important for the collocated of two satellites and more precise inclination keeping control.

Until now, we have analyzed the characteristics of the perturbing period of geostationary satellite, established the spectral decomposing algorithm to identify periodical motions from high-precise momentary ephemeris, and presented an identifying algorithm of periodical motions based on singular value decomposition.

References

1. Kozai Y (1959) The effect of the Earth's oblateness on the orbit of a near satellite. J Astron 64:378–397
2. Kozai Y (1962) Second order solution of artificial satellite theory without drag. J Astron 67:446–461
3. Blitzer L (1962) Circular orbit in an axially symmetric gravitational field. J ARS 32:1102
4. Cook GE (1966) Perturbation of near-circular orbits by the Earth's gravitational potential. Planet Space Sci 14:433
5. Cook GE (1963) Perturbations of satellite orbits by tesseral harmonics in the Earth's gravitational potential. Planet Space Sci 11:797
6. Kamel A, Ekman D, Tibbitts R (1973) East-west station keeping requirements of nearly synchronous satellites due to Earth's Tri-axiality and Luni-Lunar Effects. Celest Mech 8:129–148
7. Kamel A, Wagner C (1982) On the orbital eccentricity control of synchronous satellites. J Astronaut Sci 3(1):61–73

Chapter 6
Correction Geostationary Orbit

Abstract The relation between the relative motion of geostationary orbit and the station keeping elements is proposed; the orbit correction equations for the radial, tangential, and normal impulse thrust as well as the continuous thrust are reviewed; and the common properties of in-plane orbit correction and out-plane orbit correction are analyzed.

6.1 Introduction

Under the influence of various perturbations, the geostationary satellite is no longer stationary for the observers from the Earth but presents complicated perturbation motions. Therefore, routine orbit corrections or maneuvers must be performed to keep the satellite remain in the vicinity of its nominal position; the vicinity is named as "dead band," which is often defined by the longitude and latitude range relative to the nominal longitude. For example, if a satellite is required to be kept within the dead band of $\pm 0.1^\circ$, then that means the satellite should stay within a restricted region where the longitude span is $\pm 0.1^\circ$ along its track and the latitude span is $\pm 0.1^\circ$ along the normal direction. The orbit correction to keep the satellite remain within the "dead band" is called station keeping maneuver.

In this chapter, we firstly derive the relation between the relative motion of geostationary orbit and the station keeping elements, secondly put forward the orbit correction equations of the radial/tangential/normal correction effect of impulse and continuous thrust, and finally briefly introduce the onboard thrust configuration.

H. Li, *Geostationary Satellites Collocation*, DOI 10.1007/978-3-642-40799-4_6,

6.2 Relative Motion Equation

The small deviations of the orbit elements of geostationary satellite will induce the relative motion along the radial/tangential/normal direction from the nominal position. By linearizing Kepler motion, the linear equations of relative motion with time and the classical Kepler orbit elements are

$$\begin{cases} \Delta r = \Delta a - ea_s \cos\left(\omega_e\left(t - t_p\right)\right) \\ \Delta\lambda = -\dfrac{3}{2}\dfrac{\Delta a}{a_s}\omega_e\left(t - t_p\right) + 2e\sin\left(\omega_e\left(t - t_p\right)\right) - \dfrac{i^2}{4}\sin\left(2\omega_e t\right) \\ \Delta\varphi = i \cdot \sin\left(\omega + \omega_e\left(t - t_p\right)\right) \end{cases} \tag{6.1}$$

By the following definitions,

$$f = \omega_e\left(t - t_p\right),\ l = \Omega + \omega + f,\ l - l_p = f - f_p = \omega_e\left(t - t_p\right),\ D = -\frac{3}{2}\cdot\frac{\Delta a}{a_s}$$

Then the relation between the relative motion and the station keeping elements follows the equations below:

6.2.1 *Radial Equation*

The radial relative motion equation is given by

$$\begin{aligned} \Delta r &= \Delta a - ea_s \cos\left(\omega_e\left(t - t_p\right)\right) = \Delta a - ea_s \cos\left(l - (\Omega + \omega)\right) \\ &= \Delta a - a_s\left(\cos l \cdot e\cos(\Omega + \omega) + \sin l \cdot e\sin(\Omega + \omega)\right) \\ &= \Delta a - a_s\left(e_x \cos l + e_y \sin l\right) \end{aligned} \tag{6.2}$$

or expressed by the orbit drift rate

$$\Delta r = -a_s\left(\frac{2}{3}D + e_x \cos l + e_y \sin l\right) \tag{6.3}$$

6.2.2 *Tangential Equation*

By ignoring the periodic term due to the inclination, the tangential relative motion equation is given by

$$\begin{aligned}\Delta\lambda &= -\frac{3}{2}\frac{\Delta a}{a_s}\omega_e\left(t-t_p\right)+2e\sin\left(\omega_e\left(t-t_p\right)\right)=D\left(l-l_p\right)+2e\sin\left(l-(\Omega+\omega)\right)\\ &=D\left(l-l_p\right)+2(\sin l\cdot e\cos(\Omega+\omega)-\cos l\cdot e\sin(\Omega+\omega))\\ &=D\left(l-l_p\right)+2\left(e_x\sin l-e_y\cos l\right)\end{aligned} \tag{6.4}$$

6.2.3 Normal Equation

Substituting the inclination into formula (6.1), the normal relative motion equation is given by

$$\begin{aligned}\Delta\varphi &= i\cdot\sin\left(\omega+\omega_e\left(t-t_p\right)\right)=i\cdot\sin(l-\Omega)=i\cdot(\sin l\cos\Omega-\cos l\sin\Omega)\\ &=i_x\sin l-i_y\cos l\end{aligned} \tag{6.5}$$

Then the relation between the linear equation of relative motion and the station keeping elements in the RTN coordinate is

$$r=a_s-a_s\left(\frac{2}{3}D+e_x\cos l+e_y\sin l\right) \tag{6.6}$$

$$\begin{aligned}\lambda &= \lambda_p+D\left(l-l_p\right)+2\left(e_x\sin l-e_y\cos l\right)\\ &=\lambda_p+D\left(l_0-l_p\right)+D(l-l_0)+2\left(e_x\sin l-e_y\cos l\right)\\ &=\lambda_0+D(l-l_0)+2\left(e_x\sin l-e_y\cos l\right)\end{aligned} \tag{6.7}$$

$$\varphi=i_x\sin l-i_y\cos l \tag{6.8}$$

Replacing time t with the mean right ascension l, we get

$$l=\Omega+\omega+\omega_e\left(t-t_p\right),\quad \frac{\mathrm{d}l}{\mathrm{d}t}=\omega_e$$

Then the relative velocity of geostationary satellite along the radial, tangential, and normal direction can be given by

$$\begin{aligned}V_r &= \frac{\mathrm{d}r}{\mathrm{d}t}=a_s\cdot\left(e_x\sin l\cdot\frac{\mathrm{d}l}{\mathrm{d}t}-e_y\cos l\cdot\frac{\mathrm{d}l}{\mathrm{d}t}\right)\\ &=a_s\cdot\omega_e\left(e_x\sin l-e_y\cos l\right)=V_s\left(e_x\sin l-e_y\cos l\right)\end{aligned} \tag{6.9}$$

$$\begin{aligned}V_T &= a_s\frac{\mathrm{d}\lambda}{\mathrm{d}t}=a_s\cdot\left(D\cdot\frac{\mathrm{d}l}{\mathrm{d}t}+2e_x\cos l\cdot\frac{\mathrm{d}l}{\mathrm{d}t}+2e_y\sin l\cdot\frac{\mathrm{d}l}{\mathrm{d}t}\right)\\ &=a_s\omega_e\cdot\left(D+2e_x\cos l+2e_y\sin l\right)=V_s\left(D+2e_x\cos l+2e_y\sin l\right)\end{aligned} \tag{6.10}$$

$$
\begin{aligned}
V_N &= a_s \cdot \frac{d\varphi}{dt} = a_s \cdot \left(i_x \cos l \cdot \frac{dl}{dt} + i_y \sin l \cdot \frac{dl}{dt} \right) \\
&= a_s \omega_e \cdot \left(i_x \cos l + i_y \sin l \right) = V_s \left(i_x \cos l + i_y \sin l \right)
\end{aligned} \tag{6.11}
$$

In the equation, V_s is the ideal geostationary orbit velocity:

$$V_s = a_s \cdot \omega_e = 3074.7(\mathrm{m/s})$$

6.3 Orbit Correction Equation

Suppose a geostationary satellite obtains ΔV of extra impulse velocity increment at time (t_b) or at right ascension (l_b). ΔV can be decomposed into the radial component ΔV_r, the tangential component ΔV_T, and the normal component ΔV_N:

$$\Delta \vec{V} = \begin{pmatrix} \Delta V_r \\ \Delta V_T \\ \Delta V_N \end{pmatrix} = \begin{pmatrix} V_r^+ - V_r^- \\ V_T^+ - V_T^- \\ V_N^+ - V_N^- \end{pmatrix}$$

In this section, we will discuss how the radial component ΔV_r, the tangential component ΔV_T, and the normal component ΔV_N change the orbit elements, respectively.

The longitude drift vector is

$$\Delta D = D^+ - D^-, \quad \Delta \lambda_0 = \lambda_0^+ - \lambda_0^-$$

The eccentricity vector is

$$\Delta e_x = e_x^+ - e_x^-, \quad \Delta e_y = e_y^+ - e_y^-$$

The inclination vector is

$$\Delta i_x = i_x^+ - i_x^-, \quad \Delta i_y = i_y^+ - i_y^-$$

Then the motion parameters of the satellite before (−) and after (+) the extra impulse velocity increment are deduced from the linear equation of orbit small deviation.

The radial position increment equation is

$$
\begin{aligned}
r^- &= a_s - a_s \left(\frac{2}{3} D^- + e_x^- \cos l_b + e_y^- \sin l_b \right), \\
r^+ &= a_s - a_s \left(\frac{2}{3} D^+ + e_x^+ \cos l_b + e_y^+ \sin l_b \right)
\end{aligned}
$$

The tangential position increment equation is

$$\lambda^- = \lambda_0^- + D^-(l_b - l_0) + 2\left(e_x^- \sin l_b - e_y^- \cos l_b\right)$$
$$\lambda^+ = \lambda_0^+ + D^+(l_b - l_0) + 2\left(e_x^+ \sin l_b - e_y^+ \cos l_b\right)$$

The normal position increment equation is

$$\varphi^- = i_x^- \sin l_b - i_y^- \cos l_b, \quad \varphi^+ = i_x^+ \sin l_b - i_y^+ \cos l_b$$

The radial velocity increment equation is

$$V_r^- = V_s\left(e_x^- \sin l_b - e_y^- \cos l_b\right), \quad V_r^+ = V_s\left(e_x^+ \sin l_b - e_y^+ \cos l_b\right)$$

The tangential velocity increment equation is

$$V_T^- = V_s\left(D^- + 2e_x^- \cos l_b + 2e_y^- \sin l_b\right),$$
$$V_T^+ = V_s\left(D^+ + 2e_x^+ \cos l_b + 2e_y^+ \sin l_b\right)$$

The normal velocity increment equation is

$$V_N^- = V_s\left(i_x^- \cos l_b + i_y^- \sin l_b\right), \quad V_N^+ = V_s\left(i_x^+ \cos l_b + i_y^+ \sin l_b\right)$$

6.4 Radial Impulse

If the velocity increases along the radial direction, that is, the radial component $\Delta V_r \neq 0$, while the tangential component $\Delta V_T = 0$ and the normal component $\Delta V_N = 0$, then the variation of the orbit at time (t_b) is $(\Delta D, \Delta\lambda, \Delta e_x, \Delta e_y, \Delta i_x, \Delta i_y)$, which satisfies the linear equations below:

$$\Delta r = a_s\left(\frac{2}{3}\Delta D + \Delta e_x \cos l_b + \Delta e_y \sin l_b\right)$$
$$\Delta\lambda = \Delta\lambda_0 + \Delta D(l_b - l_0) + 2(\Delta e_x \sin l_b - \Delta e_y \cos l_b)$$
$$\Delta V_r = V_s(\Delta e_x \sin l_b - \Delta e_y \cos l_b)$$
$$\Delta V_T = V_s(\Delta D + 2\Delta e_x \cos l_b + 2\Delta e_y \sin l_b)$$

Considering that the radial velocity increment is induced by impulse, which means the radial and tangential position are the same before and after the extra impulse velocity increment, that is, $\Delta r = 0, \Delta\lambda = 0$, then

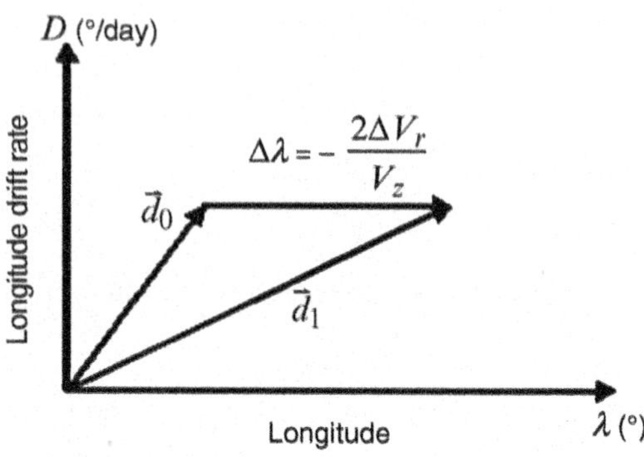

Fig. 6.1 Longitude via radial velocity increment

$$\begin{bmatrix} \frac{2}{3} & 0 & \cos l_b & \sin l_b \\ l_b - l_0 & 1 & 2\sin l_b & -2\cos l_b \\ 0 & 0 & V_s \sin l_b & -V_s \cos l_b \\ 1 & 0 & 2\cos l_b & 2\sin l_b \end{bmatrix} \cdot \begin{bmatrix} \Delta D \\ \Delta\lambda_0 \\ \Delta e_x \\ \Delta e_y \end{bmatrix} = \begin{bmatrix} 0 \\ 0 \\ \Delta V_r \\ 0 \end{bmatrix} \tag{6.12}$$

By solving above equation, then we get how the radial velocity increments put in effect to the geostationary orbit.

$$\Delta D = 0, \quad \Delta\lambda = -\frac{2\Delta V_r}{V_s}$$

$$\Delta e_x = \frac{\Delta V_r}{V_s} \sin l_b = \frac{\Delta V_r}{V_s} \cos\left(l_b - \frac{\pi}{2}\right)$$

$$\Delta e_y = -\frac{\Delta V_r}{V_s} \cos l_b = \frac{\Delta V_r}{V_s} \sin\left(l_b - \frac{\pi}{2}\right)$$

Therefore, the radial velocity increment does not change the drift rate of geostationary satellite. It changes the mean longitude with the magnitude of $-6.5 \times 10^{-4} \cdot \Delta V_r$. As illustrated in Fig. 6.1, the direction from the Earth's center to the satellite is defined as positive and the opposite direction is defined as negative.

If $\Delta V_r = 1$(m/s), then the mean longitude moves westward of 0.037°, and if $\Delta V_r = -1$(m/s), then the mean longitude moves eastward of 0.037°.

The radial velocity increments change both the size and the direction of eccentricity. According to the equation of eccentricity increment,

$$\Delta\vec{e} = \begin{bmatrix} \Delta e_x \\ \Delta e_y \end{bmatrix} = \frac{\Delta V_r}{V_s} \begin{bmatrix} \cos\left(l_b - \frac{\pi}{2}\right) \\ \sin\left(l_b - \frac{\pi}{2}\right) \end{bmatrix}, \Delta V_r \geq 0 \tag{6.13}$$

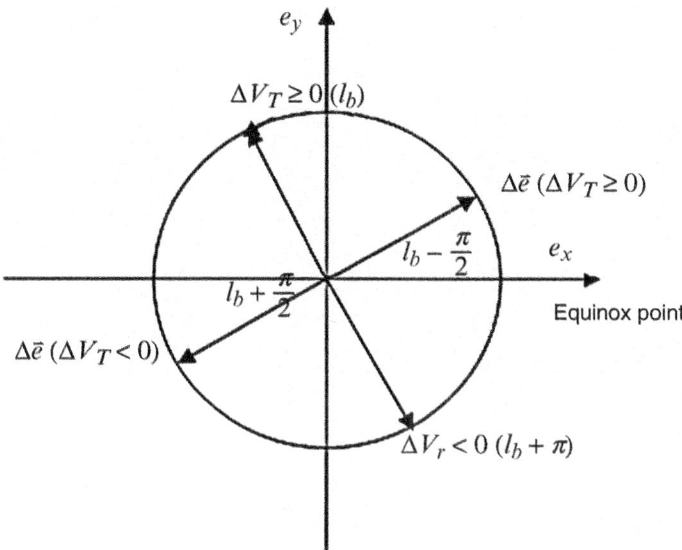

Fig. 6.2 Eccentricity via radial velocity increment

or

$$\Delta\vec{e} = \begin{bmatrix} \Delta e_x \\ \Delta e_y \end{bmatrix} = \frac{|\Delta V_r|}{V_s} \begin{bmatrix} \cos\left(l_b + \frac{\pi}{2}\right) \\ \sin\left(l_b + \frac{\pi}{2}\right) \end{bmatrix}, \Delta V_r < 0 \tag{6.14}$$

Therefore, the radial velocity increment changes the eccentricity of $3.25 \times 10^{-4} \cdot \Delta V_r$, and the direction lags behind the phase of radial impulse of $\pi/2$, as shown in Fig. 6.2.

Although the radial velocity increment is seldom used to correct orbit parameters, owing to some deviation of the tangential and normal thruster, there is coupling radial velocity increment when the satellite obtains the tangential and normal velocity increments.

The satellite obtains the radial velocity increment ΔV_r at the mean longitude l_b. If $\Delta V_r \geq 0$ (from the Earth' center to the satellite), then the eccentricity increment vector lags behind the mean longitude l_b of 90°, the magnitude of the eccentricity variation is $\Delta V_r/V_s$, and the direction is with an angle of $(l_b - \pi/2)$ which is measured from the equinox direction, as illustrated in Fig. 6.3.

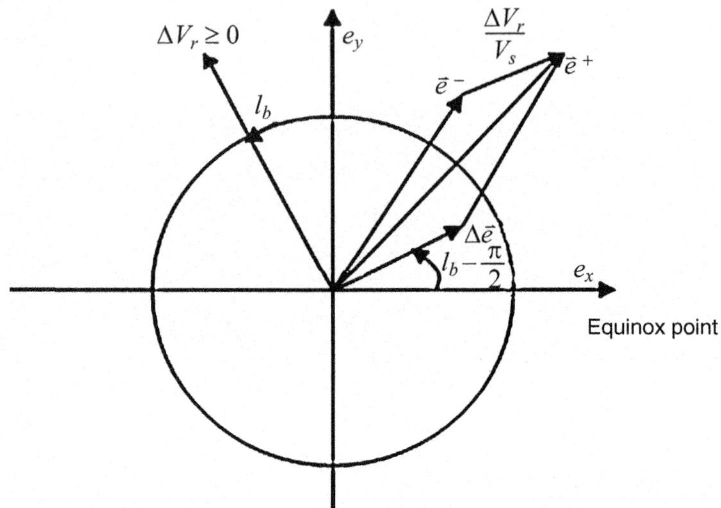

Fig. 6.3 Eccentricity via positive impulse

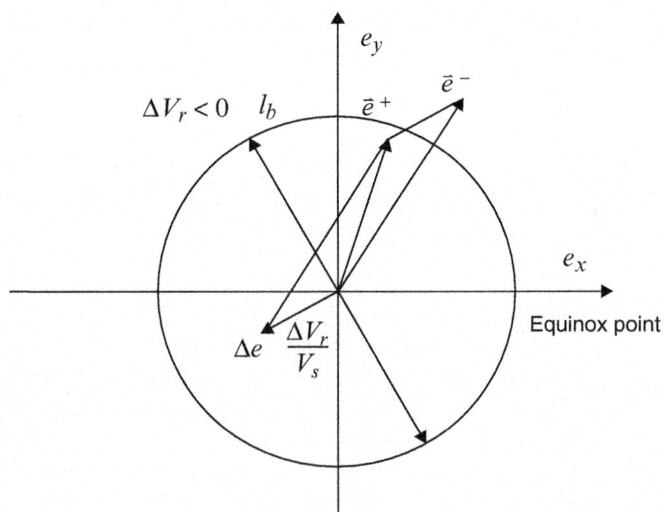

Fig. 6.4 Eccentricity via negative impulse

If $\Delta V_r < 0$ (from the satellite to the Earth's center), then the eccentricity increment vector is 90° ahead of the mean longitude l_b, the magnitude of the eccentricity variation is $\Delta V_r/V_s$, and the direction is with an angle of $(l_b - \pi/2)$ measured from the equinox direction.

6.5 Tangential Impulse

If the velocity increases along the tangential direction, i.e., the tangential component $\Delta V_T \neq 0$, while the radial component $\Delta V_r = 0$ and the normal component $\Delta V_N = 0$, then the variation of the orbit at time (t_b) $(\Delta D, \Delta\lambda, \Delta e_x, \Delta e_y, \Delta i_x, \Delta i_y)$ follows the following linear equations:

$$\Delta r = a_s\left(\frac{2}{3}\Delta D + \Delta e_x \cos l_b + \Delta e_y \sin l_b\right)$$

$$\Delta\lambda = \Delta\lambda_0 + \Delta D(l_b - l_0) + 2(\Delta e_x \sin l_b - \Delta e_y \cos l_b)$$

$$\Delta V_r = V_s(\Delta e_x \sin l_b - \Delta e_y \cos l_b)$$

$$\Delta V_T = V_s(\Delta D + 2\Delta e_x \cos l_b + 2\Delta e_y \sin l_b)$$

Considering the impulse velocity increment, suppose $\Delta r = 0, \Delta\lambda = 0, \Delta V_r = 0$; therefore,

$$\begin{bmatrix} \frac{2}{3} & 0 & \cos l_b & \sin l_b \\ l_b - l_0 & 1 & 2\sin l_b & -2\cos l_b \\ 0 & 0 & \sin l_b & -\cos l_b \\ V_s & 0 & 2V_s \cos l_b & 2V_s \sin l_b \end{bmatrix} \cdot \begin{bmatrix} \Delta D \\ \Delta\lambda_0 \\ \Delta e_x \\ \Delta e_y \end{bmatrix} = \begin{bmatrix} 0 \\ 0 \\ 0 \\ \Delta V_T \end{bmatrix} \tag{6.15}$$

The solution of the above equations is

$$\Delta D = -\frac{3\Delta V_T}{V_s} \cdot 360.9856(°/\text{day})$$

$$\Delta\lambda_0 = \frac{3\Delta V_T}{V_s}(l_b - l_0)$$

$$\Delta e_x = \frac{2\Delta V_T}{V_s}\cos(l_b)$$

$$\Delta e_y = \frac{2\Delta V_T}{V_s}\sin(l_b)$$

$\Delta\lambda_0 = -\Delta D(l_b - l_0)$ is a compatible equation of different drift rates at time t_0. It has no practical meanings in physics. According to the definition of $\Delta\lambda_0$,

$$\begin{aligned} \lambda_0^+ &= \lambda_0^- + \Delta\lambda_0 = \lambda_0^- - \Delta D(l_b - l_0) = \lambda_0^- - (D^+ - D^-)(l_b - l_0) \\ &= \lambda_0^- + D^-(l_b - l_0) - D^+(l_b - l_0) = \lambda^- - D^+(l_b - l_0) \end{aligned}$$

Fig. 6.5 Drift rate via tangential velocity increment

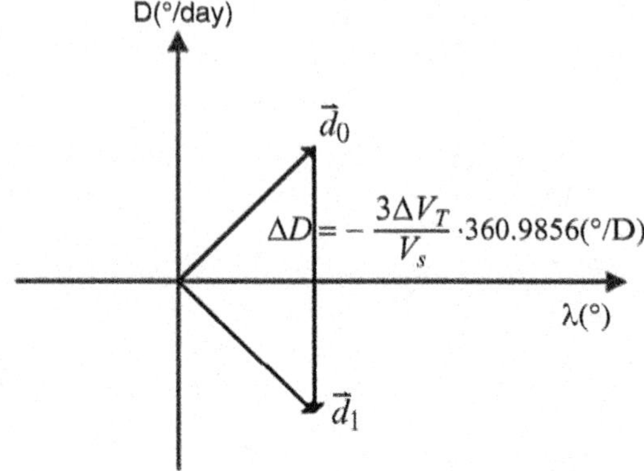

Because $\lambda^-|_{t=t_b} = \lambda^+|_{t=t_b}$, the compatible equation is given by

$$\lambda^+ = \lambda_0^+ + D^+(l_b - l_0)$$

According to equation

$$\Delta D = -\frac{3}{2}\left(\frac{\Delta a}{a_s}\right) = -\frac{3\Delta V_T}{V_s}$$

and the definition of drift rate, the variation of semi-major axis due to the tangential velocity is

$$\Delta a = -\frac{2a_s}{3}D = 2a_s\frac{\Delta V_T}{V_s} = 2\frac{\Delta V_T}{\omega_e}$$

The tangential velocity increment changes the semi-major axis and the drift rate of satellite. The increment equations are

$$\Delta D = -0.3522 \cdot \Delta V_T(°/\text{day}) \text{ and, } \Delta a = 27.427 \cdot \Delta V_T(\text{km})$$

The satellite accelerates eastward along the tangential direction. As illustrated in Fig. 6.5, if $\Delta V_T > 0$, then the drift rate is westward and the satellite moves westward along the tangential direction relative to the rotation of the Earth. If $\Delta V_T < 0$, then the drift rate is eastward. For the first sight, it seems a paradox that the eastward acceleration generates westward drift rate and the westward deceleration generates eastward drift rate. The fact is that the satellite accelerates eastward along the tangential direction. Because $\Delta V_T > 0$, the semi-major axis increases and the angular velocity of orbit mean motion decreases. Compared with the Earth's rotation angular velocity, it generates westward longitude drift velocity. The satellite decelerates westward along the tangential direction. Because $\Delta V_T < 0$, the semi-major axis decreases and the angular velocity of orbit mean motion increases.

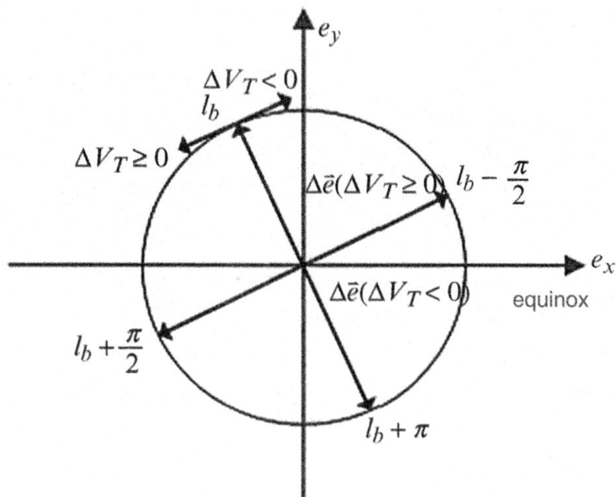

Fig. 6.6 Eccentricity via tangential impulse

Compared with the Earth's rotation angular velocity, it generates eastward longitude drift velocity.

The tangential velocity increment changes the satellite eccentricity. According to the equation of eccentricity increment,

$$\Delta \vec{e} = \begin{bmatrix} \Delta e_x \\ \Delta e_y \end{bmatrix} = \frac{2\Delta V_T}{V_s} \begin{bmatrix} \cos(l_b) \\ \sin(l_b) \end{bmatrix}, \quad \Delta V_T \geq 0$$

$$\Delta \vec{e} = \begin{bmatrix} \Delta e_x \\ \Delta e_y \end{bmatrix} = \frac{2|\Delta V_T|}{V_s} \begin{bmatrix} \cos(l_b + \pi) \\ \sin(l_b + \pi) \end{bmatrix}, \quad \Delta V_T < 0$$

The tangential velocity changes the eccentricity of $6.5 \times 10^{-4} \cdot |\Delta V_T|$; the direction of the eccentricity increment lags behind the planned phase of impulse of $\pi/2$, as illustrated in Fig. 6.6.

When the tangential velocity increment is scheduled at the apse of orbit, the direction of the eccentricity increment due to the tangential velocity increment is collinear with the orbit primary eccentricity, and the magnitude of eccentricity increment reaches its maximum, while the direction of eccentricity is kept unchanged. When the tangential velocity increment is scheduled at orbit perigee, the magnitude of eccentricity after the tangential pulse is

$$e^+ = e^- + \frac{2\Delta V_T}{V_s}, \Delta V_T \geq 0$$

$$e^+ = e^- - \frac{2|\Delta V_T|}{V_s}, \Delta V_T < 0$$

Therefore, in order to keep the orbit with a small eccentricity with each maneuver increment, the westward tangential velocity increment should be scheduled at

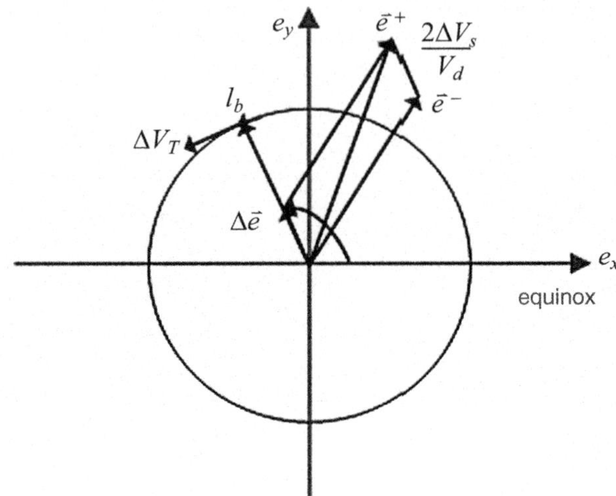

Fig. 6.7 Eccentricity via positive tangential velocity

perigee. If the westward tangential velocity at perigee reaches $|\Delta V_T| = \frac{V_s}{2} \cdot e^-$, the orbit after correlation is a roundness orbit. If the westward tangential velocity is greater than $\frac{V_s}{2} \cdot e^-$, the line of apsides will rotate 180° in space. Meanwhile, if the eastward velocity increment is scheduled at perigee, the orbit will obtain the maximum eccentricity after correction.

When the tangential velocity increment is scheduled at apogee, where the right ascension $l_b = \Omega + \omega + \pi$,

$$e^+ = e^- - \frac{2\Delta V_T}{V_s}, \Delta V_T \geq 0$$

$$e^+ = e^- + \frac{2|\Delta V_T|}{V_s}, \Delta V_T < 0$$

Therefore, at apogee, opposite to the case of that at perigee, the eastward tangential velocity increment decreases the eccentricity, and the westward tangential velocity increment increases the eccentricity. Therefore, in order to keep the orbit with a small eccentricity with each maneuver increment, the eastward tangential velocity increment should be scheduled at apogee.

The satellite obtains the tangential velocity increment ΔV_T at the right ascension l_b. As illustrated in Fig. 6.7, if $\Delta V_T \geq 0$ (along the motion direction of the satellite), then the eccentricity increment vector lags behind the right ascension of 90°, and its magnitude is $\frac{2\Delta V_T}{V_s}$. As illustrated in Fig. 6.8, if $\Delta V_T < 0$ (opposite to the motion direction of the satellite), then the eccentricity increment vector lags behind the tangential velocity increment of 90°, with the magnitude of $\frac{2|\Delta V_T|}{V_s}$, and its angular is $l_b + \pi$.

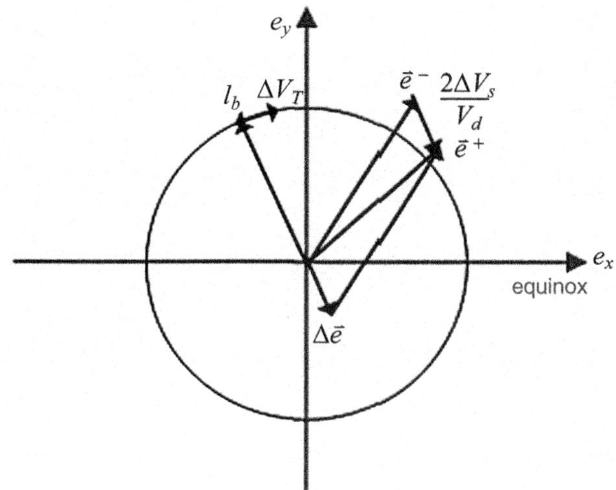

Fig. 6.8 Eccentricity via negative tangential velocity

Table 6.1 The tangential velocity increment vs. orbit correction

ΔV_T(m/s)	ΔD(°/day)	Δa(km)	Δe (Unit less)
+1.0	−0.3522	27.427	6.5×10^{-4}
−1.0	0.3522	−27.427	6.5×10^{-4}
−2.839	+1.0	−77.86	1.845×10^{-3}
+2.839	−1.0	+77.86	1.845×10^{-3}
+0.03646	−0.0128	+1.0	2.37×10^{-5}
−0.03646	+0.0128	−1.0	2.37×10^{-5}
±0.154	Uncertain	±4.223	1×10^{-4}

In conclusion, in practical engineering, the tangential velocity increment is used to correct not only the drift rate but also the eccentricity of satellite. Therefore, the data listed in Table 6.1 are very useful in geostationary orbit correction.

6.6 Normal Impulse

If the velocity increases along the normal direction, i.e., the normal component $\Delta V_N \neq 0$, while the radial component $\Delta V_r = 0$ and the tangential component $\Delta V_T = 0$, then the variation of the orbit at time (t_b) is (ΔD, $\Delta\lambda$, Δe_x, Δe_y, Δi_x, Δi_y), which satisfies the linear equations below:

$$\Delta\varphi = \Delta i_x \sin(l_b) - \Delta i_y \cos(l_b) \tag{6.16}$$

$$\Delta V_N = V_s\left(\Delta i_x \cos(l_b) + \Delta i_y \sin(l_b)\right) \tag{6.17}$$

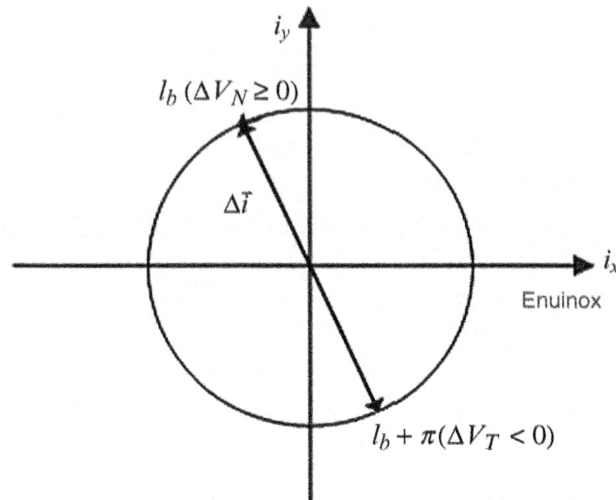

Fig. 6.9 Inclination via normal velocity increment

Considering the impulse velocity increment, suppose $\Delta\varphi = 0, \Delta V_N \neq 0$; then the small deviation equation of normal velocity increment is

$$\begin{bmatrix} \sin(l_b) & -\cos(l_b) \\ \cos(l_b) & \sin(l_b) \end{bmatrix} \begin{pmatrix} \Delta i_x \\ \Delta i_y \end{pmatrix} = \begin{pmatrix} 0 \\ \frac{\Delta V_N}{V_s} \end{pmatrix} \tag{6.18}$$

The solution of the above equations is

$$\Delta \vec{i} = \begin{pmatrix} \Delta i_x \\ \Delta i_y \end{pmatrix} = \frac{\Delta V_N}{V_s} \begin{pmatrix} \cos(l_b) \\ \sin(l_b) \end{pmatrix}, \Delta V_N \geq 0 \tag{6.19}$$

$$\Delta \vec{i} = \begin{pmatrix} \Delta i_x \\ \Delta i_y \end{pmatrix} = \frac{|\Delta V_N|}{V_s} \begin{pmatrix} \cos(l_b + \pi) \\ \sin(l_b + \pi) \end{pmatrix}, \Delta V_N < 0 \tag{6.20}$$

As shown in Fig. 6.9, $\Delta V_N \geq 0$ denotes the northward correction and $\Delta V_N < 0$ denotes the southward correction. The above formula indicates that the northward correction at the mean right ascension l_b and the southward correction at the mean right ascension $l_b + \pi$ are of the same effect, which means that there are two opportunities to correct the inclination as well as the right ascension of orbit. One is along the north direction at the mean right ascension l_b, and the other is along the south direction at the mean right ascension $l_b + \pi$.

The normal velocity increment changes the size and the direction of inclination. The changed size is $0°.0186 \cdot |\Delta V_N|$ and the direction is related to the right ascension where the normal pulse is planned. As shown in Fig. 6.10, if and only if $l_b = \Omega^-$ and $l_b = \Omega^- + \pi$, i.e., the normal velocity increment is scheduled at the ascending node and descending node of the orbit, then the direction of inclination increment is collinear with the original inclination vector $\vec{i}^-$, the direction of inclination doesn't change, and the size of inclination increment reaches its maximum.

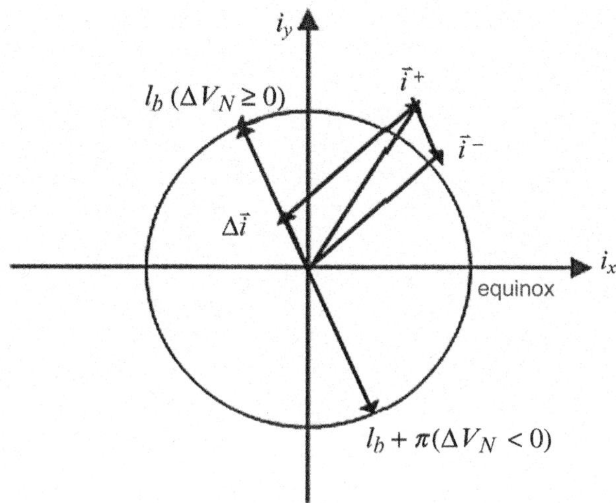

Fig. 6.10 Inclination via normal velocity increment

If $l_b = \Omega^-$, which means the normal pulse is planned at the ascending node,

$$i^+ = i^- + \frac{\Delta V_N}{V_s}$$

The northward normal velocity increment ($\Delta V_N \geq 0$) increases the inclination, and the southward velocity increment ($\Delta V_N < 0$) decreases the inclination.

If $l_b = \Omega^- + \pi$, which means the normal pulse is planned at the descending node,

$$i^+ = i^- - \frac{\Delta V_N}{V_s}$$

The northward normal velocity increment ($\Delta V_N \geq 0$) decreases the inclination, and the southward velocity increment ($\Delta V_N < 0$) increases the inclination.

For example, to obtain an inclination increment of one degree, a normal velocity increment of about 53.66 m/s is required, while with a normal velocity increment of 1 m/s, the inclination increment changes only about 0.0186. Therefore, the inclination correction of satellite consumes more fuel.

6.7 Continuous Thrust

If the station keeping requires a long time thrust, then the thrust process cannot be considered as impulsive thrust and the arc loss must be considered in continuing thrust process. For example, for a geostationary satellite of 1,000 kg, if the orbit correlation is carried out by traditional chemical propellants, whose rated thrust is

20 (N), then in order to obtain 1 m/s velocity increment (east/west station keeping), the thrust process will last 50 s; and to obtain 5 m/s velocity increment (inclination keeping), the thrust process will last 250 s. The cost time is relatively short compared with a mean sidereal day, and thus the process can be considered as pulse thrust. Therefore, normally it is feasible to apply pulse thrust to the station keeping of geostationary satellite. However, if small thrusters are adopted, such as high specific impulse ion propulsion (ionic) with a rated thrust of 0.5 (N) which is applied by a lot of geostationary satellites, then in order to obtain 1 m/s velocity increment (east/west station keeping), the thrust process will last 2,000 s; and to obtain 5 m/s velocity increment (inclination keeping), the thrust will last 10,000 s. The cost time is no longer short compared with one mean sidereal day. Therefore, the arc loss must be considered during the thrust continuous process.

Suppose the radial/tangential/normal components of the rated acceleration are a_R, a_T, a_N, and the thrust process lasts dt, $\Delta t = t_2 - t_1$, and then the velocity increments are

$$dV_R = a_R dt, \Delta V_R = a_R \Delta t$$
$$dV_T = a_T dt, \Delta V_T = a_T \Delta t$$
$$dV_N = a_N dt, \Delta V_N = a_N \Delta t$$

1. Correction equation of the drift rate and mean longitude

$$\Delta D = -\frac{3a_T}{V_s} \cdot 360.9856(^\circ/\text{day}) \cdot \Delta t \tag{6.21}$$

$$\Delta a = \frac{2a_T}{\omega_e} \cdot \Delta t \tag{6.22}$$

In the case of continuous thrust, the mean longitude increment is generated not only from the radial acceleration but also from the drift rate changes due to the tangential acceleration, so the differential equation for the mean longitude increment is

$$\begin{aligned} d\lambda &= -\frac{2a_r}{V_s} \cdot dt + \Delta d \cdot dt \\ \Delta\lambda &= -\frac{2a_r}{V_s} \cdot \Delta t - \frac{3}{2}\frac{\omega_e}{V_s} a_T (\Delta t)^2 = -\frac{\Delta t}{V_s}\left(2a_r + 3\omega_e a_T\left(\frac{\Delta t}{2}\right)\right) \end{aligned} \tag{6.23}$$

2. Correction equation of the eccentricity vector

The differential correction equation of the eccentricity vector is

$$\mathrm{d}e_x = \frac{1}{V_s}(\mathrm{d}V_r \sin l + 2\mathrm{d}V_T \cos l) = \frac{1}{V_s}(a_r \sin l + 2a_T \cos l)\mathrm{d}t \tag{6.24}$$

$$\mathrm{d}e_y = \frac{1}{V_s}(-\mathrm{d}V_r \cos l + 2\mathrm{d}V_T \sin l) = \frac{1}{V_s}(-a_r \cos l + 2a_T \sin l)\mathrm{d}t \tag{6.25}$$

Assume the right ascension is $l(t_1)$ at thrust start time t_1 and the right ascension is $l(t_2)$ at thrust end time t_2. At the middle of the thrust process, the mean longitude is $l_m = \frac{(l(t_1)+l(t_2))}{2}$. Performing integral to the formula above with the eccentricity vector along the thruster work arc, we get

$$\Delta e_x = \frac{2}{V_s \cdot n}(a_r \sin l_m + 2a_T \cos l_m) \sin\left(\frac{1}{2}n\Delta t\right) \tag{6.26}$$

$$\Delta e_y = \frac{2}{V_s \cdot n}(-a_r \cos l_m + 2a_T \sin l_m) \sin\left(\frac{1}{2}n\Delta t\right) \tag{6.27}$$

Obviously, if Δt is quite small, then keep the first order of Δt. With $\sin\left(\frac{1}{2}n\Delta t\right) \approx \frac{1}{2}n\Delta t$, the correction equation of impulse thrust is given by

$$\begin{aligned}\Delta e_x &= \frac{2}{V_s \cdot n}(a_r \sin l_m + 2a_T \cos l_m) \sin\left(\frac{1}{2}n\Delta t\right)\\ &= \frac{2}{V_s \cdot n}(a_r \sin l_m + 2a_T \cos l_m) \cdot \frac{1}{2}n\Delta t\\ &= \frac{1}{V_s}(\Delta V_r \sin l_m + 2\Delta V_T \cos l_m)\end{aligned} \tag{6.28}$$

$$\begin{aligned}\Delta e_y &= \frac{2}{V_s \cdot n}(-a_r \cos l_m + 2a_T \sin l_m) \sin\left(\frac{1}{2}n\Delta t\right)\\ &= \frac{2}{V_s \cdot n}(-a_r \cos l_m + 2a_T \sin l_m) \cdot \frac{1}{2}n\Delta t\\ &= \frac{1}{V_s}(-\Delta V_r \cos l_m + 2\Delta V_T \sin l_m)\end{aligned} \tag{6.29}$$

3. Correction equation of the inclination vector

Similar to the eccentricity vector, the correlation equation of the inclination vector is

$$\Delta i_x = \frac{2a_N}{V_s n} \cos l_m \sin\left(\frac{1}{2} n \Delta t\right) \tag{6.30}$$

$$\Delta i_y = \frac{2a_N}{V_s n} \sin l_m \sin\left(\frac{1}{2} n \Delta t\right) \tag{6.31}$$

Obviously, if Δt is quite small, then keep the first order of Δt. With $\sin\left(\frac{1}{2} n \Delta t\right) \approx \frac{1}{2} n \Delta t$, the correction equation of impulse thrust is given by

$$\Delta i_x = \frac{2a_N}{V_s n} \cos l_m \sin\left(\frac{1}{2} n \Delta t\right) = \frac{2a_N}{V_s n} \cos l_m \cdot \frac{1}{2} n \Delta t = \frac{\Delta V_N}{V_s} \cos l_m \tag{6.32}$$

$$\Delta i_y = \frac{2a_N}{V_s n} \sin l_m \sin\left(\frac{1}{2} n \Delta t\right) = \frac{2a_N}{V_s n} \sin l_m \cdot \frac{1}{2} n \Delta t = \frac{\Delta V_N}{V_s} \sin l_m \tag{6.33}$$

6.8 Onboard Thrust Configuration

According to the correction equations of geostationary orbit, the impulse velocity increment should be carried out for the station keeping. The radial velocity increment changes the mean longitude λ and the eccentricity vector (e_x, e_y). The tangential velocity increment changes the drift rate $D = \frac{d\lambda}{dt}$ and the eccentricity vector (e_x, e_y), and the variation of the eccentricity vector is two times of that caused by the radial velocity increment. Meanwhile the change of the mean longitude drift rate indirectly changes the mean longitude. Therefore, radial thrust devices are normally not installed in GEO satellites, but east/west trust configuration is provided with the tangential thrust devices. The in-plane correction equations are simplified as:

1. Correction equation of impulse thrust

$$\begin{cases} \Delta D = -\dfrac{3\Delta V_T}{V_s} \cdot 360.9856(°/\text{day}), \quad \text{or.} \\ \Delta a = -\dfrac{2a_s}{3} \Delta D = 2a_s \dfrac{\Delta V_T}{V_s} = 2\dfrac{\Delta V_T}{\omega_e} \\ \Delta e_x = \dfrac{2\Delta V_T}{V_s} \cos(l_b) \\ \Delta e_y = \dfrac{2\Delta V_T}{V_s} \sin(l_b) \end{cases} \tag{6.34}$$

2. Correction equation of continuous thrust

$$\begin{cases} \Delta D = -\dfrac{3a_T}{V_s} \cdot 360.9856(^\circ/\text{day}) \cdot \Delta t \\ \Delta a = \dfrac{2a_T}{\omega_e} \cdot \Delta t \\ \Delta e_x = \dfrac{2}{V_s \cdot n}(2a_T \cos l_m) \sin\left(\dfrac{1}{2} n \Delta t\right) \\ \Delta e_y = \dfrac{2}{V_s \cdot n}(2a_T \sin l_m) \sin\left(\dfrac{1}{2} n \Delta t\right) \end{cases} \tag{6.35}$$

The correction of orbit plane (the inclination i and the right ascension of the ascending node Ω) is correlated only with the normal thruster. If it is northward thrust ($\Delta V_n \geq 0$), the correction equation of inclination is

$$\begin{cases} \Delta i_x = \dfrac{\Delta V_N}{V_s} \cos(l_b) \\ \Delta i_y = \dfrac{\Delta V_N}{V_s} \sin(l_b) \end{cases}, \quad \Delta V_N \geq 0 \tag{6.36}$$

If it is southward thrust ($\Delta V_n < 0$), the correction equation of inclination is

$$\begin{cases} \Delta i_x = \dfrac{|\Delta V_N|}{V_s} \cos(l_b + \pi) \\ \Delta i_y = \dfrac{|\Delta V_N|}{V_s} \sin(l_b + \pi) \end{cases}, \quad \Delta V_N < 0 \tag{6.37}$$

Therefore, by providing northward thrust at the mean longitude l_b or southward thrust at the mean longitude $l_b + \pi$, the inclination correction $(\Delta i_x, \Delta i_y)$ can be obtained. That is why some geostationary satellites are only provided with northward or southward normal thrusters and some geostationary satellites are provided both northward and southward normal thrusters. The latter are of more flexible correction direction and time choices. Normally the onboard thrust configuration is shown by taking Paksat-1R satellite as an example; the thrust configuration is illustrated in Fig. 6.11.

The 490 N engine (1A, 1B) in the Earth back panel is used to put the satellite to get into the geostationary orbit from the parking orbit. The 10 N engines 2A to 7A

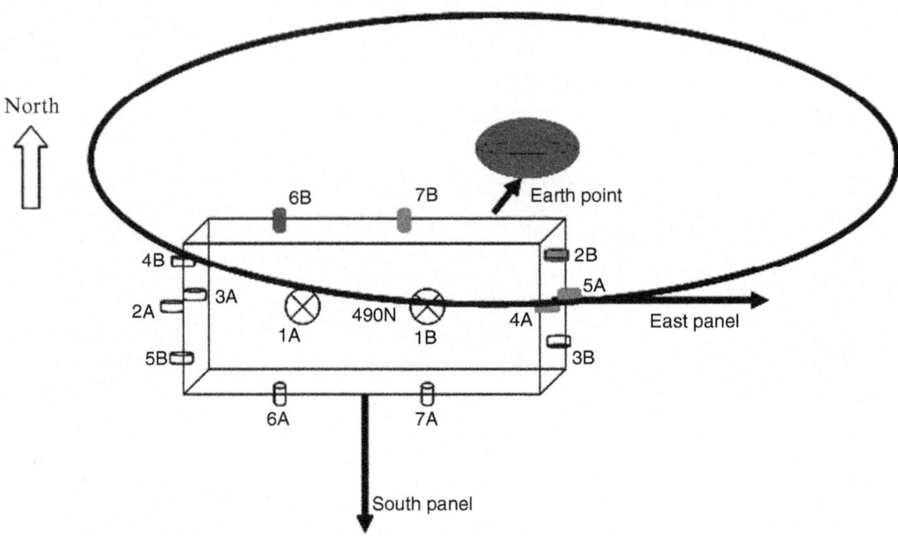

Fig. 6.11 Onboard thrust configuration

and 2B to 7B are adopted for orbit reacquisition and orbit maneuvers for routine station keepings. The A branch and B branch are backups for each other. The engine configured at the east panel provides the west force to lower the velocity of satellite. And the engine configured at the west panel provides the east force to increase the velocity of satellite. The above two engines are used to perform in-plane orbit maneuvers. The engine configured at the north panel and south panel provides the south force and north force, respectively, acting as the force of out-plane orbit maneuvers.

Chapter 7
Maintaining Geostationary Orbit

Abstract The principles, strategies, and algorithms of the station keeping of geostationary satellite are discussed. For north/south station keeping, the design of inclination confined ring and the calculation of inclination control target for single satellite and collocated satellites are discussed. The relation between control moment and local satellite time is also discussed and a specific case simulation of the control process is given. For east/west station keeping, the complicated situation of coupling control of the drift rate and eccentricity is analyzed, including the distribution strategy and the pulse execution algorithm of single pulse, bi-pulses, and tri-pulses.

7.1 Introduction

The relative motion of a single or multiple satellites collocated in the geostationary orbit must be confined to a limited range known as "dead band," which is defined by the longitude and latitude range. The one along the longitude direction is named as "longitude dead band" and the one along the latitude direction is named as "latitude dead band." For the orbit correction of geostationary satellite, the inclination must remain a small angle, so the definition of "dead band" must distinguish the definition of the Earth's equatorial plane. For the "dead band" of general precision, for example, $\pm 0.1°$ of south/north station keeping, the relative plane defined by the "dead band" can be the mean Earth's equatorial plane. But for a more precise "dead band," e.g., $\pm 0.05°$ or less than $\pm 0.05°$ of south/north station keeping, the relative plane defined by the "dead band" must be the true Earth equatorial plane. For the definition of the Earth's relative equatorial plane, please consult the third chapter in this book or relevant references. From the previous analysis, the "latitude dead band" is defined by the allowable maximum inclination and the "longitude dead band" is defined by the deviation from the nominal longitude. Therefore, for the

H. Li, *Geostationary Satellites Collocation*, DOI 10.1007/978-3-642-40799-4_7,

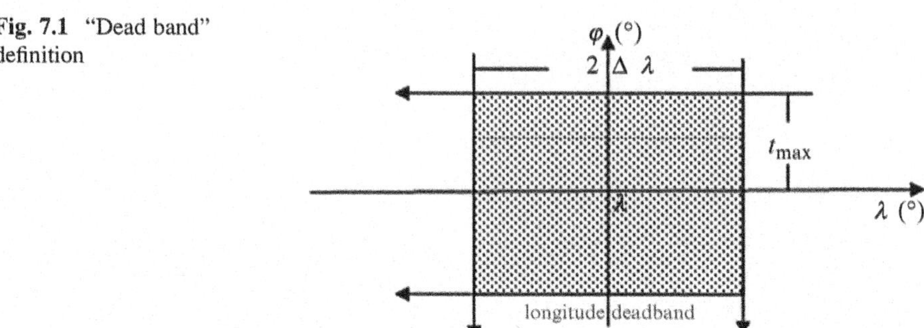

Fig. 7.1 "Dead band" definition

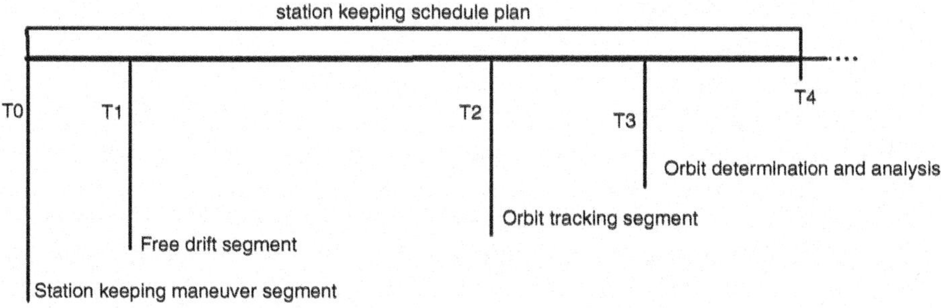

Fig. 7.2 A routine station keeping period

geostationary satellite in the nominal longitude λ_n, the definition of the station keeping "dead band" is illustrated in Fig. 7.1.

Therefore, the orbit correction of geostationary satellite is a series of operations used to correct the geostationary orbit by satellite propulsion system during the whole satellite lifecycle as illustrated in Fig. 7.2. The purpose of orbit correction is to keep the satellite perturbing freely within the "dead band" as much as possible. The larger the "dead band," the easier to restrict the satellite motion within the "dead band." On the contrary, the smaller the "dead band," the more difficult to keep the satellite within the "dead band." The operation of correcting orbit for one time and the relevant measuring event is called a station keeping period.

$T_0 - T_1$: station keeping maneuver segment – generally 1 day (single or double pulses) to 2 days (more than three pulses).

$T_1 - T_2$: free drift segment – perturbation time within the "dead band." Generally, the interval of east/west maneuver is 1–3 weeks and the interval of south/north maneuver is 1–3 months.

$T_2 - T_3$: orbit tracking segment – usually 1–2 days. To ensure the precision of orbit determination, the ground measuring time should be at least 1 day.

$T_3 - T_4$: orbit determination and analysis segment – usually 1–2 days. The major task is the precise orbit determination and the precision analysis of the current correction and calibration in order to plan and prepare for the next maneuver.

Whether the orbit correction is done by onboard autonomy control or ground-based control, the free variables need to be determined are:

- The size of orbit correction (How much?)
- The direction of orbit correction (Which direction?)
- The time of orbit correction (When? or Where?)

And the restrictions are:

Budget and distribution of the "dead band" The distribution of the "dead band" includes the budget of mean and oscillatory terms. Because the short-period terms (especially daily period terms) cannot be counteracted by the long-period orbit correction and the correctable parameters are those mean parameters with the secular perturbation motion, the distribution of forced motion and free drift should be reasonable and restrict the satellite within the "dead band" as much as possible.

Measurement condition and orbit determination precision Measurement conditions decide the time for orbit recovery, which means the period from the end of the current control to the time when the orbit determination precision satisfies the next control strategy and implementation. In general, the orbit recovery time of single-station tracking measurement is at least 1 day. So more than twice controls in a day should be taken very carefully. Moreover, the error of orbit determination directly reflects the uncertainty of keeping satellite within the "dead band." That's why the "dead band" distribution should consider the uncertainty of orbit determination. For high-precision satellite control, in order to ensure that the satellite remains in the "dead band" with 99 % probability, uncertainty of 3 σ margin of the error of orbit determination is required.

Characteristics of the satellite body The ratio of the solar radiation area to the satellite mass is mainly considered. According to Chap. 5, we know that the ratio decides the radius of eccentricity's free perturbation. Restriction of the eccentricity size is the main strategy of distributing mean longitude drift ring. But the increase or decrease of eccentricity causes more fuel consumption. Therefore, considering the characteristics of the satellite body and determining appropriate radius of the eccentricity is an important way of orbit correction strategy design.

Perturbation acceleration in the nominal longitude In the vicinity of the rest position, the perturbation of the mean longitude can be considered as the motion with a fixed constant acceleration. This kind of motion must draw a parabola curve; the mean longitude acceleration is a constant that is only related with the rest position; the mean longitude variation rate (mean longitude drift rate) changes linearly and the mean longitude variation changes in parabola. The acceleration of the mean longitude decides the opening direction and partial rate of the parabola within the "dead band."

Direction and magnitude of orbit inclination perturbation of the current year The size of orbit inclination perturbation of the current year decides the longest time of free perturbation of the mean orbit inclination in inclination drift ring. The direction of orbit inclination perturbation of the current year decides the average direction of inclination control of the current year.

Configuration and efficiency of thruster For the same velocity increment, the magnitude of force and efficiency of thruster decide the length of maneuver time.

Normally, 10(N) of rated thrust can be obtained by chemical thruster, but 1(N) of rated thrust may be obtained by electric thruster. Therefore, the magnitude of satellite thruster decides the length of maneuver time. For the satellite with thrusters at both south and north panels, it has two opportunities to obtain the same orbit correction target; but for the satellite with only one thruster at south or north panel, it has only one opportunity.

Requirement of fuel Requirement of fuel must be taken into consideration for orbit maneuver. In general consideration, the process of orbit correction should be optimized to use fuel on board. In the end of satellite lifecycle, the inclination drift ring should be appropriately amplified and the east/west drift ring control should be considered preferentially.

Restriction of attitude sensor The station keeping should be planned when the attitude sensor is not blocked or interfered to remain stable flying attitude during the control process.

Simplification and security of routine operation There are about 500 times of orbit corrections in the whole lifecycle of geostationary satellite, so the operation and labor costs must be taken into account. Generally, regular control with fixed frequency is adopted and meantime public holidays are avoided to guarantee engineers and experts with normal rests. Moreover, it's better to prepare a backup plan when the control plan is made so that it can be compensated by the backup control when the control plan is invalid or failure for some reasons.

The orbit correction is not just a mathematical multi-constrained optimization problem. There is no unique solution. Considering all the above constraints, there are numerous solutions that can keep the satellite within the "dead band." Although there are multiple solutions for the problem, the basic principles are the same [1–8].

Therefore, this chapter focuses on the numerous solutions of the station keeping for geostationary satellite and presents the practical calculations for scheduling maneuvers [9].

7.2 North/South Station Keeping Strategy

7.2.1 General Background

The purpose of north/south station keeping is to change the inclination by orbit normal thrust so that the north/south latitude remains in the "dead band." Normal thrust not only changes the size of inclination but also changes the right ascension of the ascending node. Review the definition of the inclination vector: Its size is orbit inclination and its direction is from the center of the Earth to the ascending node:

$$\mathbf{i} = \begin{pmatrix} i_x \\ i_y \end{pmatrix} = \begin{pmatrix} i\cos(\Omega) \\ i\sin(\Omega) \end{pmatrix} \tag{7.1}$$

From Chap. 4, we have known that the perturbation of inclination due to the solar and lunar attractions is related with the ecliptic longitude of the lunar ascending node. In a short time, it can be considered as a constant. So the perturbed motion of the inclination vector in a short time can be expressed as

$$i_x(t) = i_x(t_0) + \left(\frac{\mathrm{d}i_x}{\mathrm{d}t}\right)_D (t - t_0), i_y(t) = i_y(t_0) + \left(\frac{\mathrm{d}i_y}{\mathrm{d}t}\right)_D (t - t_0)$$

The direction and velocity of inclination perturbation are

$$\Omega_d = a\tan\left(\left(\frac{\mathrm{d}i_y}{\mathrm{d}t}\right)_D \Big/ \left(\frac{\mathrm{d}i_x}{\mathrm{d}t}\right)_D\right), \left(\frac{\delta i}{\delta t}\right)_D = \sqrt{\left(\frac{\mathrm{d}i_y}{\mathrm{d}t}\right)_D^2 + \left(\frac{\mathrm{d}i_x}{\mathrm{d}t}\right)_D^2}$$

From daily average perturbation rate of the long term of the inclination vector

$$\begin{cases} \left(\frac{\mathrm{d}i_x}{\mathrm{d}t}\right)_D = -3.5\sin\Omega_{sm} \times 10^{-4}(^\circ/\mathrm{day}) \\ \left(\frac{\mathrm{d}i_y}{\mathrm{d}t}\right)_D = (22.79 + 2.59\cos\Omega_{sm}) \times 10^{-4}(^\circ/\mathrm{day}) \end{cases} \tag{7.2}$$

From the above equation, the perturbation of inclination is of the following characteristics:

Perturbation rate of the inclination vector varies slightly every year The closer the mean longitude of the lunar orbit to the vernal equinox (e.g., in June 2006 the mean longitude of the lunar orbit nearly coincides with the vernal equinox), the greater the perturbation rate of the inclination vector. The maximum perturbation rate is about 0.95°/year. When the mean longitude of the lunar orbit is apart from 180° to the vernal equinox (e.g., in November 2015 the mean longitude of the lunar orbit is almost 180° apart from the vernal equinox), the perturbation rate of the inclination vector reaches its minimum of about 0.75°/year.

Perturbation direction of the inclination vector varies slightly every year The perturbation direction of the inclination vector is defined as the angle between the free perturbing direction and i_x, whose magnitude is between 81° and 99° and the average drift direction is about 90°, which means that the inclination vector always drifts along the positive direction of i_y.

Among all the period perturbations, the semiannual and semimonthly terms are the main long-period terms. The amplitude of the period terms is about 0.02°. Therefore, the main purpose of north/south station keeping is to use the normal velocity increment to overcome the perturbation due to the solar and lunar attractions, so that the inclination remains in a particular range and to keep the inclination remaining in the range as long as possible by the law of natural perturbation of inclination.

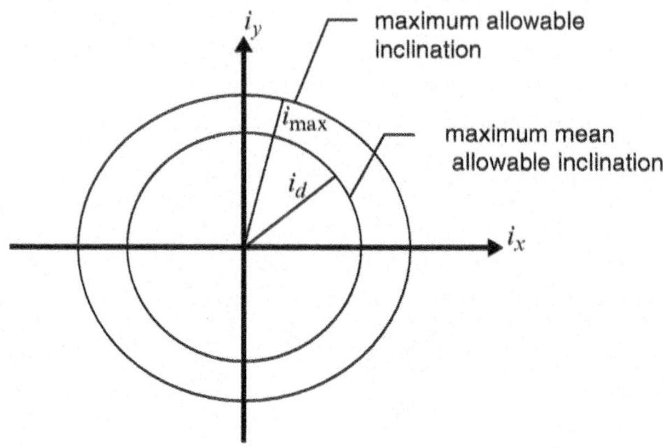

Fig. 7.3 Inclination margin strategy

7.2.2 *Inclination Dead Band Allocation*

Assuming the maximum allowable inclination is $i_{\max}$, the module of the inclination vector at any moment satisfies

$$|\mathbf{i}| \leq i_{\max}$$

To keep the inclination in the allowable range as much as possible, the inclination control strategy should take the following margins into account.

- $\Delta i_{\text{measure}}$: error of inclination measurement
- $\Delta i_{\text{control}}$: error of inclination control
- Δi_{random}: uncertainty error
- Δi_{leave}: preservation of long-period term

As illustrated in Fig. 7.3, the radius of the confined mean inclination must satisfy

$$i_d = \Delta i_{\max} - (\Delta i_{\text{measure}} + \Delta i_{\text{control}} + \Delta i_{\text{random}} + \Delta i_{\text{leave}}) \tag{7.3}$$

For example, if the maximum allowable inclination $i_{\max} = 0.1°$, the error of inclination measurement $\Delta i_{\text{measure}} = 0.005°$, the error of inclination control $\Delta i_{\text{control}} = 0.004°$, the uncertainty error $\Delta i_{\text{random}} = 0.004°$, and the preservation of long-period term $\Delta i_{\text{leave}} = 0.02$, then the radius of the confined inclination is

$$i_d = \Delta i_{\max} - (\Delta i_{\text{measure}} + \Delta i_{\text{control}} + \Delta i_{\text{random}} + \Delta i_{\text{leave}}) = 0.067° \tag{7.4}$$

The purpose of inclination control is to keep the post-control inclination vector drifts freely within the confined constraints of the mean inclination as long as possible. Therefore, the selection of inclination maneuver targets is related with the average perturbation direction of the mean inclination Ω_d and the distribution of constraints.

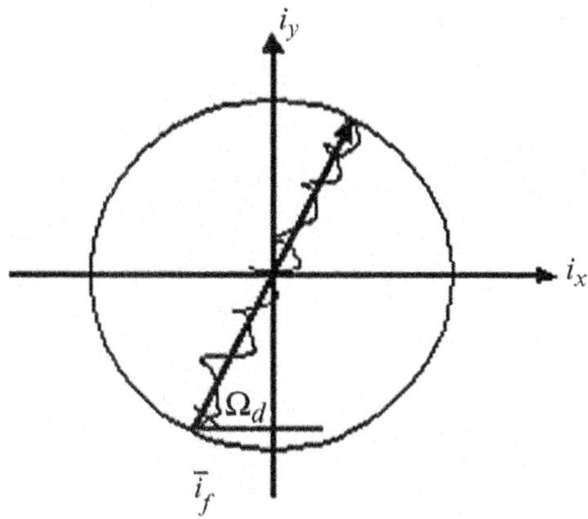

Fig. 7.4 Inclination maneuver target

7.2.3 *Inclination Maneuver Strategy*

Suppose the average perturbation direction of the mean inclination is Ω_d and the radius of the confined mean inclination is i_d as illustrated in Fig. 7.4. If the target of inclination control $\mathbf{i}_f(i_{fx}, i_{fy})$ is to make the perturbation of inclination pass through the coordinate origin, and the free perturbing distance is equivalent to the diameter of confined constraints $2i_d$ where the inclination reaches its maximum drift duration, then the target of inclination control $\mathbf{i}_f(i_{fx}, i_{fy})$ is

$$\mathbf{i}_f = \begin{pmatrix} i_{fx} \\ i_{fy} \end{pmatrix} = i_d \begin{pmatrix} \cos(\pi + \Omega_d) \\ \sin(\pi + \Omega_d) \end{pmatrix} \tag{7.5}$$

If the perturbation rate of the mean inclination of the year is $\left(\frac{\delta i}{\delta t}\right)$, then the free perturbation duration within the confined mean inclination is

$$T = 2 \cdot i_d / \left(\frac{\delta i}{\delta t}\right) \tag{7.6}$$

For example, if the average perturbation direction of the mean inclination $\Omega_d = 87°$, the radius of the confined inclination $i_d = 0.07°$, and the perturbation rate of the mean inclination of the year $\delta i / \delta t = 0.89°$, then the target of inclination control $\mathbf{i}_f(i_{fx}, i_{fy})$ and the free perturbation duration within the confined inclination are

$$\mathbf{i}_f\left(i_f = 0.067°, \Omega_f = 267°\right), \quad T = 58 \ \text{(days)}$$

7.2.4 *Maneuver Calculation*

For the inclination control target $\mathbf{i}^+$, if the current inclination vector $\mathbf{i}^-$, then according to Chap. 6, the equation of the inclination vector is

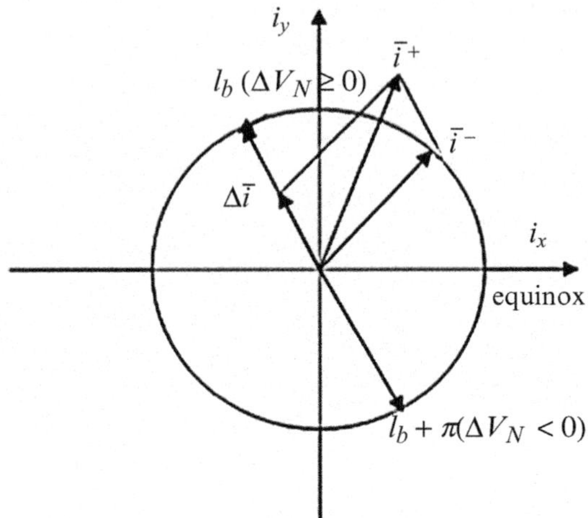

Fig. 7.5 Velocity increments calculation

$$\Delta \mathbf{i} = \begin{pmatrix} \Delta i_x \\ \Delta i_y \end{pmatrix} = \frac{\Delta V_N}{V_s} \begin{pmatrix} \cos(l_b) \\ \sin(l_b) \end{pmatrix}, \Delta V_N \geq 0, \tag{7.7}$$

$$\Delta \mathbf{i} = \begin{pmatrix} \Delta i_x \\ \Delta i_y \end{pmatrix} = \frac{|\Delta V_N|}{V_s} \begin{pmatrix} \cos(l_b + \pi) \\ \sin(l_b + \pi) \end{pmatrix}, \Delta V_N < 0, \tag{7.8}$$

In the equation, $\Delta \mathbf{i} = \mathbf{i}^+ - \mathbf{i}^-$.

If $\Delta V_N \geq 0$ is defined as northward control and $\Delta V_N < 0$ as southward control, then the formula above indicates that the northward control in the mean longitude l_b is the same as the southward control in the mean longitude $l_b + \pi$. With the same normal velocity increment, the size and the direction of inclination increment after control are the same as shown in Fig. 7.5.

The normal velocity increment changes the size and the direction of inclination. The changing size of inclination caused by the normal velocity increment is equal to $0°.0186 \cdot |\Delta V_N|$. The direction of inclination is related with pulsing time or the mean longitude. If and only if $l_b = \Omega^-$ and $l_b = \Omega^- + \pi$, which means that the normal velocity increment is scheduled at the ascending node and descending node, then the direction of the normal velocity increment and the original inclination vector are collinear and the direction of inclination doesn't change. The size of the inclination increment achieves its maximum.

If $l_b = \Omega^-$, i.e., at the ascending node,

$$i^+ = i^- + \left(\frac{\Delta V_N}{V_s}\right), \tag{7.9}$$

the northward normal velocity increment ($\Delta V_N \geq 0$) increases the inclination and the southward normal velocity increment ($\Delta V_N < 0$) decreases the inclination.

If $l_b = \Omega^- + \pi$, i.e., at the descending node,

$$i^{+}=i^{-}-\left(\frac{\Delta V_N}{V_s}\right), \tag{7.10}$$

the northward normal velocity increment ($\Delta V_N \geq 0$) decreases the inclination and the southward normal velocity increment ($\Delta V_N < 0$) increases the inclination.

If $\Delta i = i^{+} - i^{-} = 1°$ and $\Delta V_N = 53.66$(m/s), then to obtain 1(°) inclination increment, the satellite needs 53.66(m/s) normal velocity increment.

Similarly, if $\Delta V_N = 1$(m/s) and $\Delta i = 0.0186$(°), then 1(m/s) normal velocity increment only changes 0.0186(°) inclination. Therefore, the inclination correction consumes more fuel.

7.2.5 *Maneuver Planning*

If southward control is chosen, then by using the thruster on north panel, the velocity increment and the phase angle of impulse executing moment are

$$\delta v = \text{Deg 2 Rad}(|\Delta i|) \cdot V_s \tag{7.11}$$

$$l_{\text{pulse}} = \text{Rad 2 Deg}\left(\arctan\left(\Delta i_y / \Delta i_x\right)\right) \tag{7.12}$$

If northward control is chosen, then by using the thruster on south panel, the velocity increment and the phase angle of impulse executing moment are

$$\delta v = \text{Deg 2 Rad}(|\Delta i|) \cdot V_s \tag{7.13}$$

$$l_{\text{pulse}} = \text{Rad 2 Deg}\left(\arctan\left(\Delta i_y / \Delta i_x\right)\right) + 180° \tag{7.14}$$

In the expression,

$$V_s = 3074.7(\text{m/s}), \quad \mathbf{\Delta i} = \mathbf{i}^{+} - \mathbf{i}^{-} = \begin{pmatrix} \Delta i_x \\ \Delta i_y \end{pmatrix}$$

Deg 2 Rad: the unit changes from degree to radian.

Rad 2 Deg: the unit changes from radian to degree.

The relation between the impulse executing moment and the time the satellite passes through perigee t_p is

$$t_{\text{pulse}} = t_p + M_{\text{pulse}} \cdot \sqrt{\frac{a^3}{\mu}}$$

M_{pulse} is the mean anomaly of the orbit phase at impulse executing moment. According to Kepler equation,

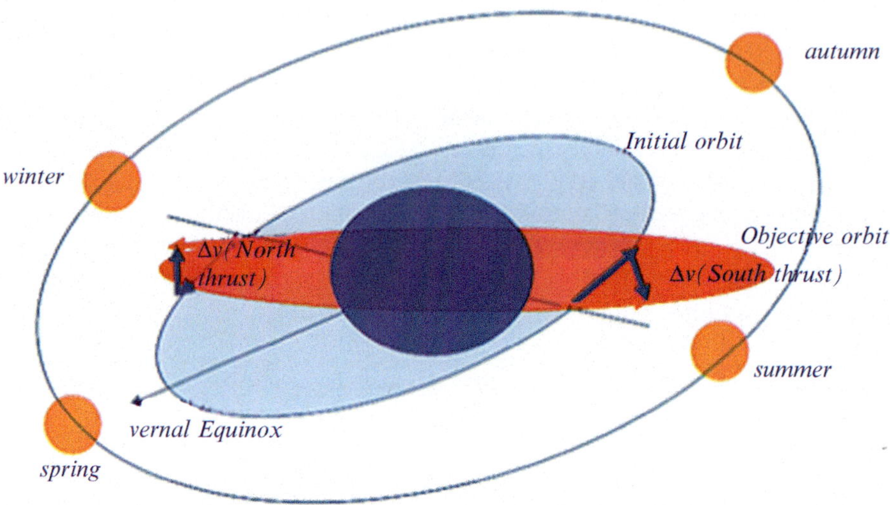

Fig. 7.6 Inclination maneuver planning

Table 7.1 Inclination control plan with season

Season	North thrust	South thrust
Spring	Morning	Evening
Summer	Midnight	Noon
Autumn	Evening	Morning
Winter	Noon	Midnight

$$M_{\text{pulse}} = E_{\text{pulse}} - e\sin E_{\text{pulse}}, \quad \tan\left(\frac{E_{\text{pulse}}}{2}\right) = \sqrt{\frac{1-e}{1+e}}\tan\left(\frac{l_{\text{pulse}}}{2}\right)$$

We notice that the orbit plane always rotates around vertical axis pointing to the vernal equinox for the three-body gravitational effect. The inclination corrections counterpart the rotation of orbit plane. Define the perturbation along i_y as positive. If the inclination is negative, i.e., the right ascension of the ascending node is 270°, in a free perturbing period, the inclination gradually decreases firstly. If the right ascension of the ascending node reaches 90°, the inclination gradually increases. The process moves in a cycle because of the inclination correction and forms a period process of correction-free perturbation correction again; Fig. 7.6 illustrates the relation between the orbit correction and local time and Table 7.1 lists the relation.

In spring, the Sun points to the vernal equinox; northward pulse lags behind the solar direction of 90° and southward pulse is 90° ahead of the solar direction. Therefore, for north/south station keeping in spring, northward control should be performed in the morning of local time and southward control should be performed in the evening of local time.

Table 7.2 Orbit element

a(m)	e	i(°)	Ω(°)	ω(°)	M(°)
42,163695.79	0.00003	0.02561	84.34127	87.12978	339.03124

In summer, the angle between the Sun and the vernal equinox is 90°; the angle between the Sun and northward pulse is 180° and southward pulse points to the Sun. Therefore, for north/south station keeping in summer, northward control should be performed in the midnight of local time and southward control should be performed at noon of local time.

In autumn, the angle between the Sun and the vernal equinox is 180°; northward pulse is 90° before the solar direction and southward pulse is 90° behind the solar direction. Therefore, for north/south station keeping in autumn, northward control should be performed in the evening of local time and southward control should be performed in the morning of local time.

In winter, the angle between the Sun and the vernal equinox is 270°; northward pulse points to the Sun and the angle between the Sun and southward pulse is 180°. Therefore, for north/south station keeping in winter, northward control should be performed at noon of local time and southward control should be performed in the midnight of local time.

The local time is determined by the time zone of the satellite's longitude; please refer to Chap. 3 for the relation between UTC and the local time.

7.2.6 *Case Study and Simulation*

This section gives a case study of the inclination control of the satellite residing in 99° east longitude, with the aid of the software interfaces which are developed by China Xi'an Satellite Control Center (XSCC).

Obtaining current orbit The information of the current orbit determination is orbit epoch 2008-11-13 00:00:0.000 (UTC) and Kepler orbit elements (the true equator and equinox of the epoch) (Table 7.2).

Prediction of inclination perturbation motion Apply accuracy model to predict the precise state of the satellite motion, and use harmonic analysis to decompose short-period terms. The mean perturbation of motion is illustrated in Fig. 7.7.

If the maximum allowable inclination $i_{\text{max}} = 0.1°$, considering the margin of inclination measurement $\Delta i_{\text{measure}} = 0.005°$, the margin of inclination control $\Delta i_{\text{control}} = 0.004°$, the uncertainty margin $\Delta i_{\text{random}} = 0.004°$, and the preservation of long-period term $\Delta i_{\text{leave}} = 0.01°$, then the radius of the confined mean inclination is given by

$$i_d = \Delta i_{\text{max}} - (\Delta i_{\text{measure}} + \Delta i_{\text{control}} + \Delta i_{\text{random}} + \Delta i_{\text{leave}}) = 0.077°$$

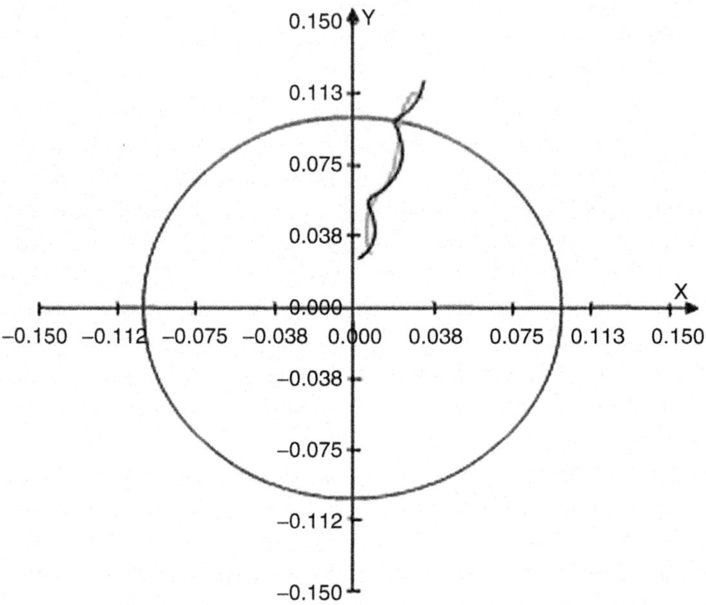

Fig. 7.7 Prediction of inclination perturbation motion

Therefore, 2008-11-28 is selected as the maneuver date, and the orbit elements at 0 o'clock (UTC) of that day is listed below.

menauver plan 2008 Y 11 M 28 D 12:00:00.000 (UTC)

J2000.0 Mean Equtor ECI			J2000.0 True Equator ECI		
a	42166797.525229	(m)	a	42166797.525229	(m)
e	6.8e-005		e	0.000068	
i	0.126153	(°)	i	0.076410	(°)
Ω	82.29453	(°)	Ω	76.011492	(°)
ω	333.658467	(°)	ω	339.941663	(°)
M	290.698114	(°)	M	290.698114	(°)

Software Interface 7.1: Maneuver planning main interface

Target of inclination correction The target of inclination correction is determined by the size and direction of the target inclination. The size of the target inclination for single satellite is keeping the inclination within the confined inclination to get the longest period of free perturbation. According to different requirements, the options for the direction of the target inclination include the following: If considering the long-period term, generally choose predictive drifting direction of next cycle; if only considering the average long-term perturbing direction, choose negative direction; if only considering the average annual perturbing direction, choose negative average annual perturbing direction; target can be chosen flexibly for other constraints such as keeping the sun sensor seeing the Sun during the correction process and time constraints of intersection after correction.

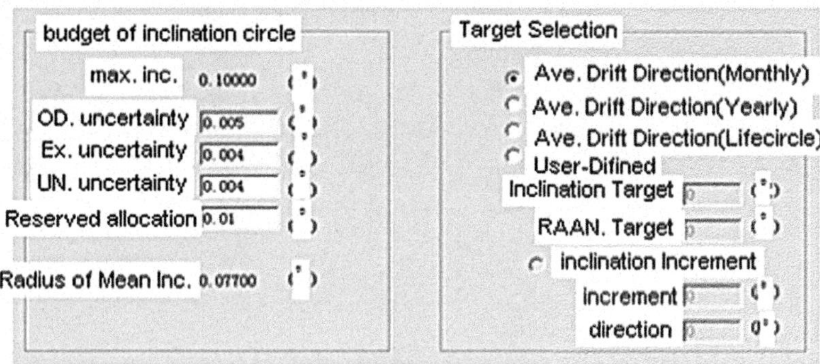

Software Interface 7.2: Maneuver strategy main interface

Selecting direction of correction According to previous discussion, there are two opportunities for correction in a mean sidereal day, corresponding to northward and southward control. Suppose the satellite has both south and north branch of thrusters. Branch A on south panel provides the northward velocity increment and branch B on north panel provides the southward velocity increment. Therefore, if branch A is used, then northward control is selected.

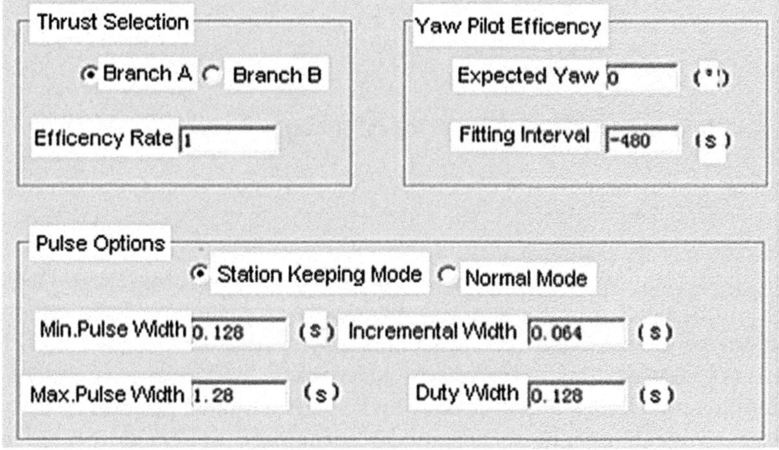

Software Interface 7.3: Maneuver calculation main interface

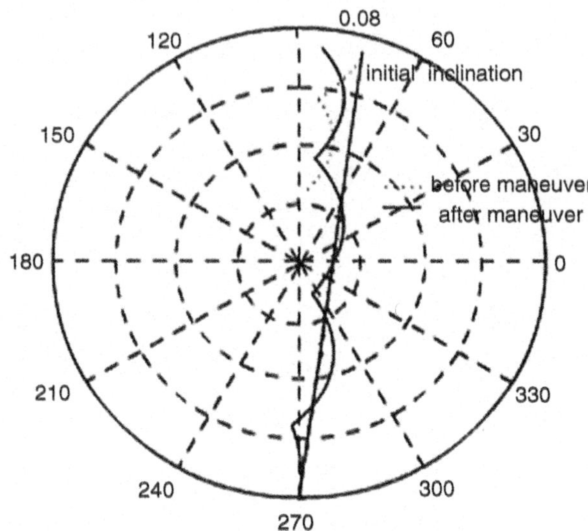

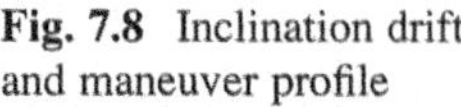
Fig. 7.8 Inclination drift and maneuver profile

The correction and simulation To achieve the target inclination, the normal velocity increment should be 7.348 m/s. Because of thruster coupling, it also generates a radial velocity increment of 0.441 m/s. Therefore, in the simulation and evaluation of control process, the coupling radial velocity increment should be taken into account. If the coupling radial velocity increment has an obvious effect on east/west drift rate, the normal control should be decomposed.

The control time is 2008-11-28, 06:21:57.594 (UTC). Because the satellite is positioned in 99° east longitude in UTC + 7, and the time difference from UTC is +7 h, the local control time is 2008-11-28, 13:21:59, which is noon of local time. The simulation and evaluation of inclination correction is illustrated in Fig. 7.8.

7.3 East/West Station Keeping Strategy

7.3.1 General Background

The longitude drift of geostationary satellite is composed of two parts. One is the longitude drift due to the Earth's non-spherical perturbation, and the other is the eccentricity perturbation due to the solar radiation pressure which causes daily period libration of longitude. The two effects are independent, and because of both of them, the satellite's true longitude will drift away from the nominal position.

By reviewing the definitions of station keeping elements, the drift rate vector is defined as the derivation of the mean longitude from the rest position λ_n; the longitude drift rate is defined as the eastward/westward drift rate due to the derivation between the semi-major axis and the geostationary orbit radius, and its unit is degree per day.

$$\mathbf{d} = \begin{pmatrix} \Delta\lambda \\ D \end{pmatrix} = \begin{pmatrix} \lambda - \lambda_n \\ D \end{pmatrix}$$

where

$$D = -\frac{3}{2}\cdot\frac{\Delta a}{a_s}\cdot 360.9860(^\circ/\mathrm{day})$$

Because of tri-axiality of the Earth, the satellite positioned above the equator is influenced by the perturbations of tesseral terms of J22, J21, J33, and J44. In the vicinity of the rest position, the perturbed force is considered to be a constant, so the acceleration of drift rate is a constant and the differential equation of the drift rate vector satisfies

$$\begin{cases} \dfrac{\mathrm{d}\lambda}{\mathrm{d}t} = D \\ \dfrac{\mathrm{d}D}{\mathrm{d}t} = \ddot{\lambda}_n \\ \lambda|_{t=t_0} = \lambda_0, D|_{t=t_0} = D_0 \end{cases} \tag{7.15}$$

The solution of the drift rate vector is

$$\Delta\lambda = \Delta\lambda_0 + D_0 t + \frac{1}{2}\ddot{\lambda}_n t^2, D = D_0 + \ddot{\lambda}_n t$$

The solution of the above equation draws a left parabola or a right parabola on the drift vector phase plane. If the mean longitude drift acceleration $\ddot{\lambda}_n < 0$, it draws a right parabola as shown in Fig. 7.9.

In the figure of the phase control of the drift rate vector, the opening of the parabola is on the left and the drift rate vector transforms its status from A to B to C in a free perturbing period. In the figure of mean longitude drift phase, the satellite has eastward (+) drift rate at the west border of the drift parabola.

$$D_{\mathrm{A}} = -\frac{1}{2}\ddot{\lambda}_n T \tag{7.16}$$

When the satellite reaches the mean longitude east border after (*T*/2) days, the mean longitude drift rate alters its direction and the satellite has westward (−) drift rate. After (*T*/2) the satellite reaches the mean longitude west border and has the maximum westward drift rate of

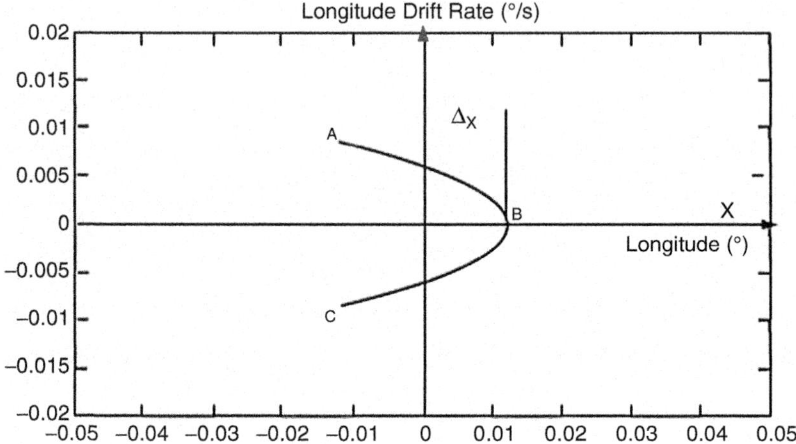

Fig. 7.9 Longitude drift cycle (negative acceleration)

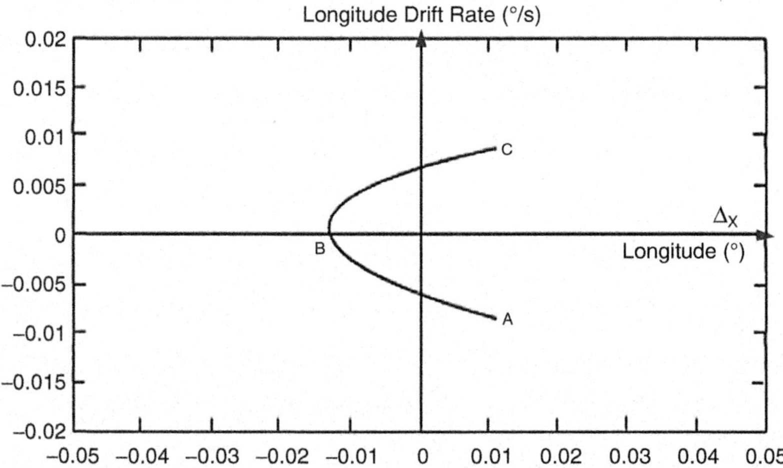

Fig. 7.10 Longitude drift cycle (positive acceleration)

$$D_{\mathrm{B}} = \frac{1}{2}\ddot{\lambda}_n T \tag{7.17}$$

When the satellite reaches C, by the tangential velocity increment, the orbit semi-major axis decreases and the status of the drift rate vector reaches A, completing an east/west control period.

If the drift acceleration $\ddot{\lambda}_n > 0$, it draws a right parabola as illustrated in Fig. 7.10; if the drift acceleration $\ddot{\lambda}_n = 0$, it draws a beeline.

In the figure of the phase control of the drift rate vector, the opening of the parabola is on the right and the drift rate vector transforms its status from A to B to C in a free perturbing period. In the figure of mean longitude drift phase, the satellite has westward (−) drift rate at the east border of the drift parabola.

$$D_{\mathrm{A}} = -\frac{1}{2}\ddot{\lambda}_n T \tag{7.18}$$

When the satellite reaches the mean longitude west border after ($T/2$) days, the mean longitude drift rate alters its direction and the satellite has eastward (+) drift rate. After ($T/2$) the satellite reaches the mean longitude east border and has the maximum eastward drift rate of

$$D_{\mathrm{B}} = \frac{1}{2}\ddot{\lambda}_n T \tag{7.19}$$

When the satellite reaches C, by the tangential velocity increment, the orbit semi-major axis increases and the status of the drift rate vector reaches A, completing an east/west control period.

The size of the eccentricity vector is the orbit eccentricity and its direction points from the Earth's center to orbit perigee.

$$\mathbf{e} = \begin{pmatrix} e_x \\ e_y \end{pmatrix} = \begin{pmatrix} e\cos(\Omega+\omega) \\ e\sin(\Omega+\omega) \end{pmatrix} \tag{7.20}$$

From Chap. 4, the secular perturbation equation of the mean eccentricity due to the solar radiation pressure is

$$\begin{cases} \dfrac{\mathrm{d}e_x}{\mathrm{d}t} = -\dfrac{3}{2}\dfrac{1}{na}C_R\left(\dfrac{S}{m}\right)P_0\cos i_s\sin\lambda_s \\ \dfrac{\mathrm{d}e_y}{\mathrm{d}t} = \dfrac{3}{2}\dfrac{1}{na}C_R\left(\dfrac{S}{m}\right)P_0\cos\lambda_s \end{cases} \tag{7.21}$$

Suppose if we assign the initial eccentricity vector $\mathbf{e_0} = (e_x(t_0), e_y(t_0))^T$, and perform integral to the above equation; then the eccentricity vector at any moment $\mathbf{e} = (e_x(t), e_y(t))^T$ satisfies

$$\begin{cases} e_x(t) = e_x(t_0) + R_e\cos i_s(\cos\lambda(t) - \cos\lambda(t_0)) \\ e_y(t) = e_y(t_0) + R_e(\sin\lambda(t) - \sin\lambda(t_0)) \end{cases} \tag{7.22}$$

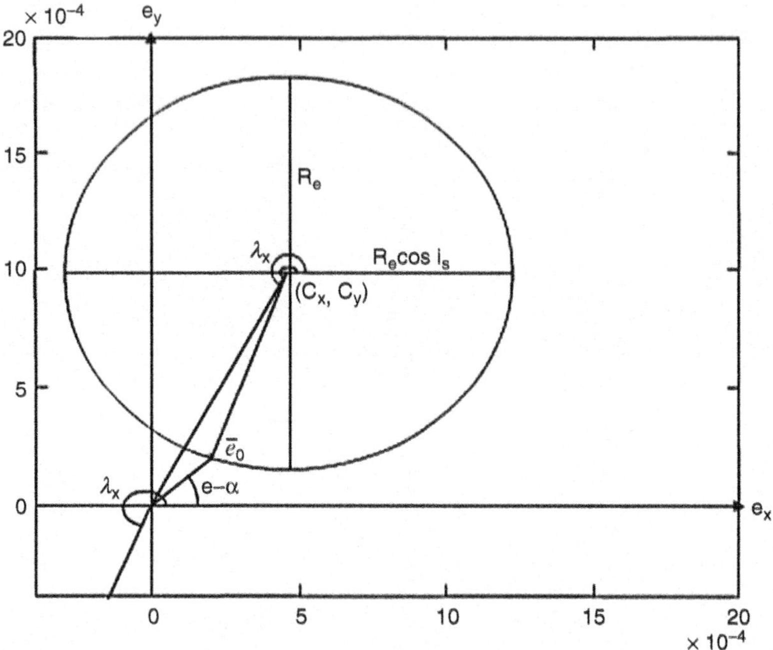

Fig. 7.11 Eccentricity free drift motion

In the expression,

$$R_e = \frac{3}{2}\frac{1}{n_e a} C_R \left(\frac{S}{m}\right) P_0 \cdot \frac{1}{n_s} \approx 0.011 \cdot C_R \left(\frac{S}{m}\right) \tag{7.23}$$

The area unit is meter square (m^2) and the quality unit is kilogram (kg). If the ratio of area to quality is 0.05 and the coefficient of solar radiation pressure is 1.5, then the free perturbation radius of eccentricity is about $R_e = 8.36 \times 10^{-4}$.

Suppose

$$C_x = e_x(t_0) - R_e \cos i_s \cos \lambda(t_0), C_y = e_y(t_0) - R_e \sin \lambda(t_0)$$

The motion equation of the eccentricity vector is transformed into

$$\left(\frac{e_x(t) - C_x}{R_e \cos i_s}\right)^2 + \left(\frac{e_y(t) - C_x}{R_e}\right)^2 = 1 \tag{7.24}$$

Therefore, the eccentricity motion due to the solar radiation pressure is an elliptical motion along the solar mean longitude as Fig. 7.11 illustrates. The center of ellipse is related to the current eccentricity vector and the solar mean longitude.

The semi-minor axis along the vernal equinox direction is $R_e \cos i_s$ and the semi-major axis is vertical to the vernal equinox and is R_e.

The characteristics of the perturbations of the drift rate and the eccentricity vector are:

Longitude drift vector The geostationary satellite positioned in the nominal longitude is influenced by extra tangential gravitational acceleration because of the elliptic equator of the Earth. The acceleration causes linear change of the semi-major axis and further causes inconsistency between the orbit plane's motion and the Earth's rotation angular velocity, and finally the satellite deviates from its rest position. The mean longitude changes in parabola and the acceleration of the mean longitude drift rate is related to the satellite's longitude of its rest position.

Eccentricity vector The motion of eccentricity due to the solar radiation pressure is an elliptical motion along the solar mean longitude. The center of ellipse is related to the current eccentricity vector and the solar mean longitude. The semi-minor axis is along the vernal equinox direction and the semi-major axis is vertical to the vernal equinox.

The goal of east/west control is by using the tangential thrust to change the orbit and limit the longitude drift rate to overcome the mean longitude drift rate due to the Earth's non-spherical perturbation and limit the size of orbit eccentricity to overcome the daily libration of satellite's longitude due to the solar radiation pressure. In order to keep the satellite's longitude remaining within the "dead band," compared with north/south maneuver, east/west maneuver consumes less fuel but its frequency is higher. The reason why east/west maneuver is more complicated than north/south maneuver is:

1. The tangential velocity increment cannot change the satellite's longitude directly but only changes the longitude drift rate.
2. The tangential velocity increment changes the longitude drift rate, and at the same time, the daily libration of satellite's longitude changes because of the coupling effect of eccentricity.
3. The longitude drift rate is highly sensitive to the tangential velocity increment. The coupling tangential velocity increment of attitude control and north/south maneuver also changes the longitude drift rate.

7.3.2 Longitude Dead Band Allocation

Considering the precision of satellite's position, the error of position determination, the error of correction, the coupling error of attitude control and north/south control, and the perturbation and other factors, east/west control should keep the longest control period, reducing control times as much as possible and keeping the satellite remaining within the allowable precise region. The drift parabola has different definitions according to different control strategies, which is mainly composed of fixed semi-width and fixed period.

Fixed mean longitude drift circle strategy If the designed semi-width of the east/west longitude is $\pm\Delta\lambda_{\max}$, to keep the longitude within the allowable range as much as possible, the longitude control strategy should consider the following margins:

- $\Delta\lambda_{\text{Measure}}(3\sigma)$: the error of tracking and orbit determination
- $\Delta\lambda_{\text{perform}}$: the error of onboard executing
- $\Delta\lambda_{\text{Daily From Ecc}}$: the longitude daily libration due to the nonzero eccentricity
- $\Delta\lambda_{\text{Sun and Moon}}$: the long-period libration due to the lunisolar attraction

Then the semi-width of the mean longitude drift parabola is

$$\Delta\bar{\lambda} = \Delta\lambda_{\max} - \Delta\lambda_{\text{Sun and Moon}} - \Delta\lambda_{\text{Measure}} - \Delta\lambda_{\text{perform}} - \Delta\lambda_{\text{Daily From Ecc}} \tag{7.25}$$

Suppose the designed semi-width of the east/west longitude is $\Delta\lambda_{\text{Max}} = 0.05°$, the error of tracking and orbit determination is $\Delta\lambda_{\text{Measure}}(3\sigma) = 0.003°$, the long-period libration due to the lunisolar attraction is $\Delta\lambda_{\text{Sun and Moon}} = 0.008°$, the error of correction is $\Delta\lambda_{\text{perform}} = 0.007°$ (error from RCS execution), and the radius of the confined eccentricity is $e_k = 2.0 \times 10^{-4}$ which induces the longitude daily libration of about $\Delta\lambda_{\text{Daily From Ecc}} = \text{rad 2 deg}(2 \cdot e_k) = 0.02°$; then the semi-width of the mean longitude drift parabola is

$$\begin{aligned}\Delta\bar{\lambda} &= \Delta\lambda_{\max} - \Delta\lambda_{\text{Sun and Moon}} - \Delta\lambda_{\text{Measure}} - \Delta\lambda_{\text{perform}} - \Delta\lambda_{\text{Daily From Ecc}} \\ &= 0.05° - 0.003° - 0.008° - 0.007° - 0.02° = 0.01°\end{aligned} \tag{7.26}$$

The longitude daily libration due to the nonzero eccentricity is the main factor that causes the satellite to move out of the confined region. Therefore, to keep the satellite remaining within a small confined region, the restriction of eccentricity in a reasonable limitation is the key to design the east/west control strategy.

If the acceleration of the mean longitude is $\ddot{\lambda}_n$ (refer to Table 4.5), the semi-width of the mean longitude drift parabola is $\Delta\bar{\lambda}$, and then the period of east/west control is

$$T = 4\left(\sqrt{\frac{\Delta\bar{\lambda}}{|\ddot{\lambda}_n|}}\right) \tag{7.27}$$

Fixed duration of east/west control strategy If the fixed duration is T and the acceleration of the mean longitude is $\ddot{\lambda}_n$, then the semi-width of the mean longitude drift parabola is

$$\Delta\bar{\lambda} = \left|\frac{T^2}{16}\ddot{\lambda}_n\right| \tag{7.28}$$

If the designed semi-width of the east/west longitude is $\pm\Delta\lambda_{\max}$, to keep the longitude within the allowable range as much as possible, the longitude control strategy should consider the following margins:

- $\Delta\lambda_{\text{Measure}}(3\sigma)$: the error of tracking and orbit determination
- $\Delta\lambda_{\text{perform}}$: the error of onboard executing
- $\Delta\lambda_{\text{Daily From Ecc}}$: the longitude daily libration due to the nonzero eccentricity
- $\Delta\lambda_{\text{Sun and Moon}}$: the long-period libration due to the lunisolar attraction

Because the semi-width of the mean longitude is fixed, then the daily libration $\Delta\lambda_{\text{Daily From Ecc}}$ must satisfy

$$\Delta\lambda_{\text{Daily From Ecc}} \leq \Delta\lambda_{\max} - \Delta\lambda_{\text{Sun and Moon}} - \Delta\lambda_{\text{Measure}} - \Delta\lambda_{\text{perform}} - \Delta\bar{\lambda}$$

and the eccentricity should be maneuvered to satisfy the condition below.

$$e \leq e_c = \frac{1}{2}\text{Rad}\left(\Delta\lambda_{\text{Daily From Ecc}}\right)$$

Suppose the acceleration of the mean longitude is $\ddot{\lambda}_n = -0.0015\left(^\circ/D^2\right)$, the designed semi-width of the east/west longitude is $\Delta\lambda_{\text{Max}} = 0.05^\circ$, the error of tracking and orbit determination is $\Delta\lambda_{\text{Measure}}(3\sigma) = 0.003^\circ$, the long-period libration due to the lunisolar attraction is $\Delta\lambda_{\text{Sun and Moon}} = 0.008^\circ$, the error of correction is $\Delta\lambda_{\text{perform}} = 0.007^\circ$ (error from RCS execution), and the period is fixed to $T = 10$ days; then the semi-width of the mean longitude drift parabola is

$$\Delta\bar{\lambda} = \left|\frac{T^2}{16}\ddot{\lambda}_n\right| = 0.0094^\circ$$

In order to ensure the osculating longitude within the dead band, the eccentricity should be restricted less than the one calculated by the formula below.

$$e \leq e_c = \frac{1}{2}\text{Rad}\left(\Delta\lambda_{\text{Daily From Ecc}}\right) = 1.97 \times 10^{-4}$$

7.3.3 Longitude Maneuver Strategy

The drift parabola defines the relation of $(\Delta\lambda, D)$. On condition that the difference between the mean longitude and the position longitude satisfies the semi-width limitation of the drift parabola, this relation determines the drift rate control target. To achieve the best effect of the current drift rate control, that is, the longest free drift time and the minimum velocity increment, the choice of the control target with the drift rate vector in different quadrants is as follows:

Suppose, in the day of control, the mean longitude and mean drift rate are $\left(\Delta\bar{\lambda}_0, \bar{D}_0\right)$. The drift parabola is determined by the drift acceleration $\ddot{\lambda}_n$ and the semi-width of the drift parabola $\Delta\bar{\lambda}$ or determined by the drift acceleration $\ddot{\lambda}_n$ and the east/west control period T. The control strategy is summarized by the algorithm listed below.

If $\left(\ddot{\lambda}_n \leq 0\right)$, then

Quadrant I: $\Delta\bar{\lambda}_0 \cdot \bar{D}_0 > 0, \bar{D}_0 > 0$

If $\Delta\bar{\lambda}_0 > \Delta\bar{\lambda}$, then the drift rate control target is

$$\left(\text{CTLDRIFT}, \Delta\bar{\lambda}_T, D_T\right) = \left(1, \Delta\bar{\lambda}_0, 0\right)$$

If $\Delta\bar{\lambda}_0 \leq \Delta\bar{\lambda}$, then the drift rate control target is

$$\left(\text{CTLDRIFT}, \Delta\bar{\lambda}_T, D_T\right) = \left(1, \Delta\bar{\lambda}_0, -\sqrt{D_A^2 - 2\ddot{\lambda}(\Delta\bar{\lambda} - \Delta\bar{\lambda}_0)}\right)$$

Quadrant II: $\Delta\bar{\lambda}_0 \cdot \bar{D}_0 \leq 0, \bar{D}_0 > 0$

The drift rate control target is

$$\left(\text{CTLDRIFT}, \Delta\bar{\lambda}_T, D_T\right) = \left(0, \Delta\bar{\lambda}_0, 0.0\right)$$

Quadrant III: $\Delta\bar{\lambda}_0 \cdot \bar{D}_0 > 0, \bar{D}_0 < 0$

The drift rate control target is

$$\left(\text{CTLDRIFT}, \Delta\bar{\lambda}_T, D_T\right) = \left(0, \Delta\bar{\lambda}_0, D_x\right),$$

and

$$D_x = \sqrt{\bar{D}_A^2 - 2\ddot{\bar{\lambda}}_n\left(\Delta\lambda_A - \Delta\bar{\lambda}_0\right)}$$

Quadrant IV: $\Delta\bar{\lambda}_0 \cdot \bar{D}_0 \leq 0, \bar{D}_0 \leq 0$

The drift rate control target is

$$\left(\text{CTLDRIFT}, \Delta\bar{\lambda}_T, D_T\right) = \left(0, \Delta\bar{\lambda}_0, 0.0\right)$$

If $\left(\ddot{\lambda}_n > 0\right)$, then

Quadrant I: $\Delta\bar{\lambda}_0 \cdot \bar{D}_0 > 0, \bar{D}_0 > 0$

If $\Delta\bar{\lambda}_0 > \Delta\bar{\lambda}$, then the drift rate control target is

$$\left(\text{CTLDRIFT}, \Delta\bar{\lambda}_T, D_T\right) = \left(1, \Delta\bar{\lambda}_0, -\sqrt{D_A^2 - 2\ddot{\lambda}(\Delta\bar{\lambda} - \Delta\bar{\lambda}_0)}\right)$$

Quadrant II: $\Delta\bar{\lambda}_0 \cdot \overline{D}_0 \leq 0, \overline{D}_0 > 0$

The drift rate control target is

$$\left(\text{CTLDRIFT}, \Delta\bar{\lambda}_T, D_T\right) = \left(0, \Delta\bar{\lambda}_0, 0.0\right)$$

Quadrant III: $\Delta\bar{\lambda}_0 \cdot \overline{D}_0 > 0, \overline{D}_0 < 0$

The drift rate control target is

$$\left(\text{CTLDRIFT}, \Delta\bar{\lambda}_T, D_T\right) = \left(0, \Delta\bar{\lambda}_0, D_x\right),$$

and

$$D_x = \sqrt{\overline{D}_A^2 - 2\ddot{\bar{\lambda}}_n\left(\Delta\lambda_A - \Delta\bar{\lambda}_0\right)}$$

Quadrant IV: $\Delta\bar{\lambda}_0 \cdot \overline{D}_0 \leq 0, \overline{D}_0 \leq 0$

The drift rate control target is

$$\left(\text{CTLDRIFT}, \Delta\bar{\lambda}_T, D_T\right) = \left(0, \Delta\bar{\lambda}_0, 0.0\right)$$

In the expression,

$$\text{CTLDRIFT} = \begin{cases} 1, \text{control} \\ 0, \text{no control} \end{cases}$$

CTLDRIFT as variable means whether the drift rate control should be performed for the current orbit or not.

7.3.4 Eccentricity Maneuver Strategy

The long-period perturbation of eccentricity due to the solar radiation pressure is of the following characteristics: The perturbation direction of eccentricity is 90° ahead of the solar sight; no matter what the initial directions of eccentricity, the eccentricity draws an approximate round arc with the solar motion. The radius is related with the ratio of area to mass and the coefficient of solar radiation reflection C_R, which is named as the radius of the eccentricity perturbation.

$$R_e = \frac{3}{2}\frac{1}{n_e a} C_R\left(\frac{S}{m}\right) P_0 \cdot \frac{1}{n_s} \approx 0.011 \cdot C_R\left(\frac{S}{m}\right) \tag{7.29}$$

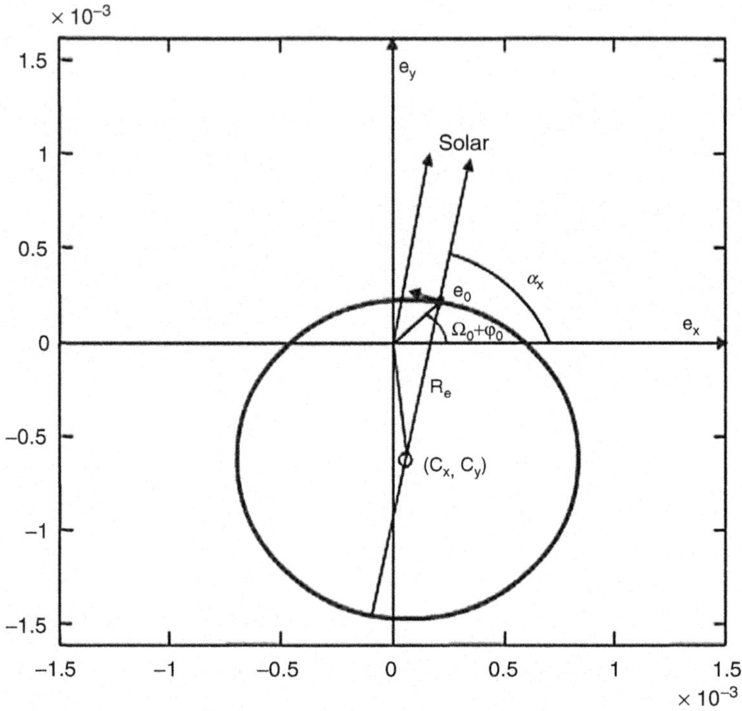

Fig. 7.12 Eccentricity perturbation drift circle

Therefore, suppose the satellite initial eccentricity is $\vec{e}_0(e_0, \Omega_0 + \omega_0)$; the initial solar longitude is α_{s0}. Ignoring the effect from the angle between the ecliptic plane and the equator plane, the center of the mean eccentricity perturbation circle (C_x, C_y) is

$$\begin{cases} C_x = e_0 \cos(\Omega_0 + \omega_0) - R_e \cos\alpha_{s0} \\ C_y = e_0 \sin(\Omega_0 + \omega_0) - R_e \sin\alpha_{s0} \end{cases} \tag{7.30}$$

The locus equation of the round arc with the radius $R_e \approx 0.011 \cdot C_R\left(\frac{S}{m}\right)$, as shown in Fig. 7.12, is given by

$$e_x = C_x + R_e \cos\alpha_s, e_y = C_y + R_e \sin\alpha_s$$

In the equation, α_s is the solar mean longitude. After half a year from the initial time, it reaches the maximum and points to

$$e_{x\max} = e_0 \cos(\Omega_0 + \omega_0) + 2R_e \cos(\pi + \alpha_{s0})$$
$$e_{y\max} = e_0 \sin(\Omega_0 + \omega_0) + 2R_e \sin(\pi + \alpha_{s0})$$

The maximum value of eccentricity is

$$e_{max} = \sqrt{e_0^2 + 4R_e^2 - 4R_e e_0 \cos(\Omega_0 + \omega_0 - \alpha_{s0})} \tag{7.31}$$

If the initial eccentricity points to the Sun, and the apogee points to the solar sight

$$\Omega_0 + \omega_0 = \alpha_{s0}$$

The maximum value of eccentricity is

$$e_{max} = |e_0 - 2R_e|$$

If the initial apogee points to the solar sight, then the maximum eccentricity reaches the smallest value.

Especially, if the initial control of eccentricity goes to the eccentricity perturbation circle with the origin as the center and points to solar sight, the maximum eccentricity is

$$e_{max} = |e_0 - 2R_e| = |R_e - 2R_e| = R_e$$

7.3.4.1 Solar Pointing Target Strategy

Among the east/west drift distributing indicators, the trace of the maximum allowable value of eccentricity along the solar sight is called confined circle of eccentricity or eccentricity control circle. The radius of the circle is the maximum east/west drift distributing eccentricity. If the radius of the perturbation circle of the mean eccentricity is close to the radius of control circle, the initial control of eccentricity goes to the eccentricity perturbation circle with the origin as the center and points to solar sight. Suppose the solar mean longitude at control time is α_{s0}, and then the target of eccentricity control at that time is

$$\mathbf{e_f} = \begin{pmatrix} e_x \\ e_y \end{pmatrix} = R_e \cdot \begin{pmatrix} \cos\alpha_{s0} \\ \sin\alpha_{s0} \end{pmatrix}$$

As shown in Fig. 7.13, when the Sun moves to the vernal equinox, the mean solar longitude $\alpha_{s0} = 0$, and the target goal of eccentricity control is as follows: The orbit perigee points to the vernal equinox and the orbit eccentricity equals the radius of the perturbation circle of eccentricity.

Suppose there is a satellite with the solar panel area of 36.4 (m^2) and the quality of 2,000 kg. Considering only the solar panel as the solar radiation area, the coefficient of solar radiation reflection is 1.5, and then the radius of the eccentricity free perturbing circle is

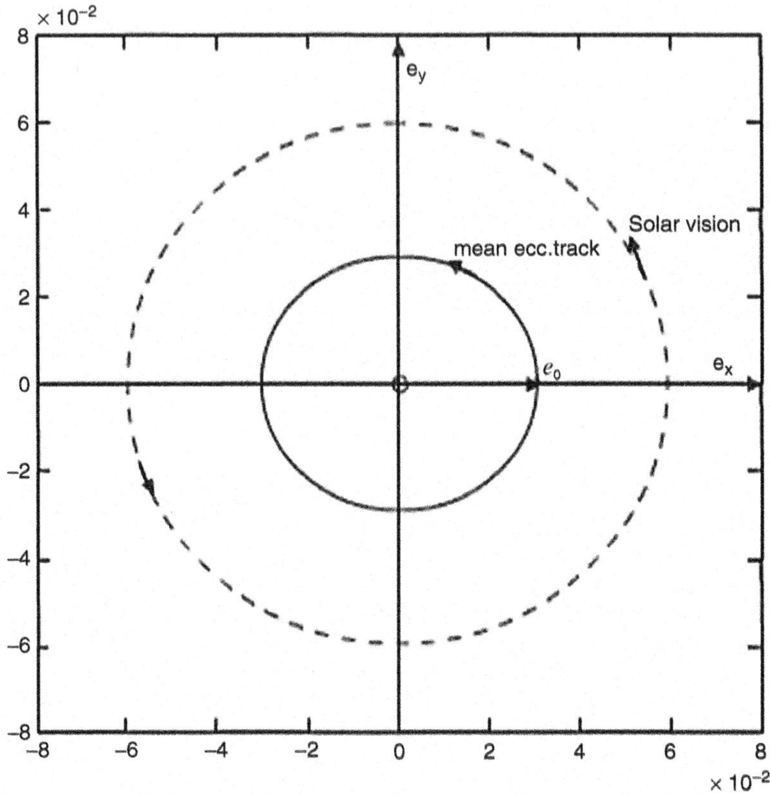

Fig. 7.13 Solar point eccentricity target

$$R_e \approx 0.011.C_R\left(\frac{S}{m}\right) = 3.0 \times 10^{-4}$$

If the design of east/west drift parabola allows that the radius of the eccentricity control circle is close to the radius of the perturbation circle, then suppose the eccentricity control is performed on 2007-06-10, and then the eccentricity target is to make the Sun point to the control target. The mean solar longitude is 77.8° and the target orbit is

At epoch 2007-6-10/0:0:0.000
$a = 42165694.424$ m
$e = 0.000299868$
$i = 0.001$
$\Omega = 359.999696°$
$\omega = 77.000295$
$M = 0.000008$

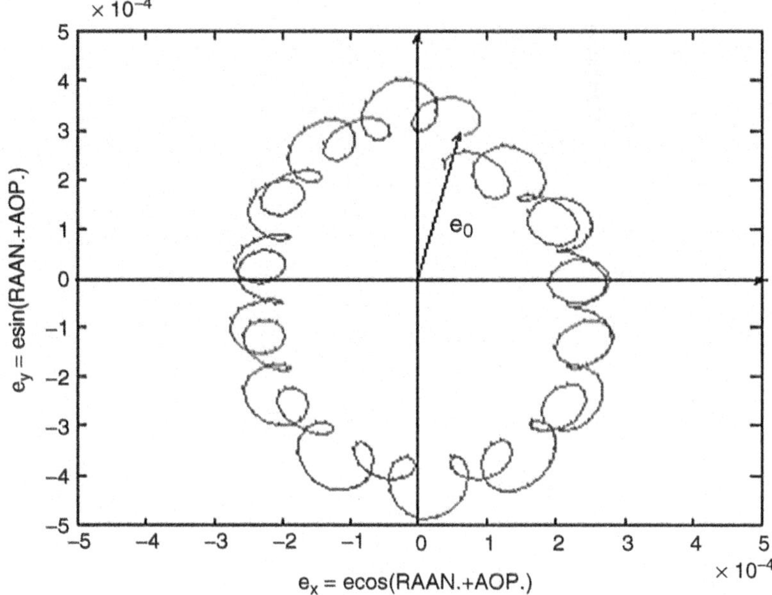

Fig. 7.14 Eccentricity free drift circle simulation

The evolution of eccentricity after control in a year is shown in Fig. 7.14. From the initial position of eccentricity, following the solar sight and along the perturbation circle, the size of eccentricity almost does not change in a year.

7.3.4.2 Solar Lagged Target Strategy

If the radius of the perturbation circle of the mean eccentricity is larger than the radius of the control circle, then to confine the eccentricity within the control circle, generally the control strategy of fixed period or the control strategy of eccentricity passing through original node is adopted. The eccentricity is confined to perturb freely within the control circle for a certain time. When the eccentricity moves out of the control circle, control operations are performed. As illustrated in Fig. 7.15, the initial eccentricity points to A and A is located at the confined circle. The direction lags behind the mean solar longitude β. The eccentricity moves into the confined circle from A and after a period of T the eccentricity moves to C. At that time, the eccentricity is ahead of the solar longitude β and passes through the confined circle. The strategy leaves the eccentricity target lagging behind the solar vision to make sure the eccentricity trespasses into the eccentricity confined circle.

Suppose the radius of the eccentricity control circle is e_c, the radius of the perturbation circle is $R_e > e_c$, the eccentricity control period is T, and the mean

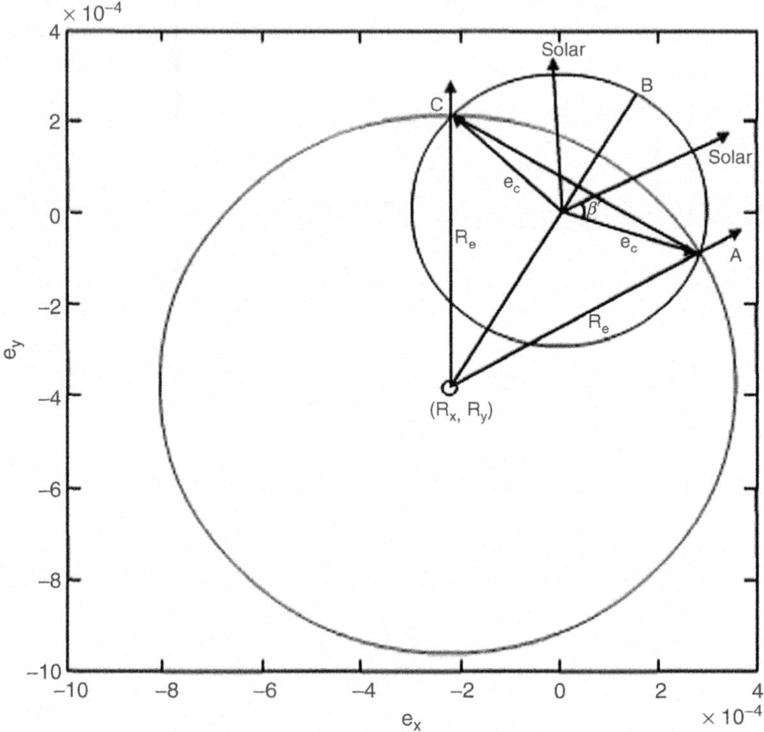

Fig. 7.15 Solar lagged target strategy

solar longitude at the control time is α_s. Then, in a free perturbation period T, the chord of eccentricity in the confined circle is

$$\overline{AC} = 2R_e \sin\left(\frac{Tn_s}{2}\right) \tag{7.32}$$

The solar lagging angle satisfies

$$\sin\left(\beta + \frac{T}{2}n_s\right) = \frac{R_e}{e_c}\sin\left(\frac{T}{2}n_s\right)$$

Then,

$$\beta = a\sin\left(\frac{R_e}{e_c}\sin\left(\frac{T}{2}n_s\right)\right) - \frac{T}{2}n_s \tag{7.33}$$

The target of eccentricity control at that moment is

$$\mathbf{e_A} = \begin{pmatrix} e_x \\ e_y \end{pmatrix} = e_c \cdot \begin{pmatrix} \cos(\alpha_s - \beta) \\ \sin(\alpha_s - \beta) \end{pmatrix} \tag{7.34}$$

The center of the free perturbation circle of eccentricity is

$$\begin{cases} R_x = \left(R_e \cos\left(\frac{T}{2}n_s\right) - e_c \cos\left(\frac{T}{2}n_s + \beta\right)\right) \cdot \cos\left(\alpha_s + \pi + \frac{T}{2}n_s\right) \\ R_y = \left(R_e \cos\left(\frac{T}{2}n_s\right) - e_c \cos\left(\frac{T}{2}n_s + \beta\right)\right) \cdot \sin\left(\alpha_s + \pi + \frac{T}{2}n_s\right) \end{cases} \tag{7.35}$$

Here, $n_s = 0.9856$(°/day) is the mean solar angular velocity.

After T days, the eccentricity freely perturbs to C. Now the eccentricity is ahead of the solar mean longitude and the eccentricity control must be performed. The amount of eccentricity control is

$$\Delta e = 2e_c \sin\beta \tag{7.36}$$

The amount of eccentricity control in a year is

$$\Delta e_T = \left[\frac{365.24}{T}\right] \cdot 2e_c \sin\beta \tag{7.37}$$

If the radius of the eccentricity control circle is $e_c = 3.0 \times 10^{-4}$, the radius of the perturbation circle is $R_e = 5.0 \times 10^{-4}$, the eccentricity control period is $T = 60$, and the mean solar longitude at the control time is $\alpha_s = 60°$, then in a free perturbation period T, the chord of eccentricity in the confined circle is

$$\overline{AC} = 2R_e \sin\left(\frac{Tn_s}{2}\right) = 4.9346 \times 10^{-4}$$

The solar lagging angle satisfies

$$\beta = a\sin\left(\frac{R_e}{e_c}\sin\left(\frac{T}{2}n_s\right)\right) - \frac{T}{2}n_s = 17.55°$$

The target of eccentricity control at that moment is

$$\vec{e}_A = \begin{pmatrix} e_x \\ e_y \end{pmatrix} = 3.0 \times 10^{-4} \cdot \begin{pmatrix} \cos(42.447°) \\ \sin(42.447°) \end{pmatrix}$$

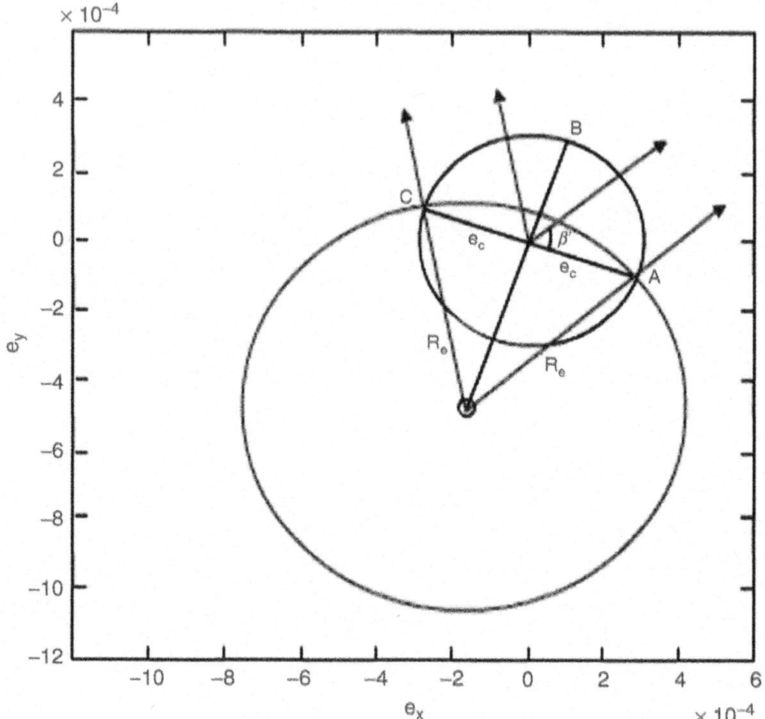

Fig. 7.16 Zero-pass eccentricity strategy

The amount of eccentricity control is

$$\Delta e = 2e_c \sin\beta = 4.0494 \times 10^{-4}$$

The amount of eccentricity control in a year is

$$\Delta e_T = \left[\frac{365.24}{T}\right] \cdot 2e_c \sin\beta = 0.0024$$

The strategy of eccentricity passing through original node allows the longest free perturbing arc in the confined circle of eccentricity, and the chord of eccentricity in the confined circle is

$$\overline{AC} = 2R_e \sin\left(\frac{Tn_s}{2}\right) \tag{7.38}$$

If the chord of eccentricity in the confined circle equals the diameter of the confined circle, then the free perturbing arc is the longest, as shown in Fig. 7.16. Therefore, the period of the free perturbation of eccentricity is

$$2e_c = 2R_e \sin\left(\frac{Tn_s}{2}\right) \tag{7.39}$$

Therefore,

$$T = \frac{2}{n_s} a\sin\left(\frac{e_c}{R_e}\right) \tag{7.40}$$

The solar lagging angle satisfies

$$\beta = \frac{\pi}{2} - a\sin\left(\frac{e_c}{R_e}\right) \tag{7.41}$$

The target of eccentricity passing through original node is

$$\mathbf{e_A} = \begin{pmatrix} e_x \\ e_y \end{pmatrix} = e_c \cdot \begin{pmatrix} \cos\left(\alpha_s - \frac{\pi}{2} + a\sin\left(\frac{e_c}{R_e}\right)\right) \\ \sin\left(\alpha_s - \frac{\pi}{2} + a\sin\left(\frac{e_c}{R_e}\right)\right) \end{pmatrix} \tag{7.42}$$

Suppose it is planned to perform the eccentricity control of a satellite on 2007-05-04 and the target is to obtain the longest time during which the eccentricity remains in the confined circle. The radius of the confined circle $e_c = 3.0 \times 10^{-4}$, the solar radiation area is 60.6 m^2, the quality is 2,000 kg, and the radius of the free perturbation circle is $R_e = 5.0 \times 10^{-4}$.

The solar lagging angle of eccentricity passing through original node satisfies

$$\beta = \frac{\pi}{2} - a\sin\left(\frac{e_c}{R_e}\right) = 53°$$

The control period of eccentricity passing through original node is

$$T = \frac{2}{n_s} a\sin\left(\frac{e_c}{R_e}\right) = 74.8\,(\text{day})$$

The satellite orbit after control is

At epoch 2007/5/4/0:0:.000
$a = 42{,}165{,}784.419$ m
$e = 0.000299868$
$i = 0.340000$
$\Omega = 269.999999°$
$\omega = 76.860028°$
$M = 359.999970°$

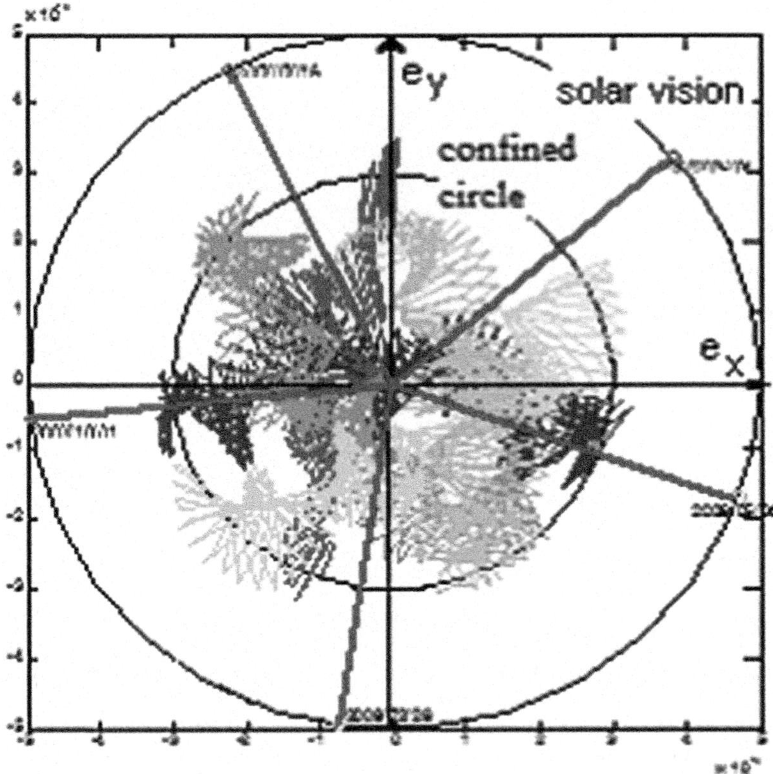

Fig. 7.17 Zero-pass eccentricity strategy simulation

The eccentricity pointing after control $(\Omega+\omega)_0 = 346.86°$, which lags behind the solar angle $\beta = 53°$ (the solar mean longitude of that day is $\alpha_s = 40°$). Extrapolate orbit for 75 days during which the eccentricity is confined in the control circle, until 2007-07-18, when the eccentricity is ahead of the solar angle $\beta = 53°$ (the solar mean longitude of that day is $\alpha_s = 116.5°$). The eccentricity will pass through the control circle and the control must be performed to limit the size of the eccentricity. The control target is

$$e_f = 3.0 \times 10^{-4}$$
$$(\Omega + \omega)_f = \alpha_s - \beta = 63.6°$$

Similarly, on October 1, 2007, December 15, 2007, and February 28, 2008, the third, fourth, and fifth eccentricity centralized controls are carried out, respectively, completing the control period of a year. The simulation trajectory of the eccentricity in the year is shown in Fig. 7.17.

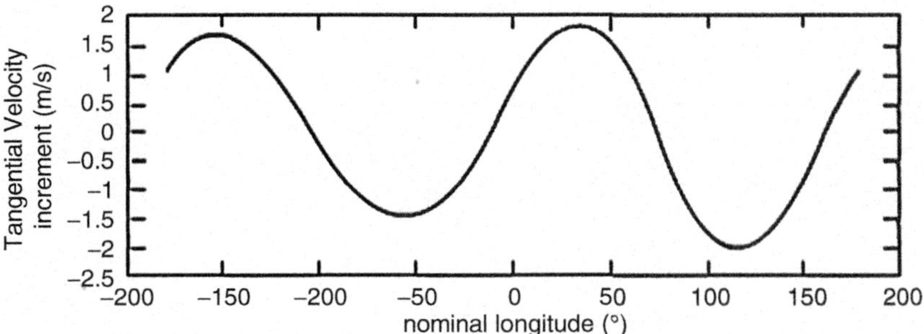

Fig. 7.18 The velocity increment for E/W station keeping

7.3.5 *Maneuver Calculation*

According to the impulse velocity increment equation of drift rate control, $\Delta D = -\frac{3}{V_s}\Delta V_T$, and drift parabola, the current tangential velocity increment is related to the longitude drift rate $\ddot{\lambda}_n$ and the semi-width of the drift parabola $\Delta\bar{\lambda}$ by

$$\Delta V_T = -\frac{4}{3}\left(\frac{1}{360.9856}\right)\sqrt{\Delta\bar{\lambda}\cdot\left|\ddot{\lambda}_n\right|}\cdot V_s \tag{7.43}$$

The relation between it and the current control period T is

$$\Delta V_T = -\frac{1}{3}\left(\frac{1}{360.9856}\right)\ddot{\lambda}_n\cdot \mathrm{T}\cdot V_s \tag{7.44}$$

The total tangential velocity increment in a year is

$$\sum\Delta V_T = -\frac{1}{3}\left(\frac{1}{360.9856}\right)\ddot{\lambda}_n\cdot V_s\cdot\sum\mathrm{T} = -\frac{1}{3}\left(\frac{1}{360.9856}\right)\ddot{\lambda}_n\cdot V_s\cdot 365.24 \tag{7.45}$$

V_s is the ideal geostationary velocity $V_s = a_s\cdot\omega_e = 3074.7$(m/s), and the unit of drift acceleration is degree/day square. Figure 7.18 illustrates the velocity increments in different nominal longitudes.

Therefore, the velocity increment for east/west station keeping in a year is only related with the longitude drift acceleration and is not related with the control times or the size of the drift parabola. The velocity increments with different nominal longitudes are listed in Table 7.3.

For example, the annual velocity increment of east/west station keeping for the satellite positioned in 110.0° east longitude is −1.989803 m/s; the annual velocity

Table 7.3 Velocity increments as a function of longitude

Longitude (°)	Velocity increment in 1 year (m/s)	Longitude (°)	Velocity increment in 1 year (m/s)
−180	1.07674363	0	0.67064426
−179	1.12404834	1	0.72760476
−178	1.16971935	2	0.78401638
−177	1.21371418	3	0.83979986
−176	1.25599288	4	0.89487591
−175	1.29651798	5	0.94916531
−174	1.33525459	6	1.00258905
−173	1.37217032	7	1.05506844
−172	1.40723534	8	1.10652525
−171	1.44042233	9	1.15688183
−170	1.47170652	10	1.20606122
−169	1.50106568	11	1.25398731
−168	1.52848008	12	1.30058493
−167	1.55393251	13	1.34578001
−166	1.57740827	14	1.38949968
−165	1.59889512	15	1.43167242
−164	1.61838331	16	1.47222814
−163	1.63586552	17	1.51109835
−162	1.65133687	18	1.54821629
−161	1.66479487	19	1.583517
−160	1.67623943	20	1.61693748
−159	1.68567281	21	1.64841679
−158	1.69309955	22	1.6778962
−157	1.69852654	23	1.70531925
−156	1.7019629	24	1.73063192
−155	1.70341997	25	1.75378271
−154	1.70291129	26	1.77472275
−153	1.70045253	27	1.79340591
−152	1.69606147	28	1.80978891
−151	1.68975798	29	1.82383142
−150	1.6815639	30	1.83549616
−149	1.67150309	31	1.84474895
−148	1.6596013	32	1.85155889
−147	1.64588615	33	1.85589836
−146	1.63038711	34	1.85774314
−145	1.61313539	35	1.8570725
−144	1.59416391	36	1.85386926
−143	1.57350724	37	1.84811985
−142	1.55120154	38	1.83981439
−141	1.52728451	39	1.82894675
−140	1.5017953	40	1.81551461
−139	1.47477447	41	1.79951947
−138	1.44626391	42	1.78096675
−137	1.41630677	43	1.7598658
−136	1.38494741	44	1.73622993

(continued)

Table 7.3 (continued)

Longitude (°)	Velocity increment in 1 year (m/s)	Longitude (°)	Velocity increment in 1 year (m/s)
−135	1.3522313	45	1.71007642
−134	1.31820498	46	1.68142658
−133	1.28291598	47	1.65030574
−132	1.24641271	48	1.61674324
−131	1.20874443	49	1.58077244
−130	1.16996119	50	1.54243073
−129	1.13011368	51	1.50175948
−128	1.08925323	52	1.45880404
−127	1.04743169	53	1.41361368
−126	1.0047014	54	1.36624159
−125	0.96111506	55	1.31674479
−124	0.91672569	56	1.26518411
−123	0.87158655	57	1.21162409
−122	0.82575108	58	1.15613294
−121	0.77927278	59	1.09878243
−120	0.73220521	60	1.03964782
−119	0.68460187	61	0.97880774
−118	0.63651615	62	0.91634412
−117	0.58800128	63	0.85234204
−116	0.53911022	64	0.78688963
−115	0.48989563	65	0.72007792
−114	0.44040986	66	0.65200071
−113	0.39070477	67	0.58275446
−112	0.34083181	68	0.51243805
−111	0.29084186	69	0.44115272
−110	0.24078528	70	0.36900183
−109	0.19071177	71	0.29609073
−108	0.14067039	72	0.22252653
−107	0.09070953	73	0.14841799
−106	0.0408768	74	0.07387525
−105	−0.0087809	75	−0.0009903
−104	−0.0582175	76	−0.0760663
−103	−0.1073878	77	−0.1512395
−102	−0.1562472	78	−0.2263961
−101	−0.2047523	79	−0.3014219
−100	−0.2528603	80	−0.3762025
−99	−0.3005294	81	−0.4506236
−98	−0.3477186	82	−0.5245711
−97	−0.394388	83	−0.5979312
−96	−0.4404983	84	−0.6705913
−95	−0.4860114	85	−0.742439
−94	−0.5308899	86	−0.8133637
−93	−0.5750972	87	−0.8832557
−92	−0.6185978	88	−0.9520071
−91	−0.661357	89	−1.0195115

(continued)

Table 7.3 (continued)

Longitude (°)	Velocity increment in 1 year (m/s)	Longitude (°)	Velocity increment in 1 year (m/s)
−90	−0.7033408	90	−1.0856648
−89	−0.7445162	91	−1.1503648
−88	−0.784851	92	−1.2135119
−87	−0.8243136	93	−1.2750089
−86	−0.8628735	94	−1.3347615
−85	−0.9005006	95	−1.3926782
−84	−0.9371658	96	−1.4486708
−83	−0.9728407	97	−1.5026542
−82	−1.0074974	98	−1.5545469
−81	−1.0411088	99	−1.6042709
−80	−1.0736484	100	−1.651752
−79	−1.1050904	101	−1.6969199
−78	−1.1354096	102	−1.7397083
−77	−1.1645812	103	−1.780055
−76	−1.1925812	104	−1.817902
−75	−1.2193861	105	−1.8531957
−74	−1.2449728	106	−1.8858871
−73	−1.2693189	107	−1.9159313
−72	−1.2924025	108	−1.9432882
−71	−1.3142022	109	−1.9679224
−70	−1.3346971	110	−1.989803
−69	−1.3538667	111	−2.008904
−68	−1.3716914	112	−2.0252038
−67	−1.3881516	113	−2.0386859
−66	−1.4032287	114	−2.0493383
−65	−1.4169044	115	−2.0571538
−64	−1.4291611	116	−2.06213
−63	−1.4399817	117	−2.064269
−62	−1.4493499	118	−2.0635778
−61	−1.4572497	119	−2.0600678
−60	−1.4636661	120	−2.053755
−59	−1.4685846	121	−2.0446599
−58	−1.4719918	122	−2.0328073
−57	−1.4738746	123	−2.0182264
−56	−1.4742212	124	−2.0009506
−55	−1.4730203	125	−1.9810174
−54	−1.4702618	126	−1.9584684
−53	−1.4659365	127	−1.933349
−52	−1.4600363	128	−1.9057083
−51	−1.452554	129	−1.8755992
−50	−1.4434839	130	−1.8430781
−49	−1.4328212	131	−1.8082046
−48	−1.4205625	132	−1.7710416
−47	−1.4067057	133	−1.7316553
−46	−1.3912503	134	−1.6901144

(continued)

Table 7.3 (continued)

Longitude (°)	Velocity increment in 1 year (m/s)	Longitude (°)	Velocity increment in 1 year (m/s)
−45	−1.3741968	135	−1.6464908
−44	−1.3555477	136	−1.6008586
−43	−1.3353069	137	−1.5532947
−42	−1.3134798	138	−1.503878
−41	−1.2900737	139	−1.4526897
−40	−1.2650974	140	−1.399813
−39	−1.2385619	141	−1.3453325
−38	−1.2104796	142	−1.2893349
−37	−1.1808651	143	−1.2319081
−36	−1.1497349	144	−1.1731412
−35	−1.1171074	145	−1.1131245
−34	−1.083003	146	−1.0519494
−33	−1.0474444	147	−0.9897078
−32	−1.0104562	148	−0.9264924
−31	−0.972065	149	−0.8623964
−30	−0.9322998	150	−0.7975131
−29	−0.8911917	151	−0.7319361
−28	−0.8487739	152	−0.665759
−27	−0.8050818	153	−0.5990752
−26	−0.7601529	154	−0.5319778
−25	−0.7140271	155	−0.4645597
−24	−0.6667463	156	−0.3969128
−23	−0.6183546	157	−0.3291287
−22	−0.5688982	158	−0.2612979
−21	−0.5184255	159	−0.1935102
−20	−0.4669868	160	−0.1258541
−19	−0.4146348	161	−0.0584171
−18	−0.3614239	162	0.00871471
−17	−0.3074105	163	0.0754565
−16	−0.2526531	164	0.14172503
−15	−0.1972119	165	0.20743861
−14	−0.1411488	166	0.27251722
−13	−0.0845278	167	0.33688261
−12	−0.0274142	168	0.40045833
−11	0.03012498	169	0.46316987
−10	0.08802118	170	0.52494467
−9	0.14620447	171	0.58571225
−8	0.20460356	172	0.64540419
−7	0.2631459	173	0.70395426
−6	0.3217578	174	0.76129843
−5	0.38036454	175	0.81737494
−4	0.43889042	176	0.8721243
−3	0.4972589	177	0.9254894
−2	0.55539272	178	0.97741547
−1	0.61321398	179	1.02785019

increment of east/west station keeping for the satellite positioned in 140° east longitude is −1.399813 m/s; (−) means westward velocity increment and (+) means eastward velocity increment.

7.3.6 Single-Pulse Maneuver Planning

Usually the single-pulse control is performed as emergency control when the mean longitude moves out of the parabola or for the transfer control of the satellite nominal longitude. At this time, the drift rate is the control target and the joint control of eccentricity may not be performed. The tangential velocity increment changes the orbit drift rate. There is no phase requirement of tangential control, but at different control phases the coupling control will change the direction of the eccentricity vector. If there is no requirement of the direction of eccentricity, the single-pulse control can be chosen according to custom or working time. But if the direction of eccentricity is clearly required, the selection of executing phase should consider the coupling effect of eccentricity. Therefore, the purpose of executing phase selection of single-pulse control is as follows: By using the drift rate control opportunity, maintain or adjust the direction of eccentricity to make it meet the direction requirement of the eccentricity vector.

The drift rate vector and eccentricity vector in the day of drift rate control are as follows.

The drift rate vector $\mathbf{d_0} = \begin{pmatrix} \Delta\lambda_0 \\ D_0 \end{pmatrix}$ is the difference between the satellite current mean longitude and the nominal longitude $\Delta\lambda_0$ (degree) and the current mean longitude drift rate D_0 (°/day).

The eccentricity vector $\mathbf{e_0} = \begin{pmatrix} e_x \\ e_y \end{pmatrix} = \begin{pmatrix} e_0 \cos(\Omega+\omega)_0 \\ e_0 \sin(\Omega+\omega)_0 \end{pmatrix}$. The size of the mean eccentricity is e_0 and the direction of perigee is $(\Omega+\omega)_0$.

The target drift rate vector is $\mathbf{d_f} = \begin{pmatrix} \Delta\lambda_0 \\ D_f \end{pmatrix}$

According to the control equation of tangential pulse,

$$\Delta D = -\frac{3\Delta V_T}{V_s} \cdot 360.9856(°/\text{day}) \tag{7.46}$$

$$\begin{cases} \Delta e_x = \dfrac{2\Delta V_T}{V_s} \cos(l_b) \\ \Delta e_y = \dfrac{2\Delta V_T}{V_s} \sin(l_b) \end{cases} \tag{7.47}$$

Therefore, for the strategy of single-pulse control, the size of tangential pulse is determined by the amount of drift rate control $\Delta D = D_f - D_0$, and the executing phase l_b is determined by the direction of eccentricity increment. The size of eccentricity increment is related with the amount of drift rate control and is not related with the executing phase. Therefore, the requirement of the direction of eccentricity increment and the determination of the executing phase of tangential pulse are the main problems for making the control strategy of single-pulse control. The two constraints of the executing phase of tangential pulse under solar pointing control mode are:

Suppose the tangential velocity increment of single pulse is ΔV_T, the size of eccentricity increment is $\Delta e = (2/V_s) \cdot \Delta V_T$, the free perturbation circle of eccentricity is R_e, and the executing phase of single pulse is l_b. Define the counterclockwise direction from the real vernal equinox at epoch as positive, and then l_b must satisfy the following two rules:

1. The single-pulse control won't change the free perturbation direction of eccentricity.

Suppose the solar mean longitude is α_s at the control time. A single pulse won't change the free perturbation direction of eccentricity should be scheduled:

If the eccentricity is ahead of the solar longitude,

$$l_b = \begin{cases} \alpha_s + \dfrac{\pi}{2}, \Delta V_T \geq 0 \\ \alpha_s - \dfrac{\pi}{2}, \Delta V_T < 0 \end{cases} \tag{7.48}$$

The formula above indicates that if the eccentricity is ahead of the solar longitude, then $\Delta V_T \geq 0$ means eastward acceleration along the satellite moving direction, and the single-pulse control time is local evening (18:00); $\Delta V_T < 0$ means westward deceleration against the satellite moving direction, and the single-pulse control time is local morning (6:00).

If the eccentricity lags behind the solar longitude,

$$l_b = \begin{cases} \alpha_s - \dfrac{\pi}{2}, \Delta V_T \geq 0 \\ \alpha_s + \dfrac{\pi}{2}, \Delta V_T < 0 \end{cases}. \tag{7.49}$$

The formula above indicates that if the eccentricity lags behind the solar longitude, then $\Delta V_T \geq 0$ means eastward acceleration along the satellite moving direction, and the single-pulse control time is local morning (6:00); $\Delta V_T < 0$ means westward deceleration against the satellite moving direction, and the single-pulse control time is local evening (18:00) (Fig. 7.19).

2. The single-pulse control won't change the size of the free perturbation circle of eccentricity.

Suppose the direction of initial eccentricity or the perigee direction is $\Omega_0 + \omega_0$ and the size of initial eccentricity is e_0. The single-pulse control won't change the size of

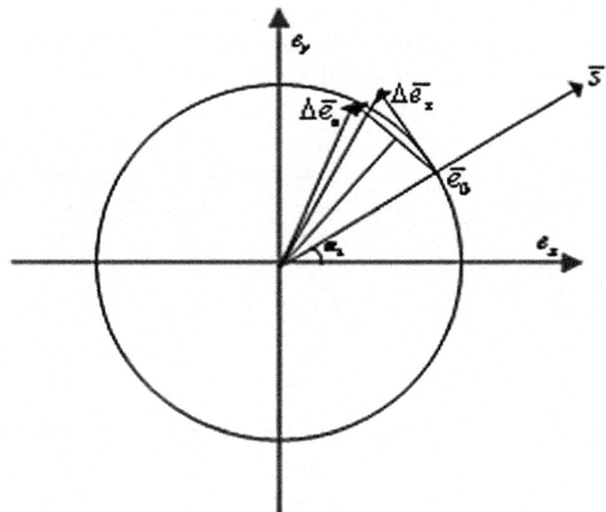

Fig. 7.19 Single-pulse planning

the free perturbation circle of eccentricity if and only if the eccentricity after control is still located in the perturbation circle. Suppose the eccentricity increment caused by the single-pulse tangential velocity increment ΔV_T is $\Delta e = (2/V_s) \cdot \Delta V_T$, the radius of the free perturbation circle is R_e, and the executing phase of the single pulse is l_b.

If the eccentricity is ahead of the solar longitude,

$$l_b = \begin{cases} \Omega_0 + \omega_0 + \pi - a\cos\left(\dfrac{\Delta e}{2e_0}\right), \Delta V_T \geq 0 \\[2ex] \Omega_0 + \omega_0 + 2\pi - a\cos\left(\dfrac{\Delta e}{2e_0}\right), \Delta V_T < 0 \end{cases} \tag{7.50}$$

Obviously, if $\Delta e \prec e_0$, $\frac{\Delta e}{2e_0} \approx 0$, then $\arccos\left(\frac{\Delta e}{2e_0}\right) \approx \frac{\pi}{2}$; the eccentricity points to the right ascension of the Sun, i.e., $\Omega_0 + \omega_0 = \alpha_s$; then the two constraint equations are equivalent to each other.

If the eccentricity lags behind the solar longitude,

$$l_b = \begin{cases} \Omega_0 + \omega_0 + 2\pi - a\cos\left(\dfrac{\Delta e}{2e_0}\right), \Delta V_T \geq 0 \\[2ex] \Omega_0 + \omega_0 + \pi - a\cos\left(\dfrac{\Delta e}{2e_0}\right), \Delta V_T < 0 \end{cases} \tag{7.51}$$

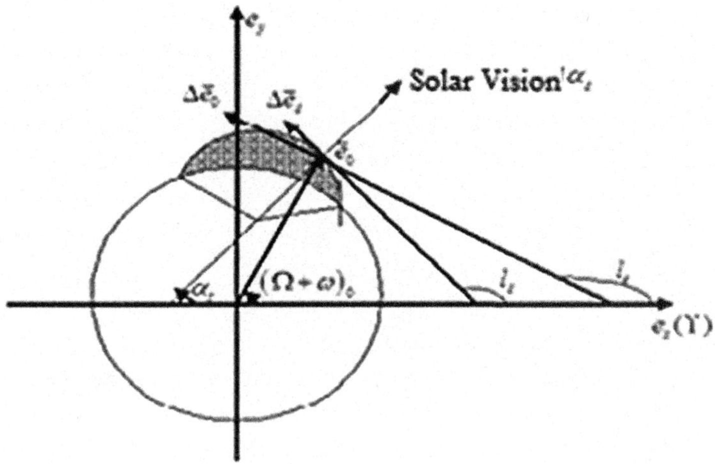

Fig. 7.20 Ahead of solar strategy planning

7.3.6.1 Executing Phase of Single Pulse When the Eccentricity Is Ahead of the Solar Longitude

In station keeping, the eccentricity is controlled out of the confined circle by making the eccentricity being ahead of the solar longitude, as shown in Fig. 7.17. To leave the eccentricity move along the perturbation circle as much as possible, the phase selection algorithm of single-pulse control is (Fig. 7.20).

For eastward acceleration control, when the eccentricity is ahead of the solar longitude, the constraint equations of single-pulse executing phase are

$$l_b^s = \alpha_s + \frac{\pi}{2} \tag{7.52}$$

$$l_b^e = \Omega_0 + \omega_0 + \pi - a\cos\left(\frac{\Delta e}{2e_0}\right) \tag{7.53}$$

Considering the perturbation direction and size of eccentricity after one eastward acceleration control, the single-pulse executing phase is chosen as follows:

$$l_b = l_b^s + \frac{1}{2}\left(l_b^e - l_b^s\right) = \frac{1}{2}(\alpha_s + \Omega_0 + \omega_0 + \pi) - \frac{1}{2}\left(a\cos\left(\frac{\Delta e}{2e_0}\right) - \frac{\pi}{2}\right) \tag{7.54}$$

For westward deceleration control, when the eccentricity is ahead of the solar longitude, the constraint equations of single-pulse executing phase are

$$l_b^s = \alpha_s - \frac{\pi}{2} \tag{7.55}$$

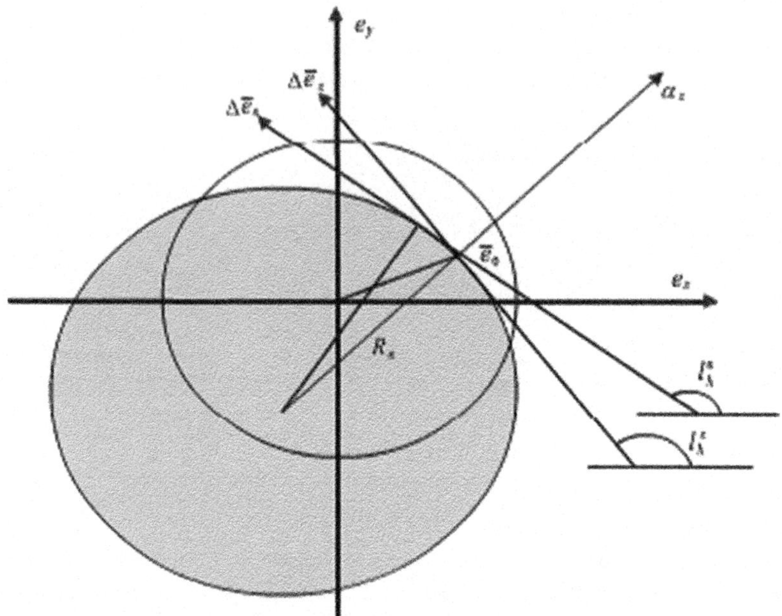

Fig. 7.21 Solar lagged target strategy planning

$$l_b^e = \Omega_0 + \omega_0 + 2\pi - a\cos\left(\frac{\Delta e}{2e_0}\right) \tag{7.56}$$

Considering the perturbation direction and size of eccentricity after control, the single-pulse executing phase is chosen as follows:

$$l_b = l_b^s + \frac{1}{2}\left(l_b^e - l_b^s\right) = \pi + \frac{1}{2}(\alpha_s + \Omega_0 + \omega_0 + \pi) - \frac{1}{2}\left(a\cos\left(\frac{\Delta e}{2e_0}\right) - \frac{\pi}{2}\right) \tag{7.57}$$

7.3.6.2 Executing Phase of Single Pulse When the Eccentricity Lags Behind the Solar Longitude

When the eccentricity lags behind the solar longitude, by the control strategy the free perturbation circle of eccentricity can be kept remaining inside the confined circle in longer control period. Therefore, the selection of single-pulse executing phase should realize that the eccentricity increment due to the tangential velocity increment lags behind the solar direction, and the size of eccentricity does not change, so that the eccentricity rotates around the free perturbation circle, as shown in Fig. 7.21.

For eastward acceleration control, when the eccentricity is ahead of the solar longitude, the constraint equations of the single-pulse executing phase are

$$l_b^s = \alpha_s - \frac{\pi}{2} \tag{7.58}$$

$$l_b^e = \Omega_0 + \omega_0 + 2\pi - a\cos\left(\frac{\Delta e}{2e_0}\right) \tag{7.59}$$

Considering the perturbation direction and the size of eccentricity after control, the single-pulse executing phase is chosen as follows:

$$l_b = l_b^s + \frac{1}{2}\left(l_b^e - l_b^s\right) = \pi + \frac{1}{2}(\alpha_s + \Omega_0 + \omega_0 + \pi) - \frac{1}{2}\left(a\cos\left(\frac{\Delta e}{2e_0}\right) - \frac{\pi}{2}\right) \tag{7.60}$$

For westward deceleration control, when the eccentricity is ahead of the solar longitude, the constraint equations of the single-pulse executing phase are

$$l_b^s = \alpha_s + \frac{\pi}{2} \tag{7.61}$$

$$l_b^e = \Omega_0 + \omega_0 + \pi - a\cos\left(\frac{\Delta e}{2e_0}\right) \tag{7.62}$$

Considering the perturbation direction and the size of eccentricity after control, the single-pulse executing phase is chosen as follows:

$$l_b = l_b^s + \frac{1}{2}\left(l_b^e - l_b^s\right) = \frac{1}{2}(\alpha_s + \Omega_0 + \omega_0 + \pi) - \frac{1}{2}\left(a\cos\left(\frac{\Delta e}{2e_0}\right) - \frac{\pi}{2}\right) \tag{7.63}$$

7.3.6.3 Case Study and Simulation

Suppose there is a satellite residing in nominal longitude E125.3°, the nominal longitude slot is ±0.1°, the area of solar panel is about 60 m^2, and the satellite mass is 2,000 kg. If the minimum station keeping duration is 20 days, then how to design a single-pulse maneuver strategy to maintain the satellite within its nominal slot?

In consideration of the longitude drift acceleration at the nominal point, according to Table 4.5, the satellite experiences the negative longitudinal acceleration, and that is

$$\ddot{\lambda}_n = -0.001855\,(^\circ/\text{day}^2)$$

The semi-width of the drift circle should satisfy the expression below to meet the 20-day duration requirement.

$$\Delta\bar{\lambda} = \left|\frac{T^2}{16}\ddot{\lambda}_n\right| \approx 0.05°$$

In this circumstance, the maximum amplitude of the daily libration caused by the eccentricity should be less than 0.05° to prevent the satellite from trespassing the boundary of the nominal slot, which means the maximum eccentricity should be restricted within a confined circle, whose radius must be less than $e_c = 3 \times 10^{-4}$. According to Chap. 4, the perturbation eccentricity radius is approximately

$$R_e \approx 0.011 \cdot C_R\left(\frac{S}{m}\right) = 4.95 \times 10^{-4}$$

This will induce the daily libration of about

$$\Delta\lambda_{\text{Daily From Ecc}} = \text{rad 2deg}(2 \cdot R_e) = 0.0567°$$

Obviously, the radius of the perturbation eccentricity is greater than the required one. It is required to maintain the eccentricity within the confined circle, so the eccentricity-lag-behind-solar strategy should be deployed to ensure that the eccentricity stays within the confined circle as long as possible. The budget will be taken to balance the fuel consumption and the duration of eccentricity maneuver. In this instance, the radius of the eccentricity confined circle $e_c = 3 \times 10^{-4}$, the duration of eccentricity maneuver $T = 70$, and then the direction of the eccentricity lags behind the solar direction by

$$\beta = a\sin\left(\frac{R_e}{e_c}\sin\left(\frac{T}{2}n_s\right)\right) - \frac{T}{2}n_s = 36°$$

Current orbit at epoch 2007-05-04 00:00:0.0 (UTC)

Osculating orbit	*A* (km)	*e*	*i* (°)	Ω (°)	*ω* (°)	**M** (°)
	42165.784	0.0003	0.34	270.0	76.9	0.0
Station keeping element	$\bar{\lambda}$(°)	*D*(°/day)	e	e_f (°)	i	i_f (°)
	125.45222	−0.01116	0.00028	344.821	0.33921	270.0

The status of the drift rate before control (Fig. 7.22):

The figure of the current drift rate vector (λ, D) indicates that:

1. The current satellite has a westward drift rate. On May 9, 2007, it enters the east/west station keeping "dead band" of – [125.3°, 125.4°] from the east border.
2. Allowing the satellite keep drifting westward, on May 14, 2007, it reaches the west border of the confined mean longitude drift parabola.

The eccentricity vector before control is shown in Fig. 7.23. On May 14, 2007, the mean solar longitude $\alpha_s = 50.735°$, and the perigee points to $(\Omega + \omega)_0 = 340.2°$, lagging behind the solar sight of 60°. The eccentricity is approximately 0.0003 and enters into the confined circle, so the eccentricity control may not be performed.

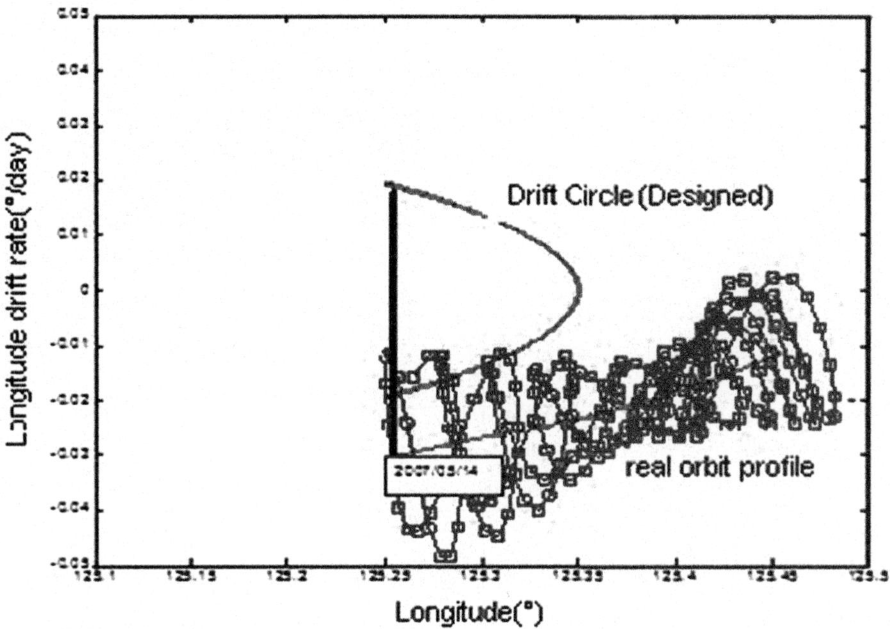

Fig. 7.22 One pulse maneuver scenario

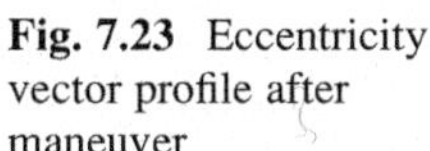
Fig. 7.23 Eccentricity vector profile after maneuver

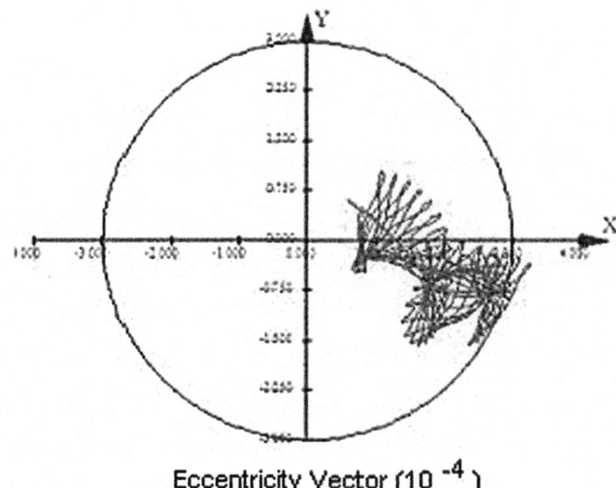

Therefore, the single-pulse control strategy is adopted. On May 14, 2007, the westward decelerating control is performed and the drift rate vector reaches the beginning point of the drift rate parabola. Because the eccentricity enters into the confined circle of eccentricity, the execution phase of pulse adopts solar lagging strategy, so the time of control and the velocity increments are listed in the right.

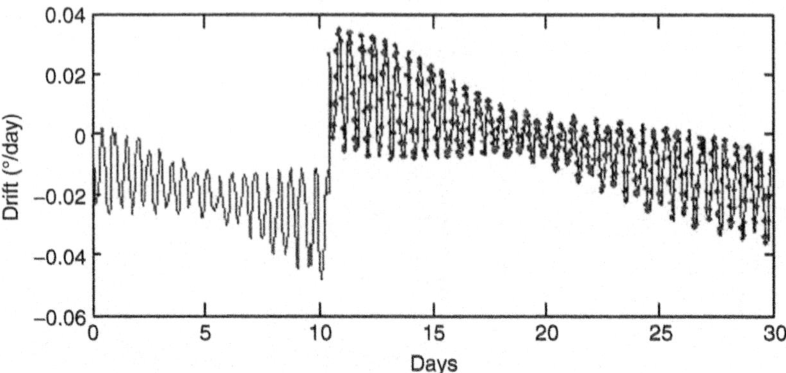

Fig. 7.24 One pulse maneuver scheduled (drift)

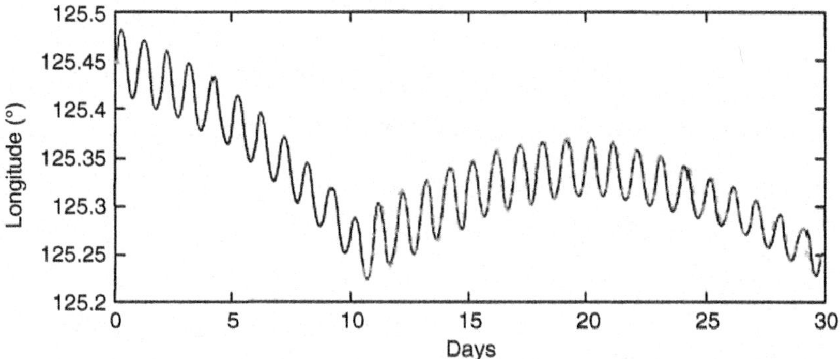

Fig. 7.25 One pulse maneuver scheduled (longitude)

Planning (UTC)	2007/05/14/09:35:17.206
Radial increment (m/s)	0.007
Tangential increment (m/s)	−0.138
Normal increment (m/s)	−0.001

Because the satellite is located in UTC + 8, the maneuver takes place at about 17:35 local time, a little bit ahead of the time when the eccentricity points to the solar vision at 18:00 local time.

Figure 7.24 shows that the westward tangential velocity increment of 0.138 (m/s) decreases the semi-major axis of 3.8 km, which makes the satellite moving to the west border of the mean longitude drift parabola and realizing an eastward drift rate of 0.019 (°/day) as shown in Fig. 7.25. The satellite drifts eastward along the parabola. Because of the negative acceleration of longitude, 10 days later, the satellite turns around and moves westward, and 20 days later, the satellite reaches the west border of the mean longitude drift parabola. Another east/west station

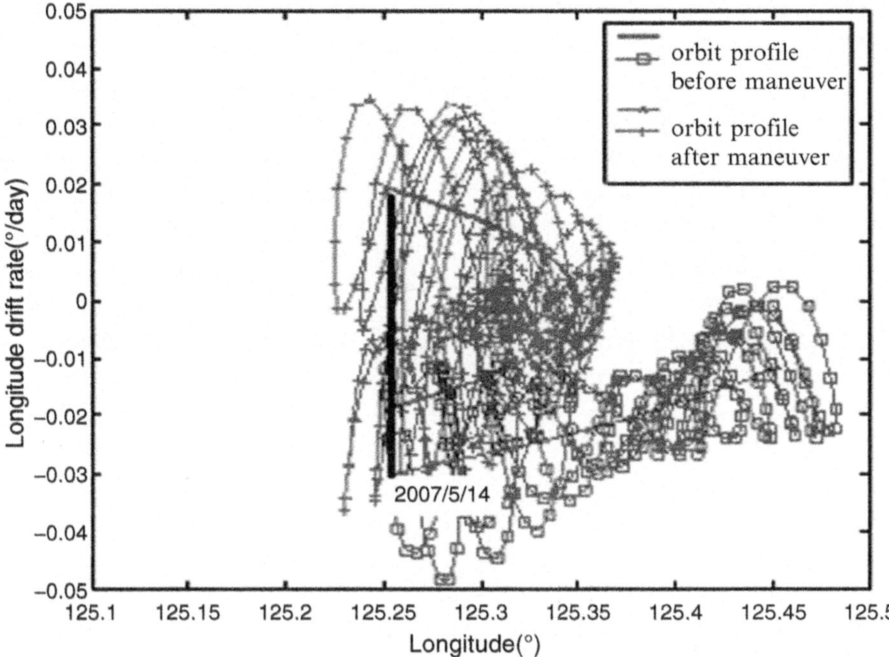

Fig. 7.26 One pulse maneuver scheduled (drift vector phase plane)

keeping control should be performed. As illustrated in Fig. 7.26, west pulses change the longitude drift at the west boundary and force the satellite to drift eastward.

The carefully selected phase of west pulse makes the eccentricity staying within the confined circle as long as possible. Figure 7.27 shows that the eccentricity vector lags behind the solar direction and remains in the confined circle of eccentricity. Adopting the eccentricity lagging solar executing phase appropriately extends the duration when the eccentricity is within the confined circle.

7.3.7 Bi-Pulse Maneuver Planning

Case study shows that single-pulse maneuver can not only realize the goal of drift rate control, while to achieve the goal of eccentricity control, adjusting the executing phase angle can control the perturbation direction of the eccentricity.

If the size of eccentricity is changed in terms of requirement, the tangential velocity increment of eccentricity control Δv_e is

$$\Delta v_e = \frac{1}{2} V_s \left\| \Delta \vec{e} \right\| \tag{7.64}$$

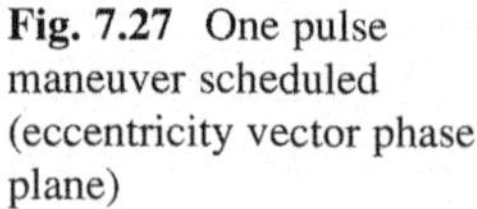

Fig. 7.27 One pulse maneuver scheduled (eccentricity vector phase plane)

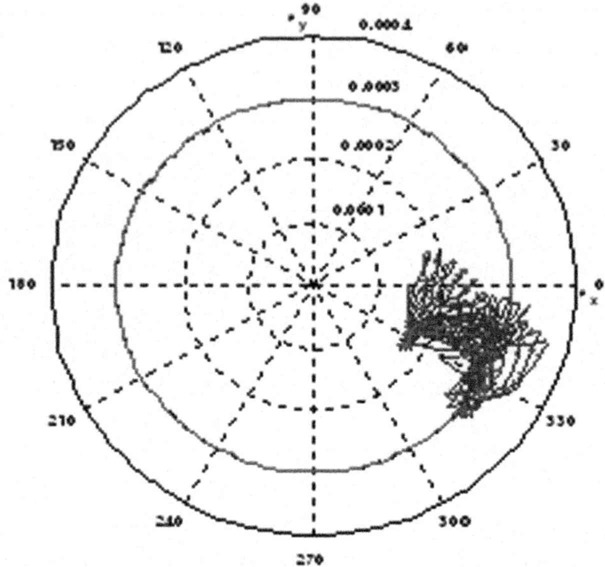

Also, as shown above, for drift rate control, the tangential velocity increment Δv_d is required to be

$$\Delta v_d = \left(\frac{V_s}{3\omega_e}\right)\Delta D \tag{7.65}$$

Here $\omega_e = 360.9856$(°/day). So if both the size and direction of eccentricity need to be maneuvered, the dual-pulse maneuver strategy is introduced below.

7.3.7.1 Drift-Oriented Dual-Pulse Maneuver

If $|\Delta v_d| \geq \Delta v_e$, the velocity increment of drift rate control is greater than the velocity increment of eccentricity control. This situation happens in the capture control of drift rate, taking the adjustment of eccentricity control target into account; in synchronous satellite transfer orbit control (transfer between different positioned longitudes), adjusting the eccentricity direction of transfer orbit to guarantee the safety of other satellites on the path; and in satellite leave orbit control, at the same time rounding the orbit.

As shown in Fig. 7.28, if $|\Delta v_d| \geq \Delta v_e$, any executing phase of single pulse cannot achieve the target goal of eccentricity control. Therefore, the velocity increment of eccentricity control needs to be decomposed at two different phases and the dual-pulse control is adopted. The arithmetic summation of dual pulse of Δv_1, Δv_2 satisfies

$$\Delta v_1 + \Delta v_2 = \Delta v_d \tag{7.66}$$

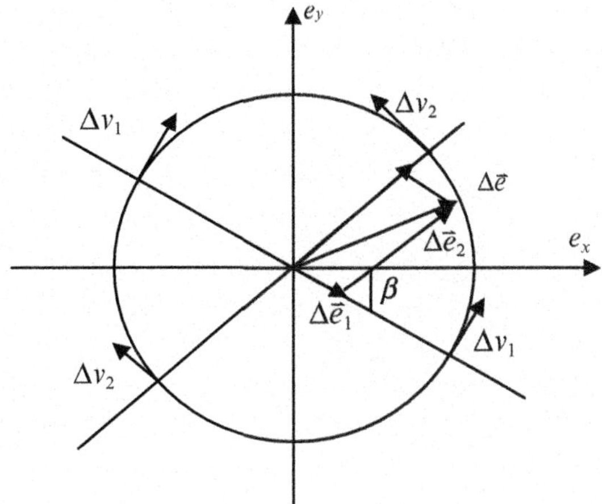

Fig. 7.28 Eccentricity-oriented bi-pulse strategy (same direction)

The eccentricity increments are $\Delta\vec{e}_1$ and $\Delta\vec{e}_2$ due to dual pulses $\Delta v_1, \Delta v_2$, and the vector summation satisfies

$$\Delta\vec{e}_1 + \Delta\vec{e}_2 = \Delta\vec{e} \tag{7.67}$$

Modulus both sides of the expression above, suppose the executing phase angle of dual pulses $\Delta v_1, \Delta v_2$ is β. By satisfying $\cos\beta = \frac{(\mathbf{\Delta e_1}, \mathbf{\Delta e_2})}{\delta e_1 \cdot \delta e_2}$, we have

$$\left\|\Delta\vec{e}_1 + \Delta\vec{e}_2\right\|^2 = \left\|\Delta\vec{e}\right\|^2 \tag{7.68}$$

and

$$\left(\frac{2}{V_s}\right)^2 \left(\Delta v_1^2 + \Delta v_2^2 + 2\Delta v_1 \cdot \Delta v_2 \cos\beta\right) = \left(\frac{2}{V_s}\right)^2 \Delta v_e^2 \tag{7.69}$$

With some calculation

$$\left(\Delta v_1^2 + \Delta v_2^2 + 2\Delta v_1 \cdot \Delta v_2 - 2\Delta v_1 \cdot \Delta v_2 + 2\Delta v_1 \cdot \Delta v_2 \cos\beta\right) = \Delta v_e^2$$

and by simplifying the relation expression, we get

$$\Delta v_e^2 = (\Delta v_1 + \Delta v_2)^2 - 2\Delta v_1 \cdot \Delta v_2 (1 - \cos\beta) \tag{7.70}$$

Because the arithmetic summation of dual pulses $\Delta v_1, \Delta v_2$ satisfies $\Delta v_1 + \Delta v_2 = \Delta v_d$, then

$$\Delta v_e^2 = \Delta v_d^2 - 2\Delta v_1 \cdot \Delta v_2 (1 - \cos\beta)$$

Because $(1-\cos\beta)\geq 0$, if $|\Delta v_d|\geq \Delta v_e$, the formula exists if and only if the dual pulse has the same sign, i.e., $\Delta v_1\cdot\Delta v_2\geq 0$. Therefore, the dual pulses satisfy

$$\Delta v_1+\Delta v_2=\Delta v_d$$
$$\Delta v_1\cdot\Delta v_2=\frac{\Delta v_d^2-\Delta v_e^2}{2(1-\cos\beta)}$$

According to the Vedic Theorem, the dual pulses $\Delta v_1, \Delta v_2$ are the root of the following quadratic equation:

$$x^2-\Delta v_d x+\frac{\Delta v_d^2-\Delta v_e^2}{2(1-\cos\beta)}=0 \tag{7.71}$$

There are two roots for the above equation.

$$\Delta v_1=\frac{\Delta v_d}{2}+\sqrt{\frac{\Delta v_d^2}{4}-\frac{(\Delta v_d^2-\Delta v_e^2)}{2(1-\cos\beta)}} \tag{7.72}$$

$$\Delta v_2=\frac{\Delta v_d}{2}-\sqrt{\frac{\Delta v_d^2}{4}-\frac{(\Delta v_d^2-\Delta v_e^2)}{2(1-\cos\beta)}} \tag{7.73}$$

Obviously, the distribution of dual pulses $\Delta v_1, \Delta v_2$ is related with the difference between expected executing phases, and the minimum difference between phases satisfies

$$\frac{\Delta v_d^2}{4}-\frac{(\Delta v_d^2-\Delta v_e^2)}{2(1-\cos\beta)}\geq 0$$

The solution of the inequality above is

$$\beta\geq a\cos\left(2\left(\frac{\Delta v_e}{\Delta v_d}\right)-1\right), \tag{7.74}$$

For average distributing dual pulses, the difference between executing phases is the minimum, which is

$$\Delta v_1=\Delta v_2=\frac{\Delta v_d}{2}, \beta=a\cos\left(2\left(\frac{\Delta v_e}{\Delta v_d}\right)-1\right)$$

The phase difference constrains the difference of executing time of dual pulses; the allowable minimum time of dual pulses with the same direction is given by

$$\Delta T=12\left(\frac{\beta}{\pi}\right)\ (\mathrm{h})$$

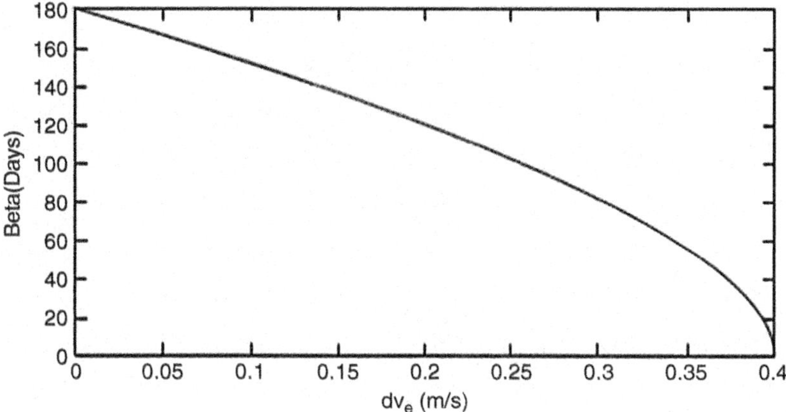

Fig. 7.29 The phase angle restriction

As shown in Fig. 7.29, suppose the velocity increment of drift rate control is

$$\Delta v_d = 0.4(\mathrm{m/s})$$

and the velocity increment of eccentricity control

$$\Delta v_e \leq \Delta v_d \leq 0.4(\mathrm{m/s})$$

The difference between executing phases is the minimum.

If $\Delta v_e = 0$, then the drift rate control has no coupling effect on the eccentricity. The executing phase of dual pulses with the same direction has an interval of 180° and the coupling effect on the eccentricity of these two controls equals zero.

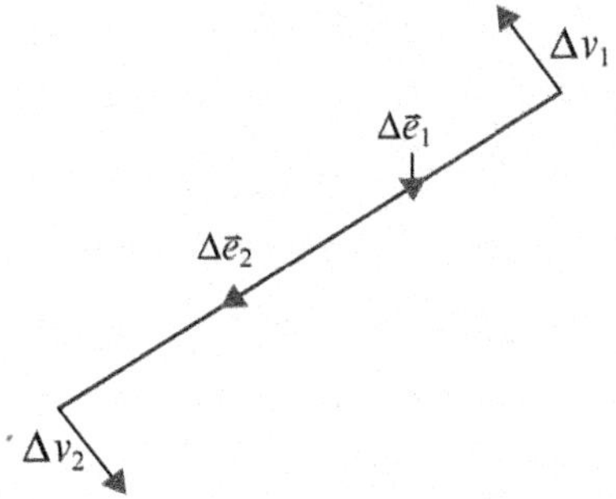

$$\mathbf{\Delta e_1 + \Delta e_2 = \Delta e = 0}$$

If $\Delta v_e = \Delta v_d$, then the velocity increment of drift rate control has coupling effect on eccentricity control. The executing phase of dual pulses with the same direction has an interval of 0° and the coupling effect on eccentricity of these two controls is superposed.

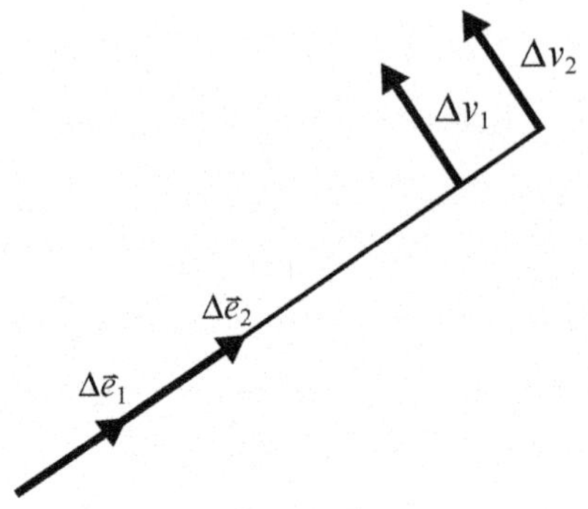

$$\mathbf{\Delta e_1} + \mathbf{\Delta e_2} = \mathbf{\Delta e}$$

For dual-pulse control, the executing phase of the first pulse can be chosen arbitrarily, but the executing phase of the second pulse is determined by size distribution and phase difference. Normally as shown in Fig. 7.28, if the angle of eccentricity increment $\mathbf{\Delta e}$ is l_e, the first pulse $\mathbf{\Delta e_1}$ is $\mathbf{\Delta e_1}$ ahead of the eccentricity increment $\mathbf{\Delta e}$, the second pulse $\mathbf{\Delta e_2}$ lags behind the eccentricity increment $\mathbf{\Delta e}$ of β_2, then the executing phases of the eastward acceleration pulses are

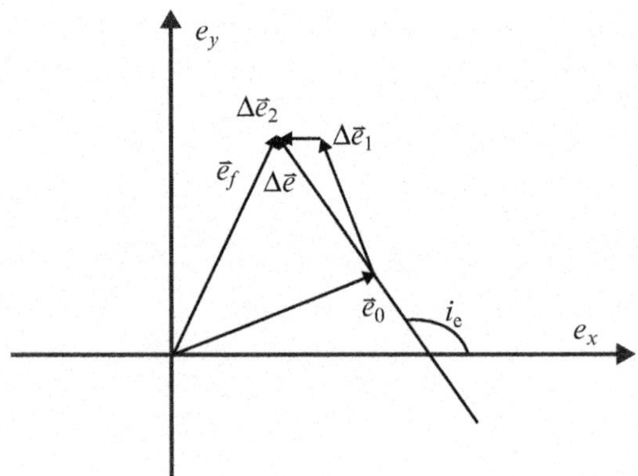

$$l_1 = l_s - \beta_1$$
$$l_2 = l_s + \beta_2$$

The executing phases of the westward deceleration pulses are

$$l_1 = l_s - \beta_1 + \pi$$
$$l_2 = l_s + \beta_2 + \pi$$

The relation among β_1, β_2, pulse distribution $\Delta v_1, \Delta v_2$, and phase difference β is

$$\begin{cases} \sin(\beta_1) = \dfrac{\Delta v_2}{\Delta v_e} \sin(\beta) \\ \cos(\beta_1) = \dfrac{\Delta v_1^2 + \Delta v_e^2 - \Delta v_2^2}{2\Delta v_1 \cdot \Delta v_e} \end{cases} \tag{7.75}$$

$$\begin{cases} \sin(\beta_2) = \dfrac{\Delta v_1}{\Delta v_e} \sin(\beta) \\ \cos(\beta_2) = \dfrac{\Delta v_2^2 + \Delta v_e^2 - \Delta v_1^2}{2\Delta v_2 \cdot \Delta v_e} \end{cases} \tag{7.76}$$

Then

$$\beta_1 = \text{mod}(\text{Rad 2 Deg}(\text{arctan2}(\sin(\beta_1), \cos(\beta_1))), 360°) \tag{7.77}$$
$$\beta_2 = \text{mod}(\text{Rad 2 Deg}(\text{arctan2}(\sin(\beta_2), \cos(\beta_2))), 360°) \tag{7.78}$$

Case Study and Simulation. The satellite is positioned in 125.3° east longitude and the east/west station keeping "dead band" is ±0.1°. The solar radiation area is about 60 m^2 and the satellite mass is 2,000 Kg. According to the task requirements, the satellite should be transferred to 135° east longitude in 3 days and the eccentricity of transitional orbit should be zero. The objective is to recapture the satellite in 135.5° east longitude; the eccentricity lags 50° behind the Sun. The orbit elements at the epoch 2007/5/16/0:35:17.206 (UTC) are listed below.

Osculation orbit	*A* (km)	*e*	*i* (°)	Ω (°)	*ω* (°)	**M** (°)
	42,165.134	0.0003	0.31	271.2	73.9	22.0
Station keeping orbit	$\bar{\lambda}$(°)	*D*(°/day)	e	e_f (°)	i	i_f (°)
	125.29496	0.0081	0.0003	345.12	0.31	271.2

1. The current status of the satellite (Fig. 7.30)
2. Deceleration control of dual pulses with the same direction

In order to transfer the satellite from 125.3° EL to 135° EL in 3 days, adopting dual-pulse decelerating control, the satellite gets an eastward drift velocity of

$$\Delta D = 3.2(°/\text{day}).$$

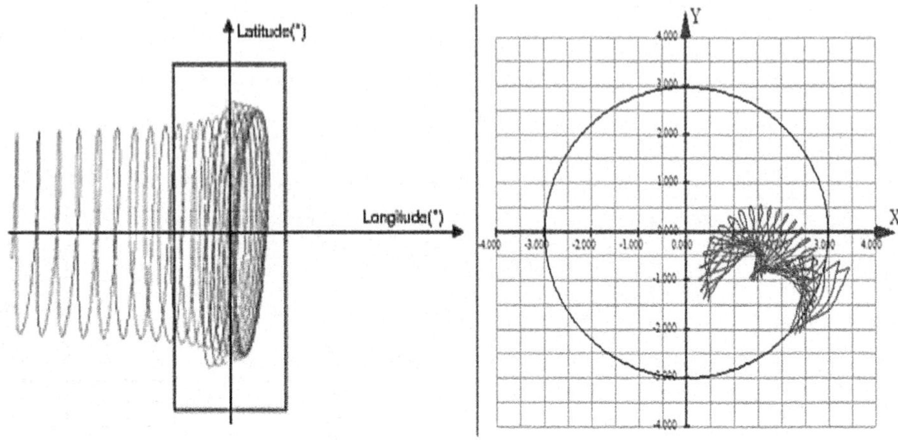

Fig. 7.30 Drift and eccentricity vector

Keeping the eccentricity target as zero, the amount of dual-pulse control is

First pulse		Second pulse	
Planning (UTC)	*2007/05/16*	*Planning (UTC)*	*2007/05/16*
Velocity increment (m/s)	*05:30:38.214*	*Velocity increment (m/s)*	*17:52:05.695*
Radial	0.238	Radial	0.248
Tangential	−4.473	Tangential	−4.662
Normal	−0.034	Normal	−0.036

3. Acceleration control of dual pulses with the same direction

After 3 days of eastward drifting, on May 19, 2007, the dual-pulse accelerating control is performed, putting the satellite into the "dead band" of 135°. Considering the eccentricity control, the satellite is made 50° behind the solar direction, and the amount of dual-pulse control is

Third pulse		Fourth pulse	
Planning (UTC)	*2007/05/19*	*Planning (UTC)*	*2007/05/19*
Velocity increment (m/s)	*05:55:56.169*	*Velocity increment* (m/s)	*05:55:56.169*
Radial	0.247	Radial	0.247
Tangential	4.696	Tangential	4.696
Normal	0.036	Normal	0.036

4. Four-pulse "swap" control process (Figs. 7.31, 7.32, and 7.33)

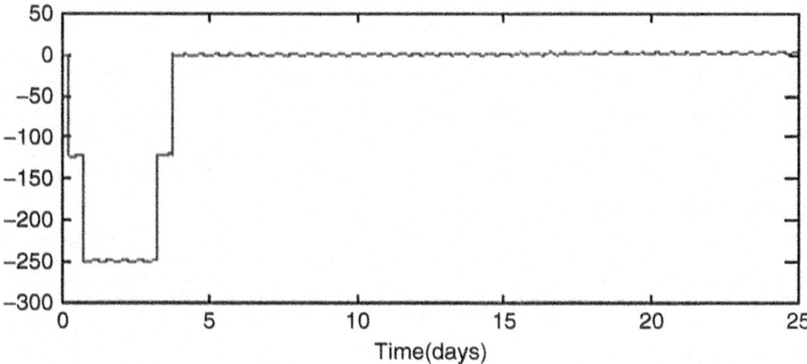

Fig. 7.31 Semi-major axis profile

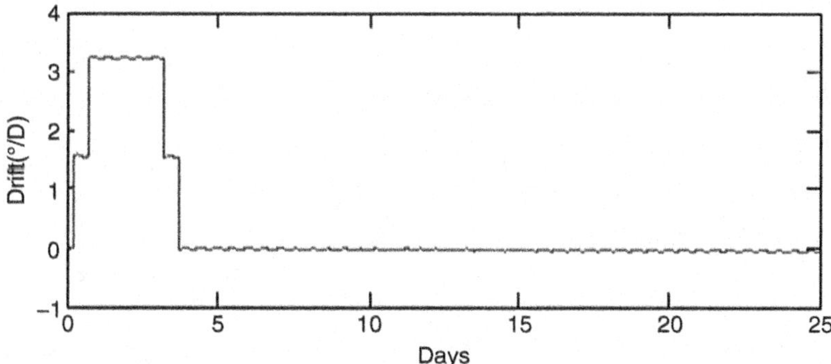

Fig. 7.32 The longitude drift rate profile

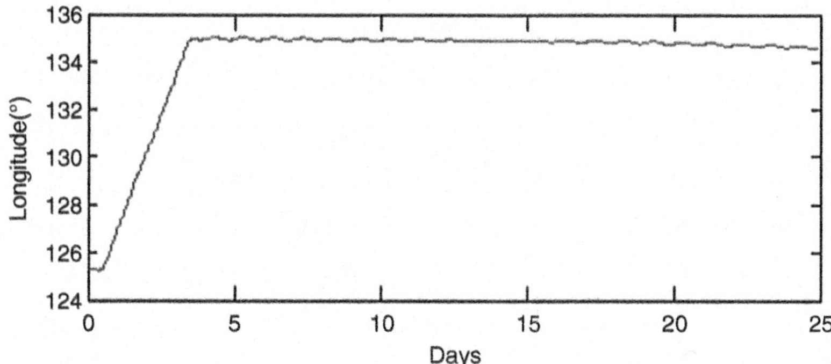

Fig. 7.33 The longitude drift profile

7.3.7.2 Eccentricity-Oriented Dual-Pulse Maneuver

Sometimes the velocity increment of drift rate control is smaller than the velocity increment of eccentricity control, which happens when the eccentricity maneuver is performed and the drift rate control is also taken into account. For example, in collocation control of multi-satellites, in period control of eccentricity direction, the drift rate control is taken into account.

If the velocity increment of drift rate control is Δv_d, the velocity increment of eccentricity control is Δv_e, and $|\Delta v_d| < \Delta v_e$, then the arithmetic summation of dual pulses of $\Delta v_1, \Delta v_2$ satisfies

$$\Delta v_1 + \Delta v_2 = \Delta v_d \tag{7.79}$$

The eccentricity increments are $\mathbf{\Delta e_1}$ and $\mathbf{\Delta e_2}$ due to dual pulses $\Delta v_1, \Delta v_2$, and the vector summation satisfies

$$\mathbf{\Delta e_1} + \mathbf{\Delta e_2} = \mathbf{\Delta e} \tag{7.80}$$

Refer to Sect. 7.3.7 and modulo both sides of the above expression, and we get

$$\Delta v_e^2 = \Delta v_d^2 - 2\Delta v_1 \cdot \Delta v_2(1 - \cos\beta) \tag{7.81}$$

Because $(1 - \cos\beta) \geq 0$, if $|\Delta v_d| < \Delta v_e$, then the formula exists if and only if the dual pulses have opposite sign, i.e., $\Delta v_1 \cdot \Delta v_2 < 0$. Therefore, the dual pulses satisfy

$$\begin{cases} \Delta v_1 + \Delta v_2 = \Delta v_d \\ \Delta v_1 \cdot \Delta v_2 = \dfrac{\Delta v_d^2 - \Delta v_e^2}{2(1 - \cos\beta)} \end{cases} \tag{7.82}$$

And if $|\Delta v_d| < \Delta v_e$, then the solution of the equations exists if and only if the difference between executing phases is 180°. Therefore, the dual pulses are as follows:

The eastward control pulse $\Delta v_{\mathrm{East}} \geq 0$ satisfies

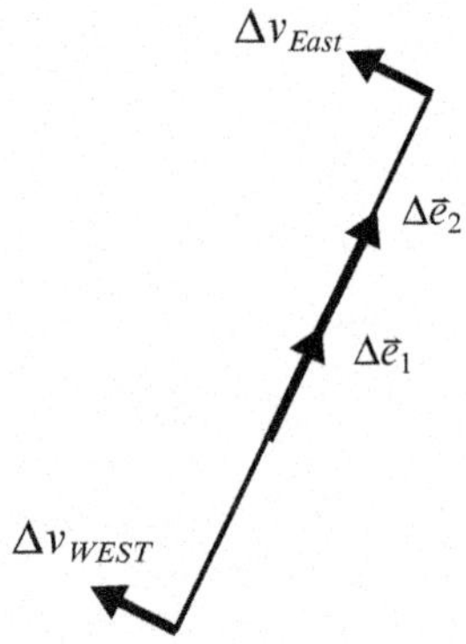

$$\Delta v_{\text{East}} = \Delta v_2 = \frac{\Delta v_d - \Delta v_e}{2}$$

The executing phase is

$$l_{\text{East}} = \arctan\left(\Delta e_y / \Delta e_x\right)$$

And the westward control pulse $\Delta v_{\text{West}} \geq 0$ satisfies

$$\Delta v_{\text{West}} = \Delta v_2 = \frac{\Delta v_d - \Delta v_e}{2}$$

The executing phase is

$$l_{\text{West}} = \pi + \arctan\left(\Delta e_y / \Delta e_x\right)$$

Case Study and Simulation. The satellite is positioned in 135° east longitude and the east/west station keeping "dead band" is ±0.1°. The solar radiation area is about 60 m^2 and the satellite quality is 2,000Kg. The current eccentricity is 20° before the solar direction and it is located at the confined circle of eccentricity. Because the perturbing circle is greater than the confined circle, the eccentricity will gradually increase. By the east/west station keeping control, the eccentricity will be changed lagging behind the Sun of 50° and will be kept at the confined circle. The orbit elements at the epoch 2007/5/26/00 27:15.076 (UTC) are listed below.

Osculation orbit	*A* (km)	*e*	*i* (°)	Ω (°)	*ω* (°)	**M** (°)
	42167.31	0.00049	0.27	271.96	129.36	343.54
Station keeping orbit	$\bar{\lambda}$(°)	*D*(°/*day*)	*E*	e_f (°)	i	i_f (°)
	134.94	−0.013975	0.00049	41.32	0.27	271.96

1. The current status of satellite

The satellite is currently located on the west border of east/west confined circle, as shown in Fig. 7.34. The satellite with a negative drift rate will trespass the west boundary of the "dead band," and because of the large eccentricity as illustrated in Fig. 7.35, the longitude already reaches the border of the "dead band." The drift rate control should be performed in the same day. Drive the satellite drift eastward along parabola and the current eccentricity is kept at the confined circle, lagging behind the Sun of 50°.

2. Control of dual pulses with opposite directions

The size and the executing phase of dual pulses are determined by the amount of drift rate control and eccentricity control. Normally the executing sequence of dual

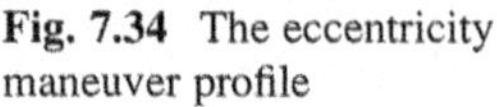

Fig. 7.34 The eccentricity maneuver profile

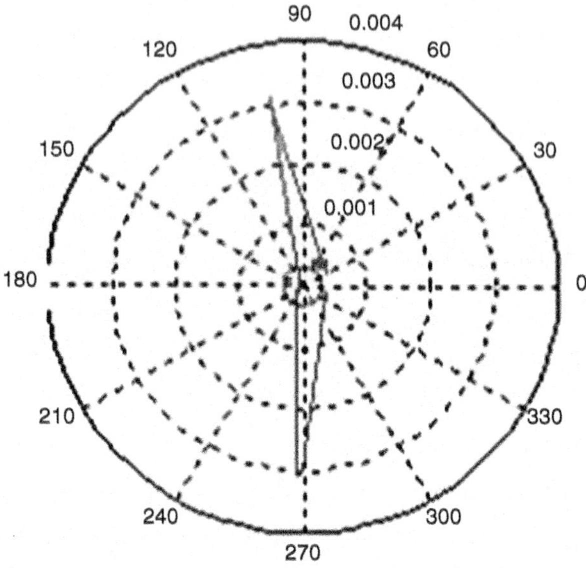

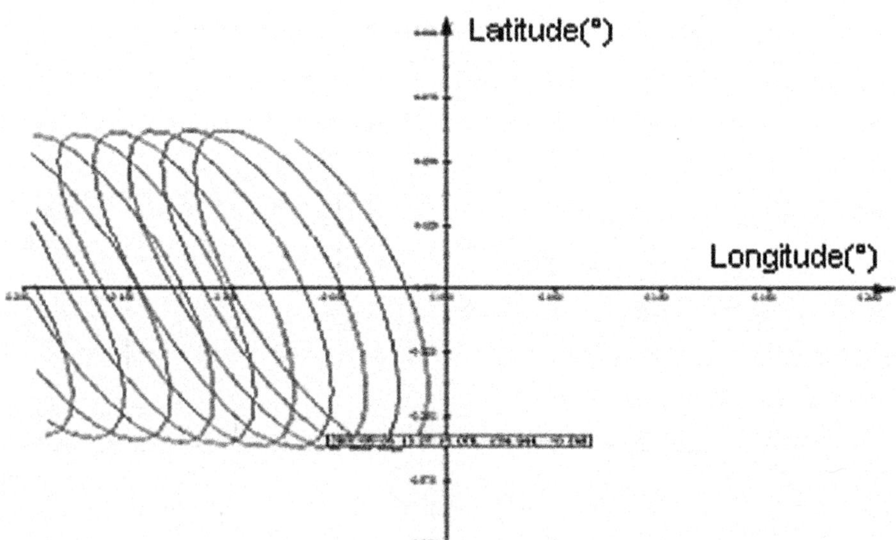

Fig. 7.35 Longitude drift scenario

pulses with opposite directions can be arbitrary, that is, the first pulse can be either westward or eastward. In this case, because the satellite already reaches the west border of the drift circle, to prevent the satellite from drifting over the border,

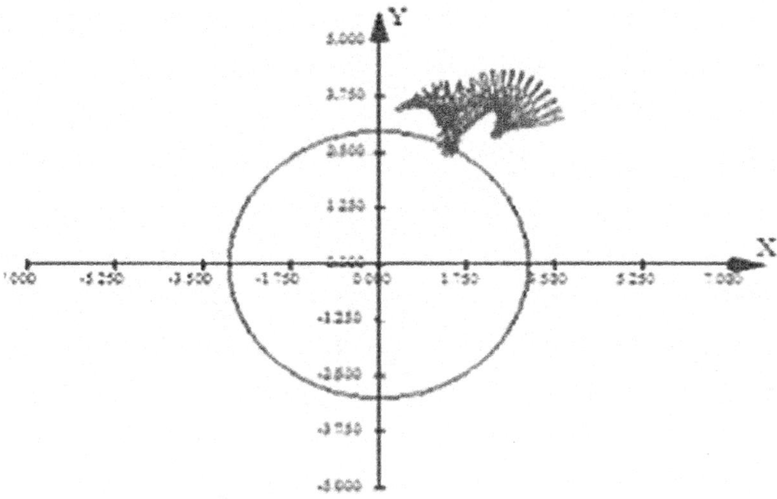

Fig. 7.36 Eccentricity drift scenario

choose westward pulse as the first pulse and force the satellite drift eastward after pulse execution. Therefore, the dual pulses with opposite directions are listed below:

First pulse (Westward)

Planning(UTC) / Velocity increment (m/s)	2007/05/26 04 : 43 : 28.692
Radial	0.012
Tangential	−0.234
Normal	−0.002

Second pulse (Eastward)

Planning(UTC) / Velocity increment (m/s)	2007/05/26 16 : 41 : 30.742
Radial	0.008
Tangential	0.147
Normal	0.001

3. Control process and orbit status after control

The first pulse (westward deceleration) decreases the semi-major axis and the longitude drift rate changes from D_0 to middle drift rate D_1. After half a day, the second pulse (eastward acceleration) increases the semi-major axis and the longitude drift rate changes to the goal of drift rate D_2, as shown in Fig. 7.36.

The eccentricity reaches the target eccentricity by dual pulses with opposite directions. It is located at the confined circle and lags behind the Sun of about 50°. The current solar longitude is about 63°, as shown in Figs. 7.37 and 7.38.

The longitude profile after those two reversed pulses is illustrated in Fig. 7.39, which indicates that the dual reversed pulses can realize not only the goal of longitude drift rate but also the goal of eccentricity.

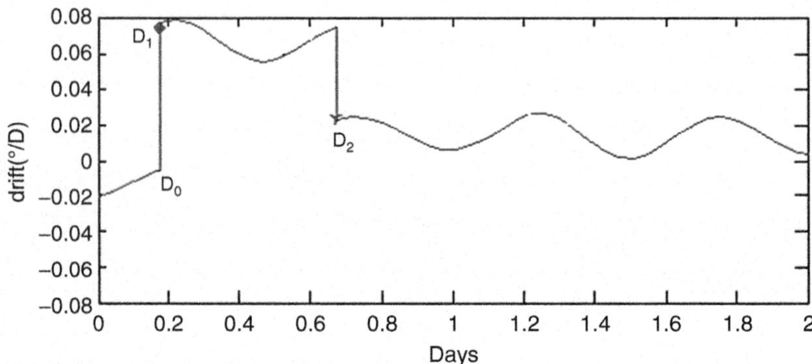

Fig. 7.37 Longitude drift rate profile

Fig. 7.38 Eccentricity profile

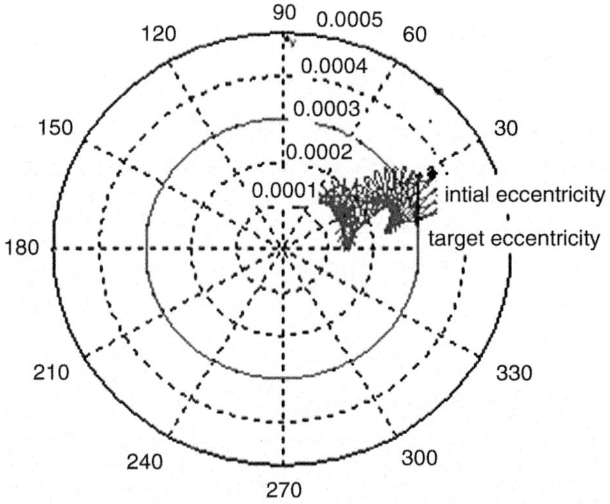

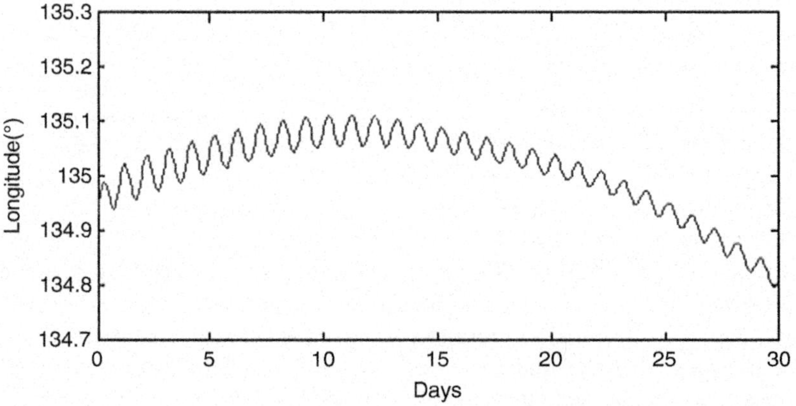

Fig. 7.39 The longitude evolution profile

7.3.8 Tri-Pulse Maneuver Planning

There is a problem of dual pulses with opposite directions: The size of east/west dual pulses is determined only by the drift rate and the eccentricity, but the mean longitude drifts a long distance and may go out of the "dead band" because of the dual pulses with an interval of a half day. For example, for east/west control of eccentricity, the velocity increment of eccentricity control is $\Delta v_e = 0.4$(m/s), the velocity increment considering westward drift rate control is $\Delta v_d = -0.1$(m/s), and the distribution of dual pulses with opposite directions is

$$\Delta v_1 = \Delta v_{\text{West}} = \frac{\Delta v_d - \Delta v_e}{2} = -0.25(\text{m/s})$$

$$\Delta v_2 = \Delta v_{\text{East}} = \frac{\Delta v_d + \Delta v_e}{2} = 0.15(\text{m/s})$$

The longitude drift increment due to the first pulse is

$$\Delta D = -\left(\frac{3}{V_s}\right) \cdot \Delta v_1 \cdot 360.9856 = 0.0881(°/\text{day})$$

Assuming the current drift rate is zero, after half a day before the second pulse, the longitude of the satellite already drifts eastward 0.044°. Obviously this is not the expecting result. Even if the second pulse achieves the control goal of eccentricity target, the satellite does not perturb along the drift ring because of longitude drifting deviation. Therefore, a third pulse is introduced to constrain the longitude drifting due to the first pulse.

7.3.8.1 Considering Westward Drift Rate Control

If the velocity increment of drift rate control $\Delta v_d \leq 0$, then the third pulse is assigned to be westward pulse.

$$\begin{cases} \Delta v_1 = k\Delta v_{\text{west}} \\ \Delta v_2 = \Delta v_{\text{east}} \\ \Delta v_3 = (1-k)\Delta v_{\text{west}} \end{cases} \quad 0 \leq k \leq 1 \tag{7.83}$$

Choose distribution factor to obtain minimum mean longitude drift after three-pulse control, as shown in Fig. 7.40a–c.

Due to dual pulses $\Delta v_1, \Delta v_2$ with the opposite directions and within an interval of half a day, the magnitude of longitude displacement is given by

$$\Delta\lambda = \frac{1}{2}D_1 + \frac{1}{2}D_2 = \frac{1}{2}D_1 + \frac{1}{2}(D_1 + \Delta D_2) = D_0 + \Delta D_1 + \frac{1}{2}\Delta D_2 \tag{7.84}$$

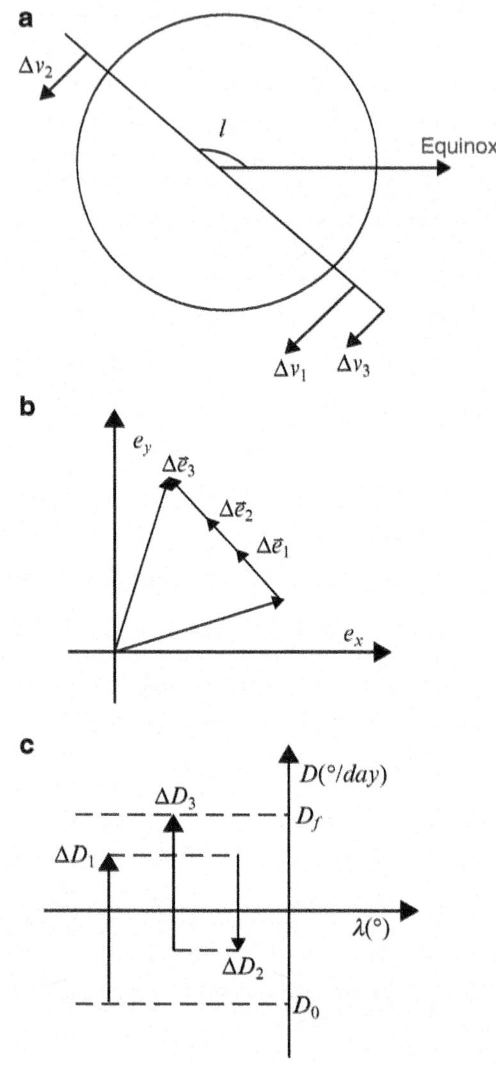

Fig. 7.40 Tri-pulse strategy for west pulse: (**a**) tri-pulse phase restriction, (**b**) tri-pulse eccentricity maneuver, (**c**) tri-pulse drift maneuver

In order to realize zero mean longitude drifting rate, the expression below should be satisfied.

$$D_0 + \Delta D_1 + \frac{1}{2}\Delta D_2 = 0$$

Then the first pulse must satisfy

$$\Delta v_1 = -\left(\frac{V_s}{3\omega_e}\right)\left(\frac{3}{2}\left(\frac{\omega_e}{V_s}\right)\Delta v_{\text{east}} - D_0\right) = -\frac{1}{2}\Delta v_{\text{east}} + \left(\frac{V_s}{3\omega_e}\right)D_0 \tag{7.85}$$

The distribution factor is

$$k = \frac{\Delta v_1}{\Delta v_{\text{west}}} = -\frac{1}{2}\left(\frac{\Delta v_{\text{east}}}{\Delta v_{\text{west}}}\right) + \left(\frac{2.8390}{\Delta v_{\text{west}}}\right)D_0 \tag{7.86}$$

If $k \geq 0$, then the initial drift rate satisfies

$$-\frac{1}{2}\left(\frac{\Delta v_{\text{east}}}{\Delta v_{\text{west}}}\right) + \left(\frac{2.8390}{\Delta v_{\text{west}}}\right)D_0 \geq 0,\ D_0 \leq D_{\max} = \frac{1}{2}\left(\frac{\Delta v_{\text{east}}}{2.839}\right)$$

If $k \leq 1$, then the initial drift rate satisfies

$$-\frac{1}{2}\left(\frac{\Delta v_{\text{east}}}{\Delta v_{\text{west}}}\right) + \left(\frac{2.8390}{\Delta v_{\text{west}}}\right)D_0 \leq 1,\ D_0 \geq D_{\min} = \left(\frac{\Delta v_{\text{west}}}{2.839}\right) + \frac{1}{2}\left(\frac{\Delta v_{\text{east}}}{2.839}\right)$$

Therefore, the tri-pulse strategy cannot guarantee the longitude maneuver objective and realize the drift rate and eccentricity maneuver objective either. Especially, when the initial drift rate satisfies $D_{\min} \leq D_0 \geq D_{\max}$, the mean longitude will be unchanged by tri-pulse strategy.

For example, the velocity increment of eccentricity control is $\Delta v_e = 0.4$(m/s), the velocity increment considering westward drift rate control is $\Delta v_d = -0.1$(m/s), and the eastward and westward of opposite velocity increments are distributed as

$$\Delta v_1 = \Delta v_{\text{West}} = \frac{\Delta v_d - \Delta v_e}{2} = -0.25(\text{m/s})$$

$$\Delta v_2 = \Delta v_{\text{East}} = \frac{\Delta v_d + \Delta v_e}{2} = 0.15(\text{m/s})$$

If the current initial drift rate is $D_0 = -0.03$(°/day), then the westward pulse distribution factor is

$$k = -\frac{1}{2}\left(\frac{\Delta v_{\text{east}}}{\Delta v_{\text{west}}}\right) + \left(\frac{2.8390}{\Delta v_{\text{west}}}\right)D_0 = 0.6407$$

The three pulses are

$$\begin{aligned}\Delta v_1 &= k\Delta v_{\text{west}} = -0.1602(\text{m/s})\\ \Delta v_2 &= \Delta v_{\text{east}} = 0.15(\text{m/s})\\ \Delta v_3 &= (1-k)\Delta v_{\text{west}} = -0.0898(\text{m/s})\end{aligned}$$

7.3.8.2 Considering Eastward Eccentricity Control

If the velocity increment of drift rate control $\Delta v_d > 0$, then the third pulse is assigned to be eastward pulse.

$$\begin{cases} \Delta v_1 = k\Delta v_{\text{east}} \\ \Delta v_2 = \Delta v_{\text{west}} \\ \Delta v_3 = (1-k)\Delta v_{\text{east}} \end{cases} \qquad 0 \le k \le 1 \tag{7.87}$$

For the same reason, the first pulse must satisfy

$$\Delta v_1 = -\left(\frac{V_s}{3\omega_e}\right)\left(\frac{3}{2}\left(\frac{\omega_e}{V_s}\right)\Delta v_{\text{west}} - D_0\right) = -\frac{1}{2}\Delta v_{\text{west}} + \left(\frac{V_s}{3\omega_e}\right)D_0 \tag{7.88}$$

The distribution factor is

$$k = \frac{\Delta v_1}{\Delta v_{\text{east}}} = -\frac{1}{2}\left(\frac{\Delta v_{\text{west}}}{\Delta v_{\text{east}}}\right) + \left(\frac{2.8390}{\Delta v_{\text{east}}}\right)D_0 \tag{7.89}$$

In the expression (Fig. 7.41),

$$D_0 \ge \frac{1}{2}\left(\frac{\Delta v_{\text{west}}}{2.839}\right) \quad \text{and } D_0 \le \left(\frac{\Delta v_{\text{east}}}{2.839}\right) + \frac{1}{2}\left(\frac{\Delta v_{\text{west}}}{2.839}\right)$$

In this example, the velocity increment of eccentricity control is $\Delta v_e = 0.4$(m/s), the velocity increment considering eastward drift rate control is $\Delta v_d = 0.1$(m/s), and the eastward and westward of opposite velocity increments are distributed as

$$\Delta v_1 = \Delta v_{\text{West}} = \frac{\Delta v_d - \Delta v_e}{2} = -0.15(\text{m/s})$$

$$\Delta v_2 = \Delta v_{\text{East}} = \frac{\Delta v_d + \Delta v_e}{2} = 0.25(\text{m/s})$$

If the current initial drift rate is $D_0 = 0.03$(°/Day), then the eastward pulse distribution factor is

$$k = \frac{\Delta v_1}{\Delta v_{\text{east}}} = -\frac{1}{2}\left(\frac{\Delta v_{\text{west}}}{\Delta v_{\text{east}}}\right) + \left(\frac{2.8390}{\Delta v_{\text{east}}}\right)D_0 = 0.6407$$

The three pulses are

$$\begin{aligned} \Delta v_1 &= k\Delta v_{\text{east}} = 0.1602(\text{m/s}) \\ \Delta v_2 &= \Delta v_{\text{west}} = -0.15(\text{m/s}) \\ \Delta v_3 &= (1-k)\Delta v_{\text{east}} = 0.0898(\text{m/s}) \end{aligned}$$

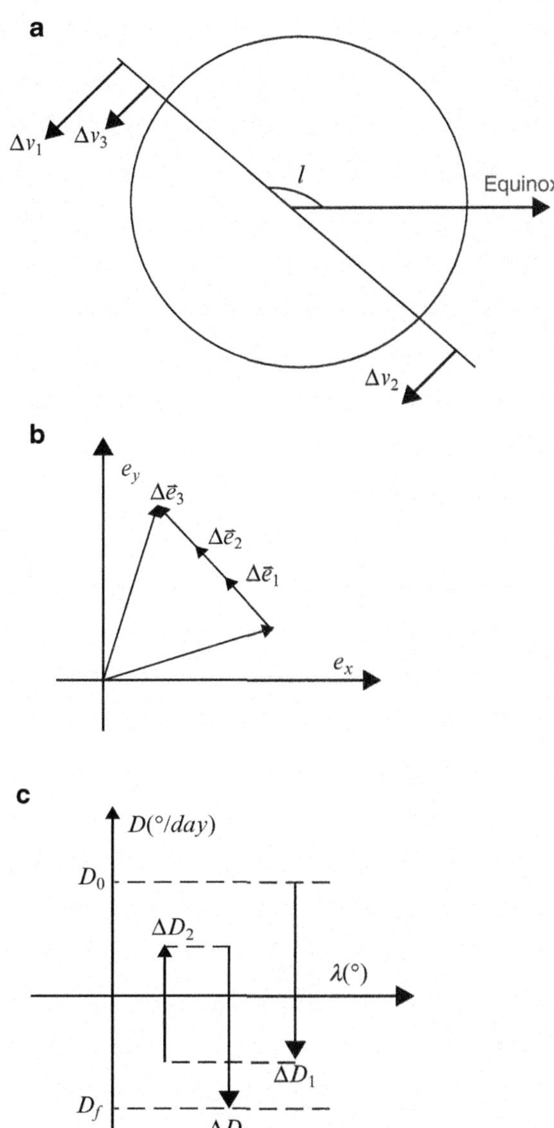

Fig. 7.41 Tri-pulse strategy for east pulse: (**a**) tri-pulse phase restriction, (**b**) tri-pulse eccentricity maneuver, (**c**) tri-pulse drift maneuver

The principle, strategy, and algorithm of the station keeping of geostationary satellite are discussed. For north/south station keeping, the design of inclination confined ring and the calculation of inclination control target for single satellite and collocated satellites are discussed. The relation between control moment and local satellite time is also discussed and a specific case simulation of the control process is given. For east/west station keeping, the complicated situation of coupling control of the drift rate and eccentricity is analyzed, including the distribution strategy and the pulse execution algorithm of single pulse, dual pulses with the same direction, dual pulses with opposite directions, and three pulses. This chapter covers the principle, strategy, and algorithm of station keeping of geostationary satellite, which should be well grasped by satellite engineers.

References

1. Kamel A, Ekman D, Tibbitts R (1973) East-west station keeping requirements of nearly synchronous satellites due to Earth's Tri-axiality and Luni-Lunar Effects. Celest Mech 8:129–148
2. Kamel A, Wagner C (1982) On the orbital eccentricity control of synchronous satellites. J Astronaut Sci 3(1):61–73
3. Chao CC, Baker JM (1983) On the propagation and control of geosynchronous satellites. J Astronaut Sci 4(1):99–115
4. Liu L (1992.8) Orbital dynamics for earth satellite. High Education Press, Beijing [In Chinese]
5. Li JS (1995.8) The precision orbit determination for earth satellite. PLA Press, Beijing [In Chinese]
6. Soop EM (1994.10) Handbook of geostationary orbits. Kluwer Academic Publishers, Dordrecht
7. Soop EM (1987) Coordinated station keeping at longitude 19 degrees west. OAD paper No.342, 1987
8. Montenbruck O (1989) Practical ephemeris calculations. Springer, Berlin
9. Li HN (2010.10) Geostationary satellite orbital analysis and collocation strategies. National Defense Industry Press, Beijing [In Chinese]

Chapter 8
Collocation Prototypes and Strategies

Abstract The mathematical prototypes serving as the guide specification to design collocation strategy for geostationary satellites are presented. A detailed assessment of the strategies used for efficient management of collocated satellites is provided. The relation between the separation distance with uncertainty of orbit determination (OD) and the orbit element offset is built for each pair of collocated satellites. The methods to build such relationship to meet the challenge of putting multi-geostationary satellites sharing the same position are put forward. The algorithms to allocate the longitude, eccentricity, and inclination for each satellite are given to ascertain that the mathematical prototypes are the guide specification to design collocation strategy for geostationary satellites.

8.1 Introduction

The geostationary satellite must be maintained in a circular orbit which is about 35,800 km above the terrestrial equator. Considering the satellite-free perturbation caused by the perturbation of space environment, generally speaking, a geostationary satellite takes about $\pm 0.1°$ of the equator's longitude. If we equally divide the equator by $\pm 0.1°$, theoretically, there will be 1,800 geostationary satellites in the orbit. Consequently, the geostationary orbit positioning longitude is limited resources and especially the one above Asia-Pacific and the Far East has already raised an international attention. Some terrestrial equator's countries have proposed sovereign rights for the geostationary orbit longitude above them, which has not been approved by most countries and organizations. Until 2006, there had been about 270 geo-satellites in working mode and many space junks in the geostationary orbit. There have been 2,300 geostationary satellites registered in ITU. Therefore, first, the geostationary orbit is insufficient, and second, considering backup satellites and other applications, two or more satellites need to share one longitude position. The

H. Li, *Geostationary Satellites Collocation*, DOI 10.1007/978-3-642-40799-4_8,

first cases of collocated satellites appeared in the 1980s, and the typical one was the Olympus communication satellite of ESA in W19°, which was collocated with one German satellite and two French satellites. By the use of eccentricity offset coordinated control strategy, the four satellites shared ±0.2° slot [4]. China has two pairs of satellites collocated in the same position, sharing ±0.1° slot. And another satellite of China shares ±0.1° slot with two satellites from different countries. So, the design and arrangement of satellite collocation control strategy to avoid satellite collision and electronic disturbance has already become a new task for geostationary orbit control. The design principle for geostationary orbit collocation strategy is that according to orbit position precision, the orbit constraint conditions for collocated satellites should be designed, leaving a relative separation distance between the collocated satellites. And then by choosing proper time and amount of East/West and North-South control, the collocated satellites should be maintained under the orbit constraint conditions during their whole lifetime to make sure that the collocated satellites operate safely. Therefore, the two major topics of geostationary satellite collocation strategies are as follows: Firstly, design orbit constraint conditions for collocated satellites according to collocation position precision, orbit perturbation characteristics, and satellite fuel requirements; secondly, design East/West and North-South maneuver algorithms to maintain the collocated satellites under the above orbit constraint conditions during their whole lifetime. Most references mainly discuss about the first part on how to design the constraint conditions according to specific collocation requirements. In this chapter, according to China's geostationary satellite collocation control practices, a comprehensive view of geostationary orbit collocation control strategy design method and the relationship between the collocated orbit offset and orbit stationary precision are given. Furthermore, the safety and effectiveness of typical geostationary satellite collocation control strategy are also analyzed in this chapter.

Multi-satellite collocation is an effective method for the geostationary orbit usage by maintaining multiple geostationary satellites at one equator longitude position. The collocation strategy is to design the constraint conditions for collocated satellites orbit and maintain the satellites under the above orbit constraint conditions during their whole lifetime to leave a safe separation distance and avoid collision through proper satellite East/West or North-South maneuvers. As a result, the two major issues of multi-satellite collocation techniques are as follows: Firstly, design orbit constraint conditions for collocated satellites according to collocation position precision, orbit perturbation characteristics, and satellite fuel requirements; secondly, design East/West and North-South maneuver algorithms to maintain the collocated satellites under the above orbit constraint conditions during their whole lifetime.

In the fixed position of radial-tangential-orthogonal coordinate, the relative motion equation of the geostationary satellite around the fixed position is constructed, and under the first-order approximation, the relative motion analytic expressions with geostationary orbit non-singularity orbit as variables are created. The relation between geostationary orbit non-singularity orbit elements and around-fixed position relative motion parameters is proposed. The relation between the minimum relative distance of the geostationary satellite around-fixed position motion and non-singularity orbit elements is given. The constraint conditions that the non-singularity orbit elements offset should meet when the collocated geo-satellites at the same longitude meet the minimum separation distance is presented. The design methods and mathematic theories of geostationary satellite orbit collocation control are described. The longitude separation drift ring assignment algorithm, the around position separation eccentricity offset control algorithm, the circumscribed separation circle four satellites collocation eccentricity relative offset algorithm, and the algorithm of inclination vector four quadrants offset base on separation slot are given by creating collocation satellite minimum approaching distance and orbit offset constraint equations.

8.2 Reference and Notation

For the convenience of description, define the equinox coordinate frame as follows:

The mean vernal equinox frame: the origin point is the center mass of the Earth; the basic plane is the satellite orbit plane; the right ascending Ω rotates clockwise from the orbit ascending node; $\mathbf{l}$ is the principal direction of mean vernal equinox frame; on the orbit plane, $\mathbf{g}$ is perpendicular to the principal direction; the orbit normal direction is $\mathbf{w}$; and consequently the $O-\mathbf{l}-\mathbf{g}-\mathbf{w}$ constructs the right-handed reference frame, in which defines the orientation of eccentricity and inclination. When the frame coincides with the J2000 inertial reference frame, the right ascending, the argument of perigee and the mean anomaly are measured on the same plane (Fig. 8.1).

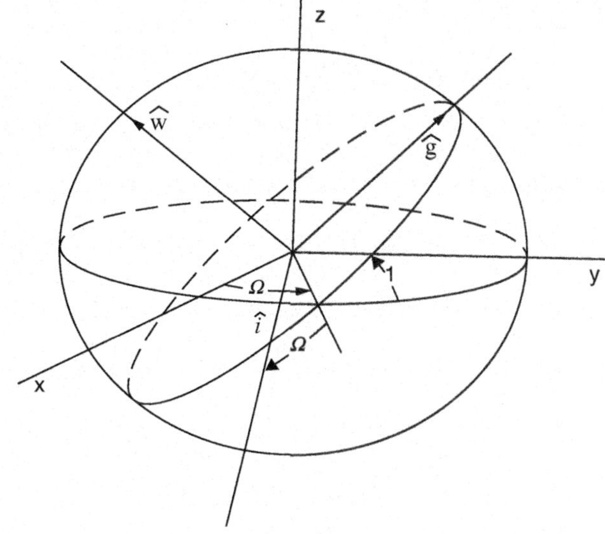

Fig. 8.1 Equinox coordinate frame

In the frame, the eccentricity vector is defined as follows: Its amplification is the orbit eccentricity, and its direction points to perigee within the orbit plane:

$$\mathbf{e} = \begin{bmatrix} e_x \\ e_y \end{bmatrix} = \begin{bmatrix} e\cos(\Omega+\omega) \\ e\sin(\Omega+\omega) \end{bmatrix} \tag{8.1}$$

The inclination vector is defined as follows: Its amplification is the orbit inclination, and its direction points to the orbit ascending node within the orbit plane:

$$\mathbf{i} = \begin{bmatrix} i_x \\ i_y \end{bmatrix} = \begin{bmatrix} i\cos\Omega \\ i\sin\Omega \end{bmatrix} \tag{8.2}$$

a_s: the semimajor axis of geostationary orbit
δa: the deviation of semimajor axis
$d_{\min}$: the minimum safety distance
$\delta\lambda$: the deviation of longitude
δe: the amplitude of the deviation of eccentricity
ω_e: the phase angle of the deviation of eccentricity
δi: the amplitude of the deviation of inclination
ω_i: the phase angle of the deviation of inclination
l: the mean right ascension ascending node

8.3 Collocation Relative Motion

With little orbit element offset, the relative motion of satellite B relative to satellite A can be obtained by linearizing unperturbed Kepler equation, and the omission of the natural perturbations in the relative motion can be justified by the fact that almost the same perturbations acting upon both satellites sharing the same longitude, and only the different cross-section to mass ratio, causes the eccentricity with the different steady drift circle. If the eccentricity vector offset is $\boldsymbol{\delta e}$, the inclination vector offset is $\boldsymbol{\delta i}$, the longitude difference is $\delta\lambda$, and the semimajor axis difference is δa between two collocated satellites, then the relative position is as follows:

$$\begin{cases} \delta R = \delta a - a_s(\delta e_x\cos(l) + \delta e_y\sin(l)) \\ \delta T = a_s\delta\lambda + 2a_s(\delta e_x\sin(l) + \delta e_y\cos(l)) \\ \delta N = a_s(\delta i_x\sin(l) - \delta i_y\cos(l)) \end{cases} \tag{8.3}$$

where

$$\boldsymbol{\delta}\mathbf{e} = \mathbf{e_A} - \mathbf{e_B} = \begin{pmatrix} \delta e_x \\ \delta e_y \end{pmatrix}$$

$$\mathbf{\delta i} = \mathbf{i_A} - \mathbf{i_B} = \begin{pmatrix} \delta i_x \\ \delta i_y \end{pmatrix}$$

$$\delta\lambda = \lambda_A - \lambda_B, \delta a = a_A - a_B$$

And a_s is the ideal geostationary semimajor axis, and l as a free argument is the right longitude measured along the tangential direction from the true vernal equinox point, taking into account of the magnitude and the phase angle of eccentricity and inclination difference, yields

$$\delta e = \sqrt{\delta e_x^2 + \delta e_y^2}, \quad \omega_e = a\tan\left(\frac{\delta e_y}{\delta e_x}\right)$$

And

$$\delta i = \sqrt{\delta i_x^2 + \delta i_y^2}, \quad \omega_i = a\tan\left(\frac{\delta i_y}{\delta i_x}\right)$$

Then Eq. (8.3) becomes simpler by

$$\begin{cases} \delta R = \delta a - a_s\delta_e \cos(l - \omega_e) \\ \delta T = a_s\delta\lambda + 2a_s\delta_e \sin(l - \omega_e) \\ \delta N = a_s\delta i \sin(l - \omega_i) \end{cases} \tag{8.4}$$

According to Eq. (8.4), the longitude offset only causes tangential separation distance, while the eccentricity offset induces not only radial but tangential separation distance. The inclination offset only brings normal separation distance, except for two points called as the relative ascension and descend node. The normal motion is independent of the equatorial motion, even with the same longitude, $\delta\lambda = 0$, and with different sets of orbit parameters can leave the relative distance beyond collision risk.

In the equations, δR is the radial motion equation of the satellite relative fixed position on the small deviation orbit, and this radial motion is related to the semimajor axis and eccentricity offset; δT is the tangential motion equation of the satellite relative fixed position, and this tangential motion is related to the orbit right ascension and eccentricity offset; δN is the orthogonal motion equation of the satellite relative fixed position, and the orthogonal motion is only related to the orbit inclination offset. According to the above relative motion equations, the normal motion is independent of the radial and tangential relative motion on the equatorial plane. The relative motion at the radial and tangential direction is an ellipse which has the mean right ascension l as an independent variable, and the ellipse equation is

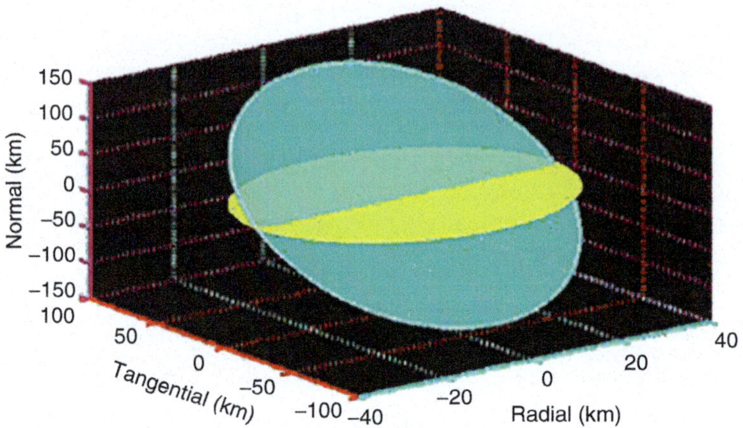

Fig. 8.2 Relative motion of geostationary satellite

$$\left(\frac{\delta r - \delta a}{\delta e \cdot a_s}\right)^2 + \left(\frac{\delta x - a_s \delta \lambda}{2\delta e \cdot a_s}\right)^2 = 1 \tag{8.5}$$

The equation shows that the projection motion on the local equator plane is an elliptic formation, which is centered at $(\delta a, a_s \delta \lambda)$. The semiminor axis is $\delta e \cdot a_s$ along the radial direction, and the semimajor axis is $2\delta e \cdot a_s$ along the tangential direction. Figure 8.2 illustrates the sceneries of relative motion with (blue) or without (yellow) inclination offset.

8.4 Collocation Principles

The principle of collocation separation strategies is leaving the relative distance beyond collision risk with different sets of orbit parameters which follow the perturbation motion of geostationary satellite and making use of station-keeping opportunities to maintain the difference during the mission life, so as to ensure the safety of collocated satellites.

Suppose for two satellites sharing the same longitude position, the relative position with each other is defined with the radial component δR, the tangent component δT and the normal component δN, and then the distance between them is given by

$$\mathrm{d} = \sqrt{\delta R^2 + \delta T^2 + \delta N^2}$$

All collocation strategies are based on the above expression on managing one or more components for distance to ensure that

$$d > d_{\min} > \mathbf{0}$$

where $d_{\min}$ is the minimum allowable separation distance between each pair of collocated satellites, which is decided by the uncertainty of orbit determination (OD) and unexpected uncertainties of orbit maneuver.

From Eq. (8.3), the longitude offset only causes tangential separation distance, while the eccentricity offset induces not only radial separation distance but also tangential separation distance. The inclination offset only causes normal separation distance, except for two points called as the relative ascension and descend node, and the normal motion is independent of the equatorial motion. So the principle of collocation separation strategies is leaving the relative distance beyond collision risk with different sets of orbit parameters which follow the perturbation motion of geostationary satellite, and making use of the station-keeping opportunities to maintain the difference during the mission life, so as to ensure the safety of collocated satellites.

8.5 Complete Longitude Separation

The simplest collocation strategy is to divide the slot into fragments, inside which each satellite is kept in an allocated region. Suppose the minimum allowable distance is $d_{\min}$, the minimum longitude separation $\delta\lambda$ should meet the following constraint:

$$\min\ \delta\lambda = \min|\lambda_2 - \lambda_1| \geq \frac{d_{\min}}{a_s} + |\delta\lambda_{\mathrm{NS}}| \tag{8.6}$$

where $|\delta\lambda_{\mathrm{NS}}|$ is the unexpected uncertainty of longitude displacements caused by the couplings of North-South station-keeping maneuver. If the duration to compensate the couplings is τ (generally $\tau = 24$ h) and the coupling ratio is κ, then the uncertainty of longitude displacements caused by the couplings could be estimated as

$$|\delta\lambda_{\mathrm{NS}}| = 3.78\kappa\tau$$

Suppose the East/West station-keeping period is T, the longitude acceleration at the nominal direction is $\ddot{\lambda}_n$, and the steady eccentricity drift radius is e_A, e_B, respectively, which are decided by the ratio of satellite area to satellite mass. To satisfy inequality (8.6), the central longitude of East/West drift circle should be allocated according to the following inequality:

$$|L_A - L_B| \geq 2(e_A + e_B) + \frac{1}{2}|\ddot{\lambda}_n|\left(\frac{T}{2}\right)^2 + \left(\frac{d_{\min}}{a_s}\right) + |\delta\lambda_{\mathrm{NS}}| \tag{8.7}$$

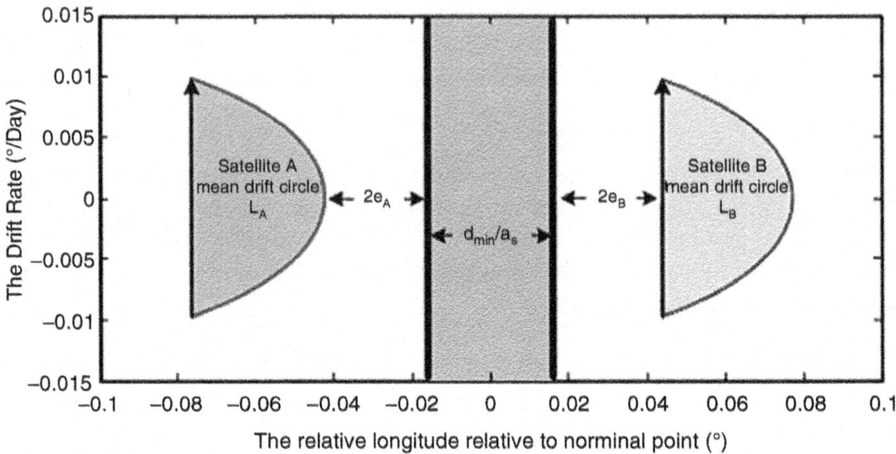

Fig. 8.3 The East/West cycle budget

In Fig. 8.3, where L_A and L_B are the central longitude of East/West drift circle for each collocated satellites. The first term on the right side of inequality (8.5) is the daily eccentricity effects with unsynchronized drift maneuvers; the second term on the right is the East/West maneuver cycle of duration T, which can be removed if the drift and eccentricity maneuvers for two satellites are synchronized. That is only practical if two satellites have approximately the same area to mass ratio and belong to the same operation owners. The third term is the longitude guardband. The fourth term is the unexpected uncertainty of longitude displacements caused by the couplings of North-South station-keeping maneuver. If the coupling control is compensated immediately after an inclination station-keeping maneuver, then this term can be omitted.

For example, suppose the minimum allowable distance between two satellites is 10 km; the East/West maneuver period is 14 days; the longitude acceleration where the two satellites are located is $-0.0014°$ per square of days; the eccentricity steady-state drift circle is 0.0003, which means that if the eccentricity vector points to the solar direction, then at any epoch the eccentricity should be smaller than the 0.0003; the north/south coupling ratio is 1 %. Then the typical longitude separation strategies for the two satellites sharing the same slot are listed in Table 8.1. The result shows that only the fourth strategy could keep the two satellites within $\pm 0.1°$ slot. The margins induced by the eccentricity and longitude coupling drifts consume a large portion of the slot. But the peer-to-peer allocation property makes it to be the resolution to separate satellites belonging to different owners, especially different countries.

The features of the first strategy:

- Each satellite occupies $\pm 0.1°$ longitude area and is maintained on each side of the designated longitude. Two satellites together occupy $\pm 0.2°$ longitude area. Therefore, the strategy is not suitable for the satellites with strict requirement of station-keeping precision.

Table 8.1 The longitude separation strategies and longitude offset

The longitude separation strategies	Drift circle offsetting	The portion allocated for A	The portion allocated for B	The slot requirement
Maneuver unsynchronized/ coupling compensate duration (1 day)	0.15°	$[\lambda_n - 0.13°, \lambda_n - 0.023°]$	$[\lambda_n + 0.023°, \lambda_n + 0.13°]$	±0.13°
*Maneuver unsynchronized/ coupling compensate at once	0.12°	$[\lambda_n - 0.11°, \lambda_n - 0.008°]$	$[\lambda_n + 0.008°, \lambda_n + 0.11°]$	±0.11°
Maneuver synchronized/coupling compensate duration (1 day)	0.12°	$[\lambda_n - 0.11°, \lambda_n - 0.008°]$	$[\lambda_n + 0.008°, \lambda_n + 0.11°]$	±0.11°
Maneuver synchronized/coupling compensate at once	0.08°	$[\lambda_n - 0.09°, \lambda_n - 0.01°]$	$[\lambda_n + 0.01°, \lambda_n + 0.09°]$	±0.09°

Note: E-W synchronized maneuver – two satellites are kept in their own drift circles and reach the west edge or east edge at the same time. E-W maneuver is basically kept synchronized
*: One Chinese satellite is collocated with two satellites of other countries by this strategy

- Each satellite can be controlled independently and the East/West keeping interval is 14–18 days.
- There is no special requirement of North-South station keeping and the independent control precision is ±0.1° and the coupling compensation after North-South maneuver can be delayed for 1 day.
- At least 10 km guardband is left between two satellites.
- The eccentricity should be controlled when East/West station-keeping maneuver is carried out, and the radius of the eccentricity control circle is $e_c = 3.0 \times 10^{-4}$.

The simulation result is illustrated in Fig. 8.4.

The features of the second strategy:

- Each satellite occupies ±0.05° longitude area and is maintained on each side of the designated longitude. Two satellites together occupy ±0.1° longitude area. Therefore, the strategy is suitable for the satellites with strict requirement of the station-keeping precision.
- Each satellite can be controlled independently and the East/West keeping interval should be shortened into 7–10 days.
- The independent control precision for North-South maneuver is ±0.1°, and the control period should be shortened or North-South maneuver coupling should be compensated immediately to degrade the effect of East/West maneuver coupling.

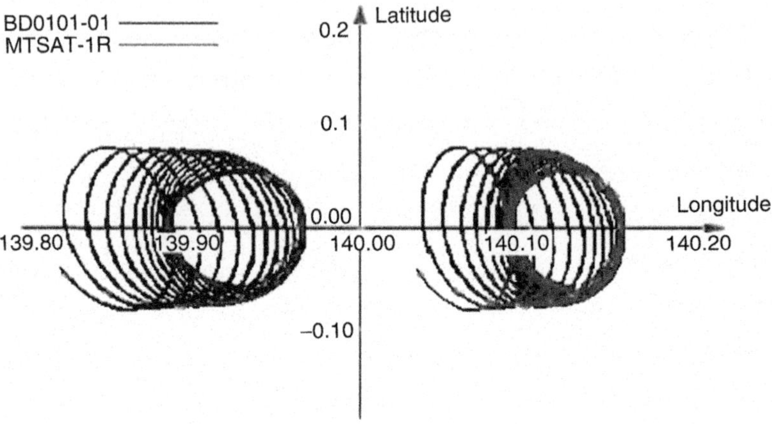

Fig. 8.4 Two satellites collocated by the first strategy

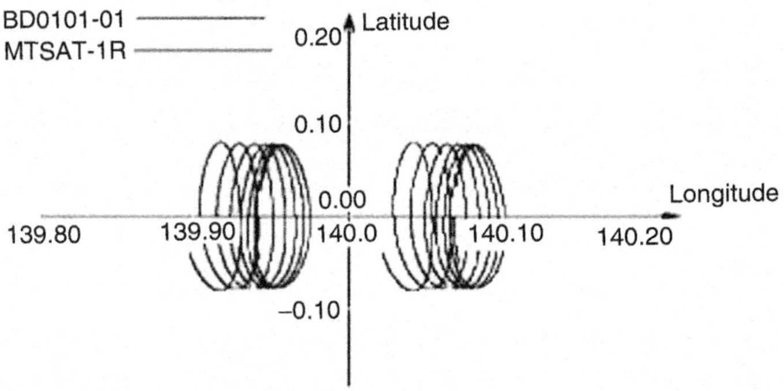

Fig. 8.5 Two satellites collocated by the second strategy

- At least 10 km guardband is left between two satellites.
- The eccentricity should be controlled when East/West station keeping is carried out, and the eccentricity should be less than 2.0×10^{-4}.

The simulation result is illustrated in Fig. 8.5.

8.6 Eccentricity Separation

The eccentricity offset causes both radial and tangential separation distance. The eccentricity collocation strategy based on maintaining the eccentricity deviation satisfies

$$0 < d_{\min} < \sqrt{\delta R^2 + \delta T^2}$$

which governs the eccentricity offset to ensure a minimum combined radial and along-track separation; the projection of relative motion to the radial and tangential plane is an ellipse which is

$$\left(\frac{\delta R-\delta a}{\delta e\cdot a_s}\right)^2+\left(\frac{\delta T-a_s\delta\lambda}{2\delta e\cdot a_s}\right)^2=1 \tag{8.8}$$

The equation shows that the projection motion on the local equator plane is an elliptic formation, which is centered at $(\delta a, a_s\delta\lambda)$. The semiminor axis is $\delta e\cdot a_s$ along the radial direction, and the semimajor axis is $2\delta e\cdot a_s$ along the tangential direction. Since the minimum distance is at the radial axis, in order to ensure that the separation distance is greater than the allowable approach distance $d_{\min}$, the eccentricity offset should satisfy the following restriction equations:

$$\begin{gathered}\delta R=\delta a+a_s\delta e\geq d_{\min}\\ \delta e\geq\frac{d_{\min}+|\delta a|}{a_s}\end{gathered} \tag{8.9}$$

where δa is the semimajor axis difference between the two collocated satellites. The presence of δa in expression (8.9) adds at most about 0.00007 eccentricity offset, since the maximum value of δa over a longitude drift cycle is approximately 2–3 km, when one satellite has the maximum eastward drift rate while the other has the maximum westward drift rate. If the East/West maneuvers are scheduled to keep in phase, δa in the eccentricity separation Eq. (8.9) can be eliminated in order to ensure relative small eccentricity offset.

For example, to achieve the minimum allowable separation distance of 10 km, the minimum eccentricity offset should satisfy

$$\delta e\geq\frac{d_{\min}+|\delta a|}{a_s}\geq 3.0\times10^{-4}$$

The relative phase angle of the eccentricity offset ω_e determines the relative argument of perigee. The time when the minimum and maximum separation distance appears, the choice of ω_e can be effectively arbitrary. However, in order to lower the longitude margins induced by the eccentricity, the eccentricity vectors of both satellites should be kept within the maximum confined circle, which means the offset $(\delta e_x, \delta e_y)$ should be orthogonal to both eccentricity vectors of collocated satellites by

$$\omega_e\approx a\tan\left(\frac{e_y}{e_x}\right)\pm\frac{\pi}{2} \tag{8.10}$$

$$\left(e_x,e_y\right)\equiv\left(e_x,e_y\right)_A\approx\left(e_x,e_y\right)_B \tag{8.11}$$

For the eccentricity separation strategy, the application requirements and the eccentricity steady-state drift circle related to the solar radiation pressure should be considered. In general, there are two strategies to separate the eccentricity vector. One is Absolute Eccentricity Offsetting Strategy (AEOS), which is suitable to the separation of a live broadcasting geostationary satellite and a navigation geostationary satellite, and the other is Relative Eccentricity Offsetting Strategy (REOS), which is suitable to the separation of two or more geostationary satellites with the same applications and maneuver requirements.

8.6.1 Absolute Eccentricity Offsetting Strategy

The strategy is suitable for the separation of a live broadcasting satellite and a navigation satellite. The former requires smaller eccentricity, while the latter requires greater eccentricity. Suppose there are a satellite A with small eccentricity, whose steady-state drift circle is e_{A}, and a satellite B with large eccentricity, whose steady-state drift circle is e_{B}. In order to maintain the allowable distance, the AEOS strategy ensures that the eccentricity offset $e_{\mathrm{B}}-e_{\mathrm{A}}$ is greater than δe at any time, that is,

$$e_{\mathrm{B}}-e_{\mathrm{A}}>\delta e \tag{8.12}$$

In consideration of perturbation motion and maneuver requirements of the eccentricity of geostationary satellite, we present two types of AEOS strategies here. The first one is eccentricity-free drifting strategy, which leaves the eccentricity of two collocated satellites pointing to solar direction and drifting freely, without considering maneuvering the eccentricity when East/West burns are scheduled. In this case, the eccentricity of satellite B is isolated by guard circle R, whose radius is $e_{\mathrm{A}}+\delta e$.

Suppose the right ascension of the Sun is α_s when the collocation strategy is put into practice. The eccentricity vector (the size and direction) is maneuvered according to the expressions below:

$$\begin{cases} e_{\mathrm{A}}^{x}=e_{\mathrm{A}}\cos\left(\alpha_s\right) \\ e_{\mathrm{A}}^{y}=e_{\mathrm{A}}\sin\left(\alpha_s\right) \end{cases} \tag{8.13}$$

$$\begin{cases} e_{\mathrm{B}}^{x}=\left(e_{\mathrm{A}}+|\delta e|\right)\cos\left(\alpha_s+\pi\right) \\ e_{\mathrm{B}}^{y}=\left(e_{\mathrm{A}}+|\delta e|\right)\sin\left(\alpha_s+\pi\right) \end{cases} \tag{8.14}$$

Figure 8.6 illustrates the eccentricity separation strategy, by which the eccentricity of satellite A and satellite B is Sun synchronous. The eccentricity of satellite A will drift from point A along the circle (a) for 1 year, while the eccentricity of B will drift from point B along the circle (b). The minimum eccentricity offset between two satellites is kept greater than the expected value δe, and the maximum eccentricity for satellite A and satellite B will be

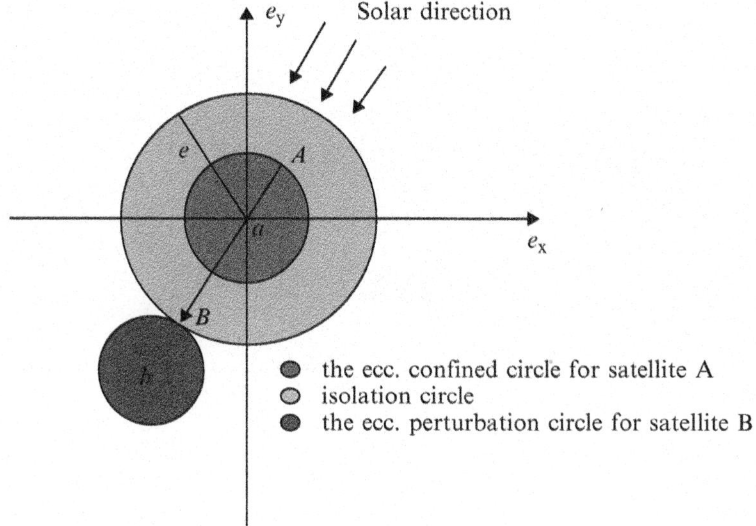

Fig. 8.6 Sun-synchronous eccentricity drifting strategy

$$e_{\mathrm{A}}^{\mathrm{Max}} = e_{\mathrm{A}} \tag{8.15}$$

$$e_{\mathrm{B}}^{\mathrm{Max}} = e_A + |\delta e| + 2e_{\mathrm{B}} \tag{8.16}$$

For example, if the steady-state drift circle of satellite A and B is $e_{\mathrm{A}} = e_{\mathrm{B}} = 3.0 \times 10^{-4}$, which corresponds with the area-to-mass ratio of about 0.028, and the eccentricity offset is $\delta e = 3.0 \times 10^{-4}$, then the maximum eccentricity of satellite B will be 12×10^{-4}, which will cause a longitude daily libration of 0.14° for satellite B, and satellite B will round around satellite A as illustrated in Fig. 8.7.

In order to decrease the eccentricity of satellite B, the eccentricity-oriented strategy should map the steady-state drift circle of satellite B outside the guard circle, and when it surpasses into the guard circle, the routine maneuvers will be taken to shift the eccentricity to the dedicated direction along the Sun. Suppose the duration of eccentricity routine maneuvers is T, and the right ascension of the Sun when the eccentricity is reoriented is α_s. As illustrated in Fig. 8.8, the eccentricity of satellite B points to point A, whose phase angle is ahead of the solar vision direction β, and the size is equal to the radius of the guard circle. Then,

$$\beta = \frac{n_s T}{2} - a\sin\left(\frac{e_{\mathrm{B}}}{R}\sin\left(\frac{n_s T}{2}\right)\right) \tag{8.17}$$

The eccentricity steady drift circle is shifted to intersect with the guard circle, leaving the arc ABC outside the guard circle, which leaves the eccentricity of satellite B to take (T/2) days to drift from point A to B, when the maximum

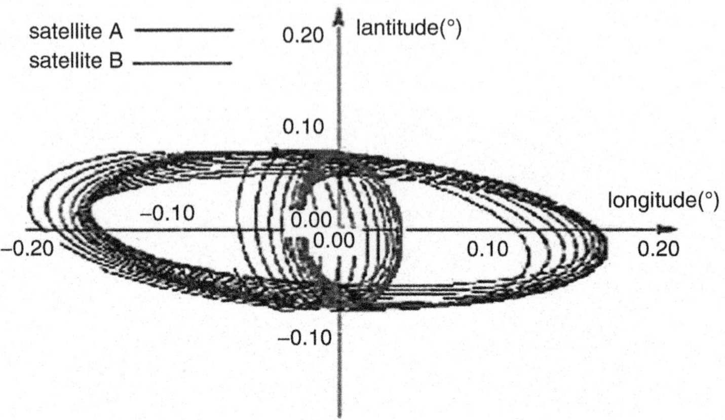

Fig. 8.7 Two collocated satellites by AEOS strategy

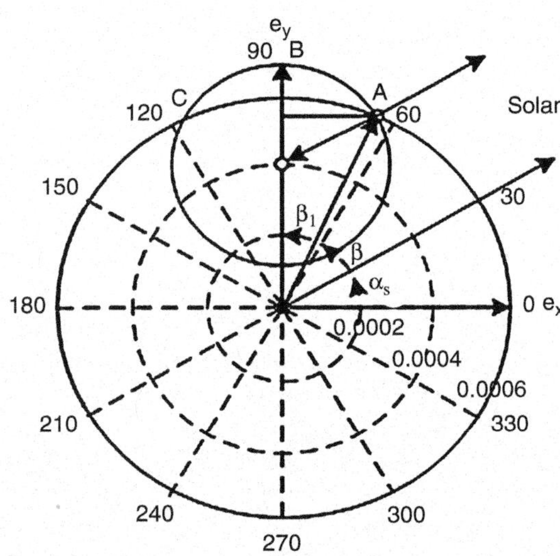

Fig. 8.8 The eccentricity reoriented strategy

eccentricity occurs, and after $(T/2)$ days, it drifts from point B to C, when the phase angle of eccentricity lags behind the solar direction, the eccentricity of satellite B will trespass into the guard circle. Then the center of the eccentricity steady drift circle of satellite B is given by

$$e_{\text{Box}} = \left(\sqrt{R^2 - e_{\text{B}}^2 \sin^2\left(\frac{n_s T}{2}\right)} - e_{\text{B}} \cos\left(\frac{n_s T}{2}\right) \right) \cos\left(\alpha_s + \frac{n_s T}{2}\right) \tag{8.18}$$

$$e_{\mathrm{Boy}} = \left(\sqrt{R^2 - e_{\mathrm{B}}^2 \sin^2\left(\frac{n_s T}{2}\right)} - e_{\mathrm{B}} \cos\left(\frac{n_s T}{2}\right)\right) \sin\left(\alpha_s + \frac{n_s T}{2}\right) \tag{8.19}$$

where $n_s = 0.9865$ is the solar mean motion, and its unit is degree per day.

The eccentricity of satellite B is

$$\begin{aligned} e_{\mathrm{B}}^x &= e_{\mathrm{B}0x} + e_{\mathrm{B}} \cos(\alpha_s), \\ e_{\mathrm{B}}^y &= e_{\mathrm{B}0x} + e_{\mathrm{B}} \sin(\alpha_s) \end{aligned} \tag{8.20}$$

The maximum eccentricity of satellite B is

$$e_{\mathrm{B}}^{\mathrm{Max}} = \sqrt{R^2 - e_{\mathrm{B}}^2 \sin^2\left(\frac{n_s T}{2}\right)} + e_{\mathrm{B}}\left(1 - \cos\left(\frac{n_s T}{2}\right)\right) \tag{8.21}$$

Obviously, the shorter the duration of eccentricity maneuver, the smaller the maximum eccentricity of satellite B. If the duration is $T = 365.2425$, since

$$\sin(n_s T/2) = \sin(\pi) = 0, \text{And} \cos(n_s T/2) = \cos(\pi) = -1,$$

the maximum eccentricity of satellite B is $e_{\mathrm{B}}^{\mathrm{Max}} = R + 2e_{\mathrm{B}}$. The result is totally similar to the case of leaving the eccentricity drifting freely.

The yearly total magnitude of eccentricity maneuver for satellite B can be estimated by the following expression:

$$\Delta e_{\mathrm{T}} \cong 4(R - e_{\mathrm{B}})\sqrt{2\left(\frac{R}{e_{\mathrm{B}}}\right) - 1} \tag{8.22}$$

For example, suppose the one-season-duration eccentricity maneuver strategy is adopted, as shown in Fig. 8.9. In spring, when the Sun is at the Earth equinox point, the eccentricity of satellite B should be oriented to point A, whose phase angle is ahead of the solar vision $\beta = 23.5°$; hence satellite B drifts along its eccentricity steady-state circle (b) from point A to point B, and the duration is one season. When the Sun is at the summer direction, the eccentricity reorienting maneuver should be scheduled so that the eccentricity vector will shift from B to C, and the eccentricity increment is

$$\left|\overrightarrow{BC}\right| = 2R \sin(\beta) \tag{8.23}$$

Similarly, in summer, the eccentricity of satellite B drifts freely from point C to D along the steady-state circle. In fall, it drifts freely from point E to F, and in

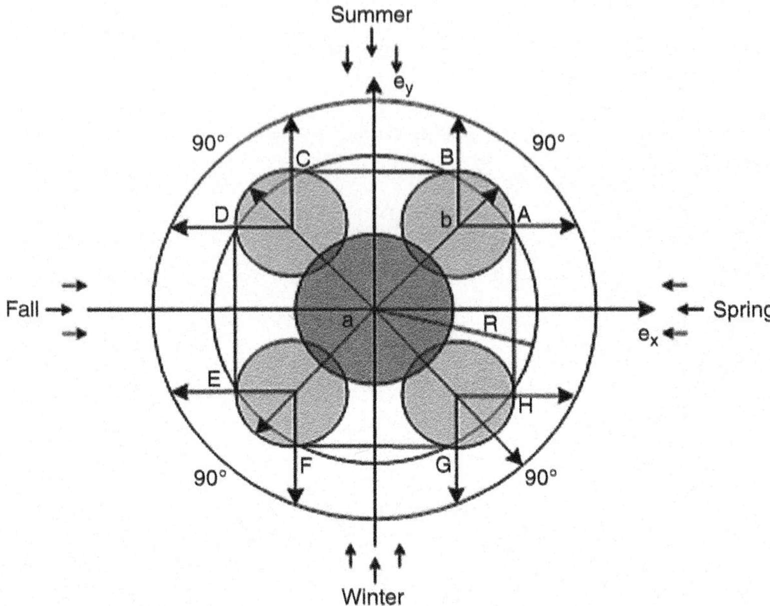

Fig. 8.9 Reorienting the eccentricity four times in a year

winter, it drifts freely from point G to H. The eccentricity route of satellite B in 1 year is $AB + CD + EF + GH$, and the eccentricity maneuver increment is

$$|\Delta e| = \left|\vec{BC}\right| + \left|\vec{DE}\right| + \left|\vec{FG}\right| + \left|\vec{HA}\right| = 8R\sin(\beta) \tag{8.24}$$

In this case, the eccentricity increment is

$$|\Delta e| = |\vec{BC}| + |\vec{DE}| + |\vec{FG}| + |\vec{HA}| = 8R\sin(\beta) = 0.0014 \tag{8.25}$$

The extra tangential velocity increment of eccentricity maneuver is

$$\Delta v_e = 1.5373 \times 10^3 \cdot \Delta e = 2.2\,(\text{m/s})$$

The maximum eccentricity of satellite B is

$$e_{\text{B}}^{\text{Max}} = \sqrt{R^2 - e_{\text{B}}^2 \sin^2\left(\frac{n_s T}{2}\right)} + e_{\text{B}}\left(1 - \cos\left(\frac{n_s T}{2}\right)\right) = 6.5 \times 10^{-4}$$

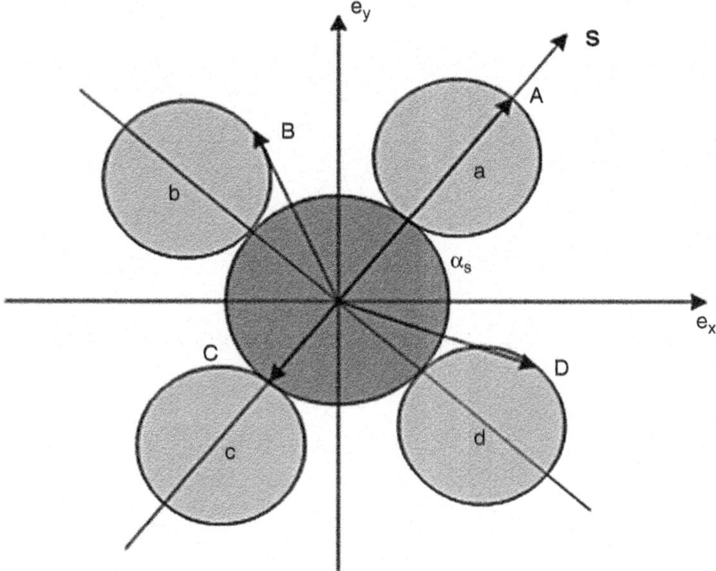

Fig. 8.10 Relative eccentricity separation strategy

8.6.2 Relative Eccentricity Offsetting Strategy

The relative eccentricity strategy is suitable for the separation of two or more geostationary satellites with the same applications and maneuver requirements. Suppose the steady-state drift circle of satellite A is e_A, and the steady-state drift circle of satellite B is e_B. For maintaining the allowable distance, the strategy ensures that the eccentricity offset $|e_B - e_A|$ is greater than δe in mission life, that is,

$$|e_B - e_A| > \delta e \tag{8.26}$$

Therefore, two satellites "orbit" relatively each other in one sidereal day. The relative eccentricity separation strategy for four collocated satellites is presented in Fig. 8.10. The eccentricity drift circles are defined to be the excircle of guard circle, whose radius is equal to the eccentricity separation δe.

Suppose the right ascension of the Sun when the collocation strategy is put into practice is α_s, and the eccentricity steady-state drift circles are a, b, c, and d for each collocating satellites, the radius are e_A, e_B, e_C, and e_D, respectively.

The eccentricity points to the solar direction, and for satellite A,

$$\mathbf{e}_A = (|\delta e| + 2e_A)\begin{pmatrix} \cos(\alpha_s) \\ \sin(\alpha_s) \end{pmatrix} \tag{8.27}$$

For satellite B,

$$\mathbf{e_B} = \sqrt{(|\delta e| + e_B)^2 + e_B^2} \begin{pmatrix} \cos\left(\alpha_s + \frac{\pi}{2} - a\tan\left(\frac{e_B}{|\delta e| + e_B}\right)\right) \\ \sin\left(\alpha_s + \frac{\pi}{2} - a\tan\left(\frac{e_B}{|\delta e| + e_B}\right)\right) \end{pmatrix} \quad (8.28)$$

For satellite C,

$$\mathbf{e_C} = |\delta e| \begin{pmatrix} \cos(\alpha_s + \pi) \\ \sin(\alpha_s + \pi) \end{pmatrix} \quad (8.29)$$

For satellite D,

$$\mathbf{e_D} = \sqrt{(|\delta e| + e_D)^2 + e_D^2} \begin{pmatrix} \cos\left(\alpha_s + \frac{3\pi}{2} + a\tan\left(\frac{e_D}{|\delta e| + e_D}\right)\right) \\ \sin\left(\alpha_s + \frac{3\pi}{2} + a\tan\left(\frac{e_D}{|\delta e| + e_D}\right)\right) \end{pmatrix} \quad (8.30)$$

The eccentricity separation strategy makes use of the eccentricity offset between each collocated satellites to manage the minimal allowable distance to safeguard the satellites. The costs for collocation are as follows: (1) the relative greater eccentricity required, which induces remarkable daily longitude libration; (2) the dedicated phase angle for the eccentricity is demanded, which have to be maneuvered with an extra burn to orient at interval. Table 8.2 summarizes the eccentricity separation strategy and budget of the longitude dead band.

The eccentricity collocation strategy ensures the physical separation of two vehicles but not necessarily their Radio Frequency (RF) separation. Because on the radial and tangential plane, one satellite relatively "orbits" the other in one sidereal day, and two satellites are aligned twice a day as seen from any equatorial Earth station. It is more practical to induce suitable inclination offset, so as to introduce the normal separation distance.

8.6.3 Evaluation of Eccentricity Separation Strategy

The budget of dead band and the extra cost for eccentricity separation strategies are evaluated in this section. Table 8.2 summarizes some typical eccentricity separation strategies, including their maximum daily libration induced by the eccentricity offset and the extra burn requirement for maintaining the eccentricity offset.

Table 8.2 The eccentricity separation strategies and budget of dead band

Typical eccentricity separation strategies	The maximum ecc./long. daily libration (satellite A)	The maximum ecc./long. daily libration (satellite B)	The ecc. maneuver and extra burn requirement (satellite A)	The ecc. maneuver and extra burn requirement (satellite B)
1. (AEOS) The strategy leaving eccentricity drift freely[a]	3×10^{-4}/ 0.034°	12×10^{-4}/ 0.14°	Sun-point eccentricity maneuver, no extra burn required	Sun-point eccentricity maneuver, no extra burn required
2. (AEOS) The strategy with reorienting the eccentricity four times 1 year	3×10^{-4}/ 0.034°	6.5×10^{-4}/ 0.075°	Sun-point eccentricity maneuver, no extra burn required	Sun-point eccentricity maneuver, extra burn required
3. (REOS) The strategy for four collocated satellites[b]	9×10^{-4}/0.10°	9×10^{-4}/0.10°	Coordinated eccentricity maneuver required	Coordinated eccentricity maneuver required

[a]When two satellites are maneuvered approaching to each other, this strategy nominates to safeguard the satellites

[b]The Olympus communication satellite was operated from 1989 to 1990 in the longitude slot 19.0° ± 0.2° in collocation with one German and two French satellites by this strategy [2]

8.6.3.1 The Features of Strategy One

- The mean longitude control and the eccentricity control of two satellites are independent and North-South control can be also carried out independently.
- Satellite B will require bigger eccentricity when it flies around satellite A and the longitude daily periodic oscillation can reach 0.14°. So, it's not suitable for the station keeping of direct broadcasting satellite.
- Random and independent control is selected for eccentricity pointing; therefore, it is more convenient for different countries or organizations to carry out the collocation control.
- Two satellites can be maintained at ±0.2° longitude slot around the designated position.

Figure 8.11 illustrates the scenario of two collocated satellites with strategy one.

8.6.3.2 The Features of Strategy Two

- If satellite B flies around satellite A, then East/West maneuver of satellite B should take into account the eccentricity and its direction. Three or four more times of eccentricity control should be carried out and the velocity increment is about 3–4 (m/s).

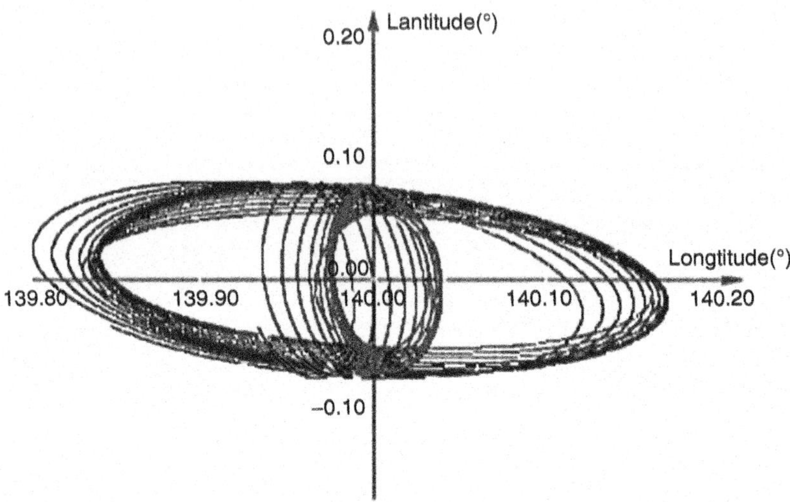

Fig. 8.11 Absolute eccentricity separation strategy

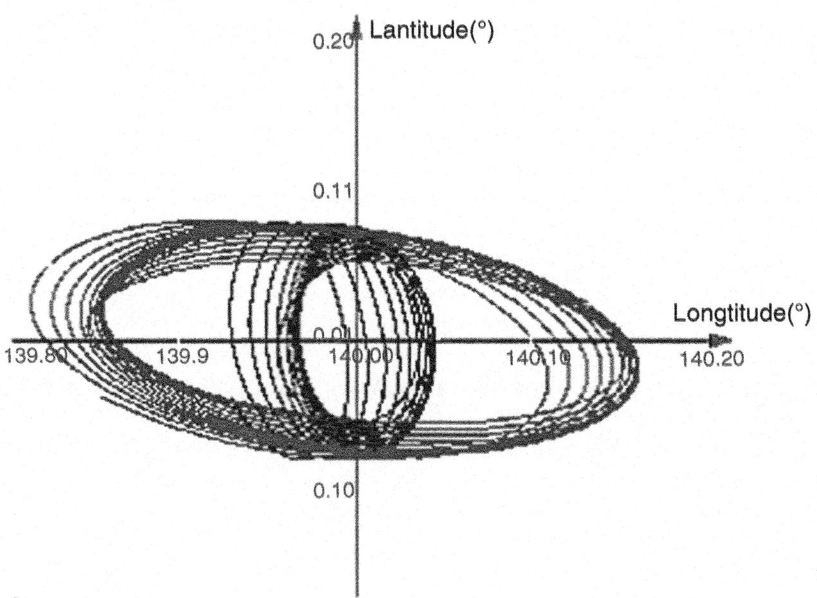

Fig. 8.12 Routine maneuvering the eccentricity strategy

– By decreasing the radius of the eccentricity control circle of satellite A appropriately, the precision of East/West control of two satellites can reach 0.1°.

Figure 8.12 illustrates the scenario of two collocated satellites with strategy one.

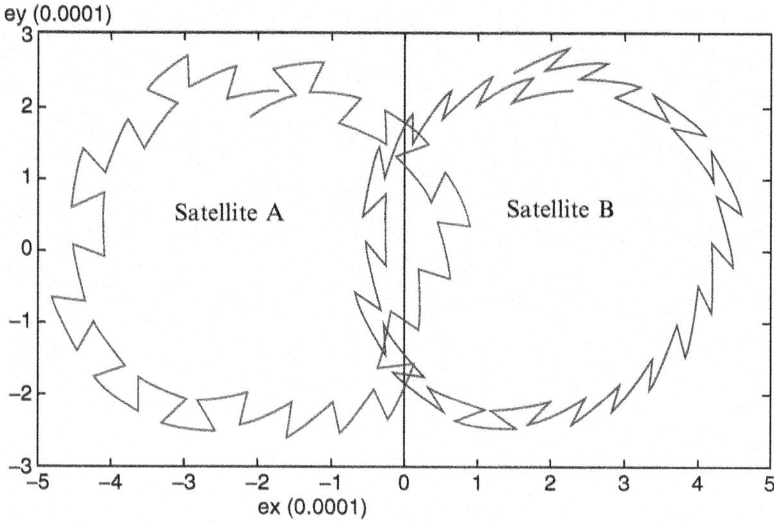

Fig. 8.13 Relative eccentricity separation strategy

8.6.3.3 The Features of Strategy Three

The eccentricity slot division of satellite A and B has the same priority, so it's easy to be accepted by every side in the cooperation collocation control by different countries. But, the eccentricity pointing selection and control of satellite A and B need cooperation which is not convenient for different organizations and control centers to maneuver the satellite independently.

- North-South control is independent and eccentricity pointing control should be coordinated in East/West maneuver.
- The precision of East/West control of two satellites can reach ±0.1°.

Figure 8.13 illustrates the scenario of two collocated satellites with strategy one. The eccentricity of satellite A and B is distributed on the positive and negative semiaxis of X axis. It's convenient for different countries and organizations to collocate their own satellites at the same designated longitude by East/West Sun pointing maneuver strategy and the even distributed eccentricity control circle.

Figures 8.14 and 8.15 show the collocation of two geostationary satellites sharing overlapped dead band and with a relative distance beyond collision by strategy three.

By eccentricity separation strategy, the Earth block problem cannot be avoided, because only for radial-tangential separation, at the time when the separation distance in the radial direction becomes zero, the separation distance is physically safe in the radial direction, but as two satellites point to the Earth in the same line, the blocking will occur highly possibly. Therefore, the separation distance in the orthogonal direction should be introduced on the fundament of the separation on the radial-tangential plane.

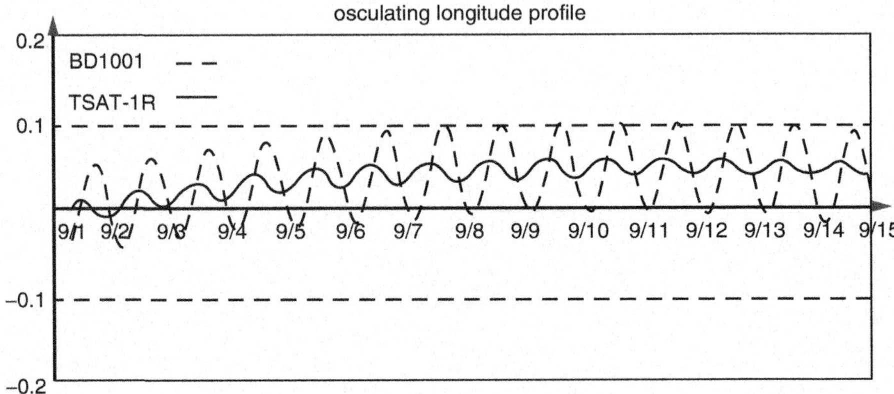

Fig. 8.14 Overlapped dead band

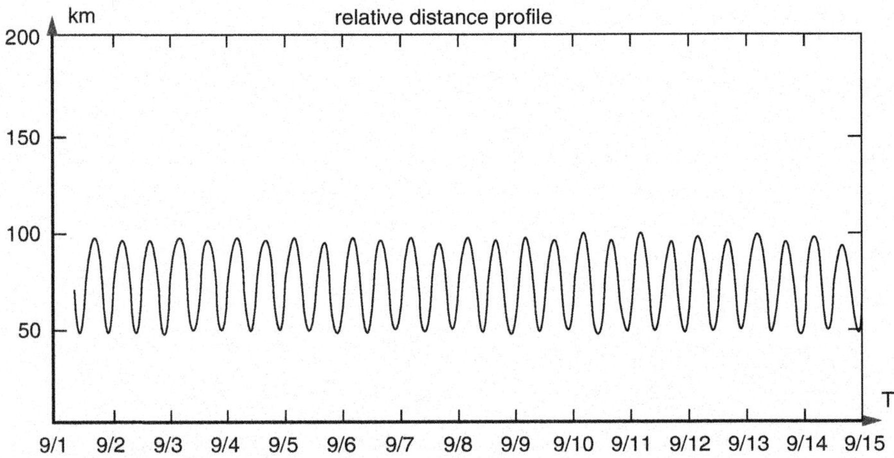

Fig. 8.15 The relative distance (km)

8.6.4 Solar Leading Eccentricity Control Strategy

The main task of geostationary satellite collocation control is to maintain relative stable eccentricity offset by making use of eccentricity perturbation and East/West control. The design and maintenance of eccentricity offset is related to collocation strategies, and in this section we will introduce the eccentricity separation circle offset and its control target.

Assume that the radius of the eccentricity separation circle is R and the radius of the free perturbation circle of eccentricity of a satellite is R_e. The eccentricity of the satellite is kept out of the eccentricity separation circle in all year to maintain the

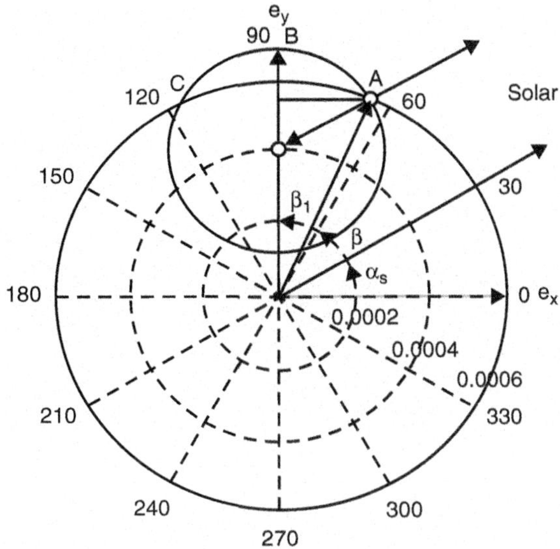

Fig. 8.16 The solar-ahead strategy

offset to other satellite's eccentricity. According to the movement principles of free perturbation of eccentricity, suppose the centralized control period of eccentricity is *T*. As shown in Fig. 8.16, the control target of the eccentricity ahead of the Sun is that the initial eccentricity points to A and the eccentricity perturbs to C freely during the control period. In the whole control period, it is not allowed to enter into the eccentricity separation circle.

Suppose the eccentricity ahead of solar angle is β and the current Sun right ascension is α_s. The strategy leaves the eccentricity target ahead of solar vision to make sure the eccentricity trespass the eccentricity confined circle, so

$$\begin{aligned} \beta + \beta_1 &= \left(\frac{T}{2}\right) n_s \\ \sin \beta_1 &= \left(\frac{R_e}{R}\right) \sin \left(\frac{T n_s}{2}\right) \end{aligned} \tag{8.31}$$

Therefore, the phase of eccentricity ahead of solar angle satisfies

$$\beta = \left(\frac{T}{2}\right) n_s - \arcsin\left(\left(\frac{e_{\mathrm{B}}}{R}\right) \sin\left(\frac{n_s T}{2}\right)\right) \tag{8.32}$$

Suppose the radius of the eccentricity separation circle is 0.0006, and the radius of the free perturbation circle of eccentricity is 0.0004, and then the relation among the satellite's separation eccentricity, the eccentricity ahead of solar angle, and the centralized control of the eccentricity is illustrated in Fig. 8.17. The longer the eccentricity control period, the bigger the eccentricity ahead of solar angle; on the contrary, the shorter the eccentricity control period, the smaller the eccentricity ahead of solar angle.

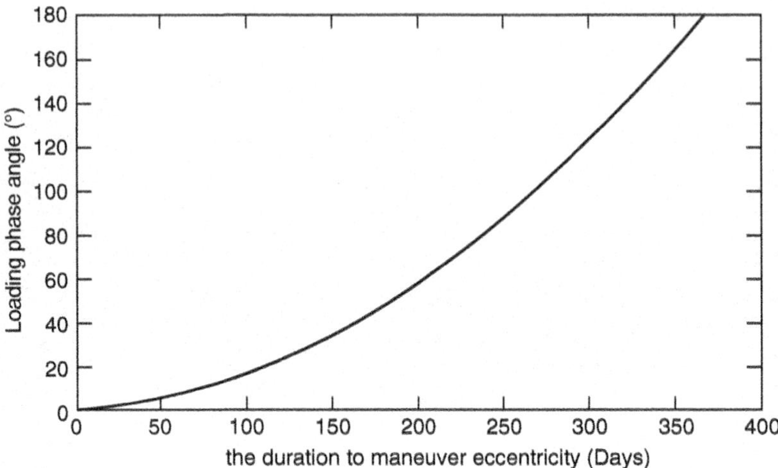

Fig. 8.17 The solar-ahead angle with expected interval

Therefore, after we leave the eccentricity ahead of solar vision, the expected eccentricity should be initialized as

$$\mathbf{e_A} = \begin{pmatrix} e_x \\ e_y \end{pmatrix} = e_c \cdot \begin{pmatrix} \cos(\alpha_s + \beta) \\ \sin(\alpha_s + \beta) \end{pmatrix} \tag{8.33}$$

Under this condition, the eccentricity vector will follow the perturbation circle which is governed by the solar radiation pressure and is centralized as

$$e_{\mathrm{Box}} = \left(\sqrt{R^2 - e_{\mathrm{B}}^2 \sin^2\left(\frac{n_s T}{2}\right)} - e_{\mathrm{B}} \cos\left(\frac{n_s T}{2}\right)\right) \cos\left(\alpha_s + \frac{n_s T}{2}\right) \tag{8.34}$$

$$e_{\mathrm{Boy}} = \left(\sqrt{R^2 - e_{\mathrm{B}}^2 \sin^2\left(\frac{n_s T}{2}\right)} - e_{\mathrm{B}} \cos\left(\frac{n_s T}{2}\right)\right) \sin\left(\alpha_s + \frac{n_s T}{2}\right) \tag{8.35}$$

Here, $n_s = 0.9856(°/\mathrm{day})$

As illustrated in Fig. 8.11, the maximum eccentricity is at point B, and the magnitude of the maximum eccentricity is

$$e_{\max} = \sqrt{R^2 - R_e^2 \sin^2\left(\frac{n_s T}{2}\right)} + R_e\left(1 - \cos\left(\frac{n_s T}{2}\right)\right) \tag{8.36}$$

Obviously, the maximum value of eccentricity relies on the centralized control period of eccentricity. Suppose the radius of the eccentricity separation circle is 0.0006, and the radius of the free perturbation circle of eccentricity is 0.0004, and then the relation among the satellite's separation eccentricity, the maximum

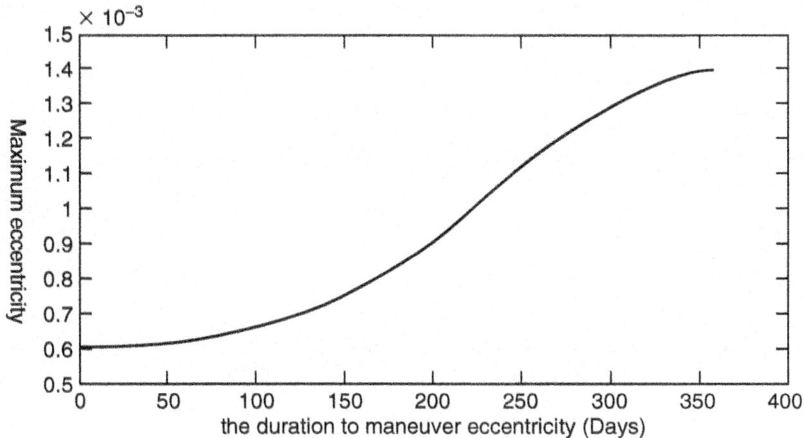

Fig. 8.18 The maximum eccentricity

eccentricity is illustrated in Fig. 8.18. The longer the period of eccentricity control, the greater the maximum eccentricity; on the contrary, the shorter the period of eccentricity control, the smaller the maximum eccentricity.

If there is no eccentricity control for 1 year, i.e., the control period is 1 year, then the eccentricity leading phase angle is 180°. Because

$$\sin\left(\frac{Tn_s}{2}\right) = \sin(\pi) = 0 \quad \text{and, } \cos\left(\frac{Tn_s}{2}\right) = \cos(\pi) = -1$$

from expression (8.32), the eccentricity ahead of solar angle is

$$\beta = \frac{n_s T}{2} - a\sin\left(\frac{R_e}{R}\sin\left(\frac{n_s T}{2}\right)\right) = \frac{n_s T}{2} = \pi \tag{8.37}$$

and from expression (8.33), the magnitude of the maximum eccentricity is

$$e_{\max} = \sqrt{R^2 - R_e^2 \sin^2\left(\frac{n_s T}{2}\right)} + R_e\left(1 - \cos\left(\frac{n_s T}{2}\right)\right) = R + 2R_e \tag{8.38}$$

For example, suppose the radius of the separation circle $R = 6.0 \times 10^{-4}$, and the radius of the perturbation circle $R_e = 4.0 \times 10^{-4}$, and then the magnitude of the maximum eccentricity will reach $e_{\max} = 14.0 \times 10^{-4}$, when we leave the initial eccentricity vector ahead of solar vision, and it follows the expression

$$\mathbf{e}_A = \begin{pmatrix} e_x \\ e_y \end{pmatrix} = R \cdot \begin{pmatrix} \cos(\alpha_s + \beta) \\ \sin(\alpha_s + \beta) \end{pmatrix} = \begin{pmatrix} -R\cos(\alpha_s) \\ -R\sin(\alpha_s) \end{pmatrix} \tag{8.39}$$

Then the eccentricity vector will follow the perturbation circle which is derived by the solar radiation pressure and is centralized according to expressions (8.34) and (8.35) as

$$\begin{cases} e_{\text{Box}} = -(R+R_e)\cos\alpha_s \\ e_{\text{Boy}} = -(R+R_e)\sin\alpha_s \end{cases} \tag{8.40}$$

so if we want to restrict the magnitude of eccentricity to achieve appropriate libration for the satellite, the interval with which the eccentricity is maneuvered should be budgeted by

$$\sqrt{R^2 - R_e^2 \sin^2\left(\frac{n_s T_{\max}}{2}\right)} + R_e\left(1 - \cos\left(\frac{n_s T_{\max}}{2}\right)\right) = e_c \tag{8.41}$$

Here,

$e_c (e_c \geq R)$ is expected to be the maximum magnitude of eccentricity.

$T_{\max}$ is the longest interval required to maintain the eccentricity.

The above equation is a nonlinear function about the maximum control period of $T_{\max}$, and because the maximum eccentricity is a monotone function of the control period T, it's easy to be solved by numerical method.

For example, if the maximum eccentricity is confined as $e_c = 7.0 \times 10^{-4}$ $(\delta\lambda = 0.08°)$, then the longest period of eccentricity control is $T_{\max} = 127$ days.

If the maximum eccentricity is confined as $e_c = 6.5 \times 10^{-4} (\delta\lambda = 0.075°)$, then the longest period of eccentricity control is $T_{\max} = 94$ days.

As shown in Fig. 8.19, the longest control period of eccentricity $T_{\max} = 127$ days. When the mean right ascension of the Sun is at the vernal equinox and points to s_1, the point of eccentricity control target is ahead of solar angle of about 26.4° and is located at point A of the separation circle of eccentricity. The eccentricity moves along the perturbation circle and when the Sun reaches s_2 after 127 days, the eccentricity arrives at point B on the separation circle. And at this time, the eccentricity vector lags behind the Sun of about 26.4°; the eccentricity will reach into the separation circle through point B. So, the centralized eccentricity control should be carried out to make the eccentricity move from point B to point C, and the strategy keeps the eccentricity out of the confined circle (red) with three eccentricity maneuvers per year.

The control value is $\Delta e = 2R\sin\beta = 5.3356 \times 10^{-4}$

For the same reason, the eccentricity perturbs freely from point C to point D. By centralized eccentricity control, the eccentricity moves from point D to point E, and after three times of centralized control, it will reach point A, so the centralized control value in 1 year is about

$$\Delta e = 3 * 2R\sin\beta = 0.0016$$

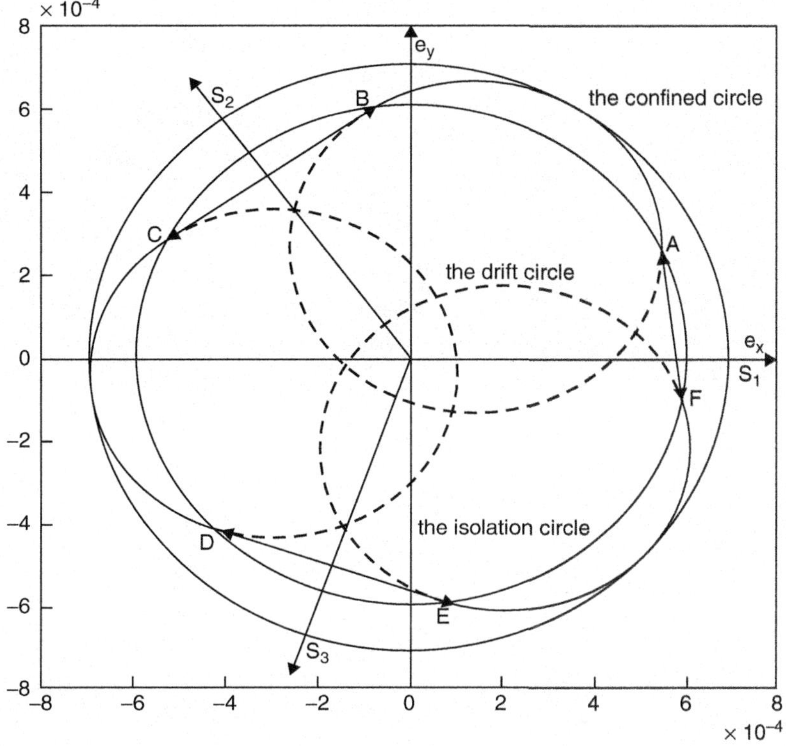

Fig. 8.19 Three eccentricity maneuvers per year

When the free-drift eccentricity is left internally to tangent with the control circle of eccentricity, the eccentricity will reach its maximum value. The maximum magnitude is equal to the radius of the control circle. As illustrated in Fig. 8.20, the eccentricity separation strategy follows the above constriction, and the simulation scenery shows the eccentricity history in 1 year and indicates that the adopted strategy is suitable for maintaining the eccentricity satisfying the collocation restriction.

If the maximum control period of eccentricity $T_{\max} = 365.24$ days and when the right ascension of the Sun arrives at the vernal equinox and points to point s_1, then the eccentricity control target point ahead of the solar angle is about 180° and is located at point A of the eccentricity separation circle. Figure 8.21 illustrates that the strategy with 180° ahead of solar keeps the eccentricity out of the confined circle for 1 year and the maximum eccentricity will reach

$$e_{\max} = R + 2R_e = 14.0 \times 10^{-4}$$

As illustrated in Fig. 8.22, the eccentricity separation strategy follows the above constriction, and the simulation scenery shows the eccentricity history in 1 year and indicates that the adopted strategy is suitable for maintaining the eccentricity satisfying the collocation restriction.

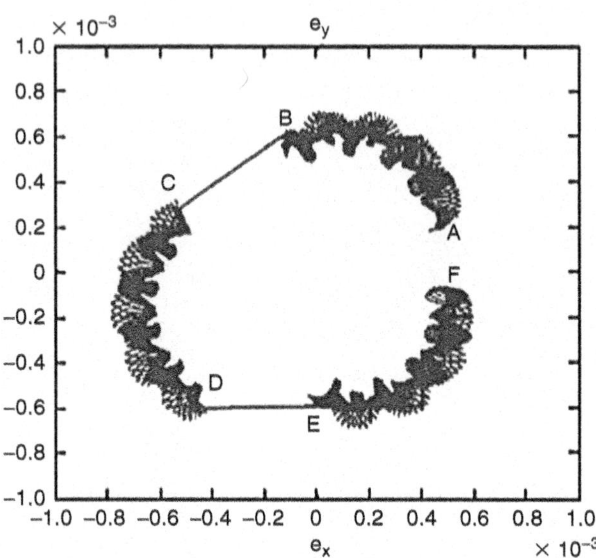

Fig. 8.20 The simulation result

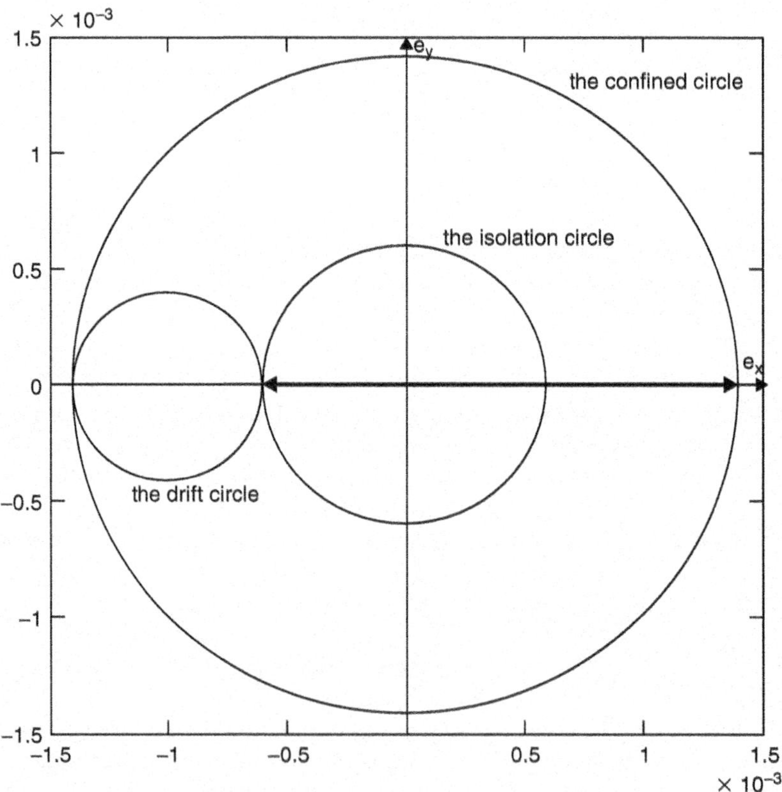

Fig. 8.21 Keeping the eccentricity out of confined circle

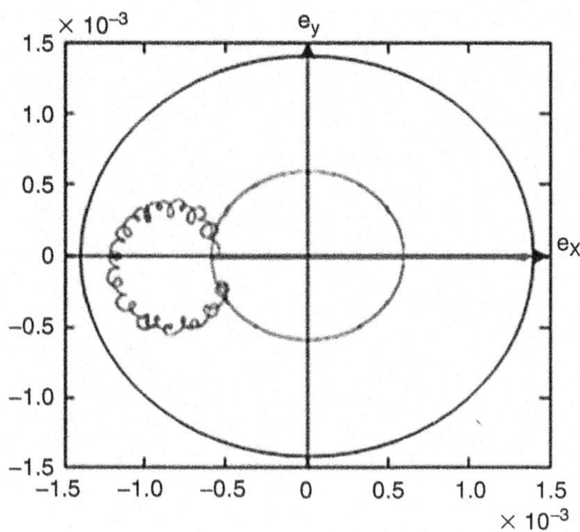

Fig. 8.22 The simulation result

8.7 Combined Eccentricity and Inclination Separation

8.7.1 *The Mathematical Prototype of E/I Strategy*

By introducing the inclination offset $(\delta i_x, \delta i_y)$ of collocated satellites, according to the normal component of the small deviation equation,

$$\delta N = a_s \delta i \sin(l - \omega_i) \tag{8.42}$$

In the equation

$$\delta i = \sqrt{\delta i_x^2 + \delta i_y^2}, \quad \omega_i = \tan^{-1}\left(\frac{\delta i_y}{\delta i_x}\right)$$

δi is the inclination offset; ω_i is the offset argument of inclination, which is measured from the anticlockwise direction of the vernal equinox.

When the mean right ascension of satellite is $l = \omega_i \pm k\pi$, the orthogonal distance of two satellites caused by the inclination offset is zero. By single inclination offset, collocated satellites cannot be separated, so it is not sufficient to maintain minimal allowable distance $d_{\min}$, but by adding the inclination offset to the eccentricity offset strategy, one can ensure that two vehicles are never in conjunction as seen from a particular Earth station. The tangential separation is conjunct to the East/West maneuver schedule, and the reliable distance is still the radial separation distance, which is induced by the eccentricity offset. When East/West control is non-synchronized, because of the mean longitude offset, the separation distance in the tangential direction becomes zero. The geostationary East-West control is only a relative short period of orbit control, and it is unrealistic to ask for synchronized East-West control of collocated satellites, especially for the satellites controlled by different control centers. So, when the orbit plane of collocated satellite is intersected, the inclination offset must be parallel or counter-parallel to the eccentricity offset when the longest relative distance in the tangential direction is required.

When cross-track separation vanishes, in order to ensure δR and δN are not in phase, and maximize the disjunction of two vehicles, one should keep the equation

$$\omega_i = \omega_e, \quad \text{or} \quad \omega_i = \omega_e + \pi$$

The result can also be got from Eq. (8.3).

By ignoring δa (the drift ring of East-West is basically equal, so the maximum deviation of semimajor axis $\delta a \leq 3$ km), from Eq. (8.3), the equations for the radial and orthogonal directions are

$$\begin{cases} \delta R = -a_s\left(\delta e_x \cos l + \delta e_y \sin l\right) \\ \delta N = a_s\left(\delta i_x \sin l - \delta i_y \cos l\right) \end{cases} \tag{8.43}$$

When the relative distance in the orthogonal direction is zero, the mean right ascension satisfies

$$0 = a_s\left(\delta i_x \sin l - \delta i_y \cos l\right)$$

$$\sin l = \frac{\delta i_y}{\delta i}, \quad \cos l = \frac{\delta i_x}{\delta i}$$

When the relative distance in the orthogonal direction is zero, the relative distance in the radial direction satisfies

$$\begin{aligned} \delta R &= -a_s\left(\delta e_x \cos l + \delta e_y \sin l\right) = -a_s\left(\delta e_x \frac{\delta i_x}{\delta i} + \delta e_y \frac{\delta i_y}{\delta i}\right) \\ &= -\frac{a_s}{\delta i}\left(\delta \vec{i} \cdot \delta \vec{e}\right) = -\frac{a_s}{\delta i}\delta i \cdot \delta e \cdot \cos\left(\widehat{\delta \vec{i}, \delta \vec{e}}\right) = -a_s \cdot \delta e \cdot \cos\left(\widehat{\delta \vec{i}, \delta \vec{e}}\right) \end{aligned} \tag{8.44}$$

When the relative distance in the orthogonal direction is zero, in order to get the longest separation distance in radial direction,

$$\left|\cos\left(\widehat{\delta \vec{i}, \delta \vec{e}}\right)\right| = 1 \tag{8.45}$$

or $\omega_i = \omega_e$, or $\omega_i = \omega_e + \pi$

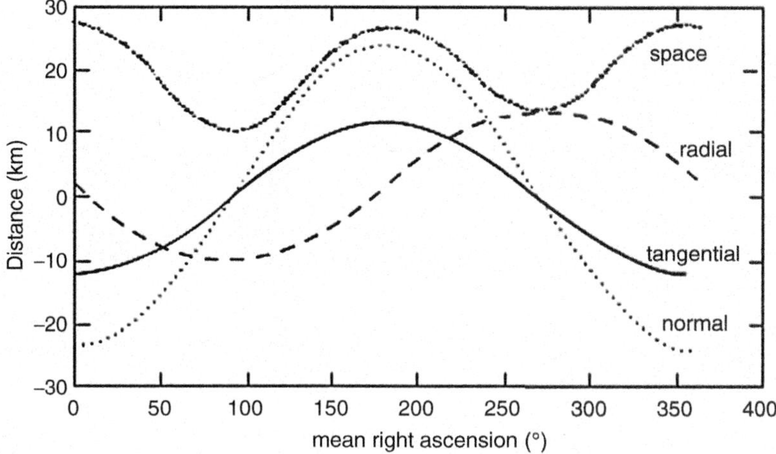

Fig. 8.23 The relative distance with right ascension

which means the inclination offset should be parallel to the eccentricity offset, so the prototype of the combined eccentricity and inclination offset strategy is defined by

$$\delta e \geq \frac{d_{\min} + |\delta a|}{a_s} \tag{8.46}$$

$$\delta i \geq \frac{d_{\min}}{a_s} \tag{8.47}$$

$$|\delta a + a_s \delta e \cos(\omega_e - \omega_i)| \geq d_{\min} \tag{8.48}$$

$$\omega_e \cong a\tan\left(\frac{\delta e_y}{\delta e_x}\right) \pm \frac{\pi}{2} \tag{8.49}$$

For example, to maintain the minimum allowable distance to be 10 km, the minimum eccentricity and inclination offset should satisfy

$$\delta e \geq \frac{d_{\min} + |\delta a|}{a_s} \geq 3.0 \times 10^{-4}$$

$$\delta i \geq \frac{d_{\min}}{a_s} \geq 0.0136^{\circ}$$

As shown in Fig. 8.23, when the inclination offset is parallel or counter-parallel to the eccentricity offset, no matter the East-West control of collocated satellites is synchronized ($\delta\lambda = 0$) or unsynchronized ($\delta\lambda \neq 0$), the distance between two satellites is assured to be longer than the minimum separation distance if the above offsetting collocation separation strategy is satisfied.

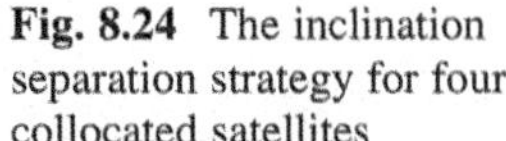
Fig. 8.24 The inclination separation strategy for four collocated satellites

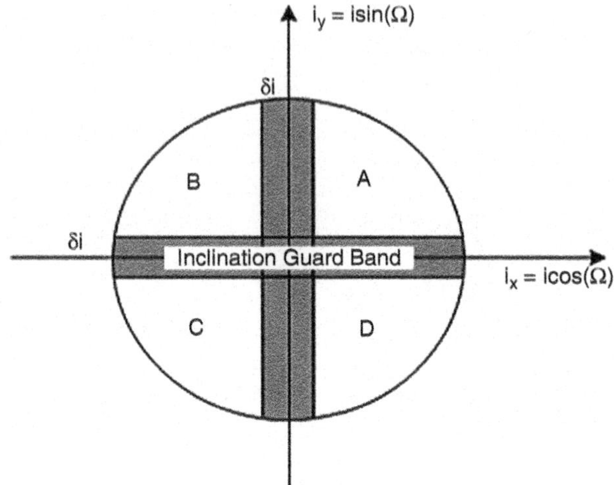

The simulation is carried out to ascertain that if the orbit offset is with the above-mentioned eccentricity and inclination offset, the minimal distance could ensure the separation beyond the risk of physical collision, with ($\delta\lambda = 0$) or without ($\delta\lambda \neq 0$) the East/West maneuver coordinated strategy.

8.7.2 Inclination Distribution Strategy

Multiple geostationary satellites may be collocated by applying the combined eccentricity and inclination offset strategy successively to each pair in the same slot. If the eccentricity offset for four satellites is adopted as shown in Fig. 8.10, then the additional inclination offset can be planed as illustrated in Fig. 8.24.

Suppose the maximum inclination restriction circle is $i_{\max}$ (in general $i_{\max} = 0.1°$) and the inclination offset is δi. One should leave guardband along i_x direction and i_y direction to insulate the inclination vectors into each quadrant.

If the radius of the inclination keeping circle of collocated satellites is $i_{\max}$ (the station-keeping precision of North-South is generally 0.1°), and the offset of inclination separation is δi, then, as shown in Fig. 8.27, by the inclination offsetting strategy, the reasonable constraint of the inclination vector of the four collocated satellites are

The inclination and the right ascension of the ascending node of satellite A $(i_{\mathrm{A}}, \Omega_{\mathrm{A}})$ are given by

$$\sqrt{2}\delta i \le i_{\mathrm{A}} \le i_{\max} \tag{8.50}$$

$$a\sin\left(\frac{\delta i}{2i_{\max}}\right) \le \Omega_{\mathrm{A}} \le a\cos\left(\frac{\delta i}{2i_{\max}}\right) \tag{8.51}$$

The inclination and the right ascension of the ascending node of satellite B $(i_{\mathrm{B}}, \Omega_{\mathrm{B}})$ are given by

$$\sqrt{2}\delta i \le i_{\mathrm{B}} \le i_{\max} \tag{8.52}$$

$$\frac{\pi}{2} + a\sin\left(\frac{\delta i}{2i_{\max}}\right) \le \Omega_{\mathrm{B}} \le \pi - a\sin\left(\frac{\delta i}{2i_{\max}}\right) \tag{8.53}$$

The inclination and the right ascension of the ascending node of satellite C $(i_{\mathrm{C}}, \Omega_{\mathrm{C}})$ are given by

$$\sqrt{2}\delta i \le i_{\mathrm{C}} \le i_{\max} \tag{8.54}$$

$$\pi + a\sin\left(\frac{\delta i}{2i_{\max}}\right) \le \Omega_{\mathrm{C}} \le \frac{3\pi}{2} - a\sin\left(\frac{\delta i}{2i_{\max}}\right) \tag{8.55}$$

The inclination and the right ascension of the ascending node of satellite D $(i_{\mathrm{D}}, \Omega_{\mathrm{D}})$ are given by

$$\sqrt{2}\delta i \le i_{\mathrm{D}} \le i_{\max} \tag{8.56}$$

$$\frac{3\pi}{2} + a\sin\left(\frac{\delta i}{2i_{\max}}\right) \le \Omega_{\mathrm{D}} \le 2\pi - a\sin\left(\frac{\delta i}{2i_{\max}}\right) \tag{8.57}$$

For using the eccentricity and inclination offset of two satellites, the conflict between the North-South coordinate and independent control should be considered. For collocation control of the satellites controlled by different centers, independent control of each satellite should be concentrated. For satellites controlled by one center, appropriate coordinate control is allowed to decrease the frequency of control.

8.7.3 Inclination Maintenance Strategy

When the inclination control of multiple satellites is carried out, the inclination vectors are usually confined in their own keeping areas. For instance, by four-satellite collocation control strategy, the inclination vectors of four satellites are confined in different four quadrants along the separation slot of i_x and i_y. Figure 8.25 indicates the optimization of the direction of inclination maneuver for four satellites sharing the same slot.

Suppose the width of the separation slot along i_x and i_y is δi, and the radius of the mean inclination control circle is i_d. If the yearly mean inclination perturbation

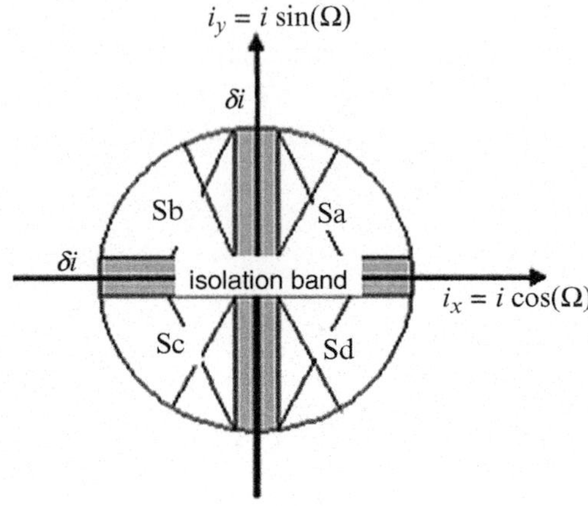

Fig. 8.25 Inclination maneuvers sharing the same slot

direction is Ω_d, in order to keep the free perturbation time as long as possible in the mean inclination control circle of four satellites, then the control targets of four satellites are

1. $\Omega_d \leq 90°$

The control target of satellite A is

$$\mathbf{i}_\mathrm{f} = \begin{pmatrix} \delta i/2 \\ \delta i/2 \end{pmatrix} \tag{8.58}$$

The control target of satellite B is

$$\mathbf{i}_\mathrm{f} = \begin{pmatrix} -\delta i/2 + (\delta i/2 - i_d \cos(\arcsin(\delta i/2i_d)))/\tan(\Omega_d) \\ \delta i/2 \end{pmatrix} \tag{8.59}$$

The control target of satellite C is

$$i_f = i_d \tag{8.60}$$

$$\Omega_f = \frac{\pi}{2} + \Omega_d + a\cos\left(\frac{\delta i|1 - \tan\Omega_d|}{2i_d\sqrt{1 + \tan^2\Omega_d}}\right) \tag{8.61}$$

The control target of satellite D is (Fig. 8.26)

$$i_f = i_d \tag{8.62}$$

$$\Omega_f = \frac{3\pi}{2} + a\sin\left(\frac{\delta i}{2i_d}\right) \tag{8.63}$$

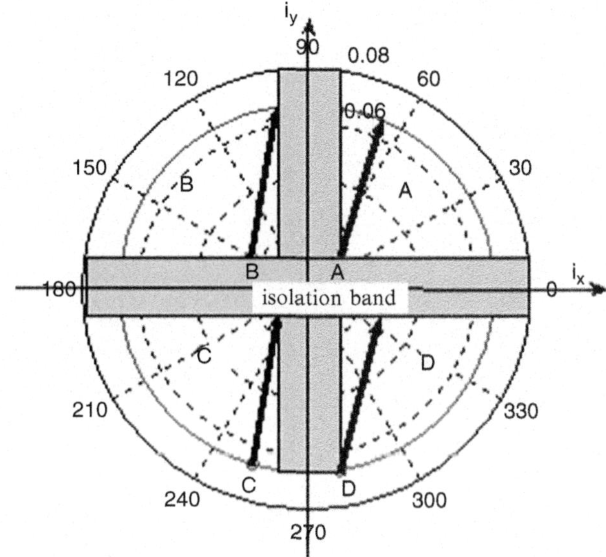

Fig. 8.26 Inclination target for drift direction

2. $\Omega_d > 90°$

The control target of satellite A is

$$\mathbf{i_f} = \begin{pmatrix} \dfrac{\delta i}{2} + \dfrac{1}{\tan \Omega_d}\left(\dfrac{\delta i}{2} - i_d \cos\left(a \sin\left(\dfrac{\delta i}{2 i_d}\right)\right)\right) & \dfrac{\delta i}{2} \end{pmatrix} \tag{8.64}$$

The control target of satellite B is

$$\mathbf{i_f} = \begin{pmatrix} -\delta i/2 \\ \delta i/2 \end{pmatrix}, \tag{8.65}$$

The control target of satellite C is

$$i_f = i_d \tag{8.66}$$

$$\Omega_f = \frac{3\pi}{2} - \arcsin\left(\frac{\delta i}{2 i_d}\right) \tag{8.67}$$

The control target of satellite D is (Fig. 8.27)

$$i_f = i_d \tag{8.68}$$

$$\Omega_f = \pi + \Omega_d + \arcsin\left(\frac{\delta i |1 + \tan \Omega_d|}{2 i_d \sqrt{1 + \tan^2 \Omega_d}}\right) \tag{8.69}$$

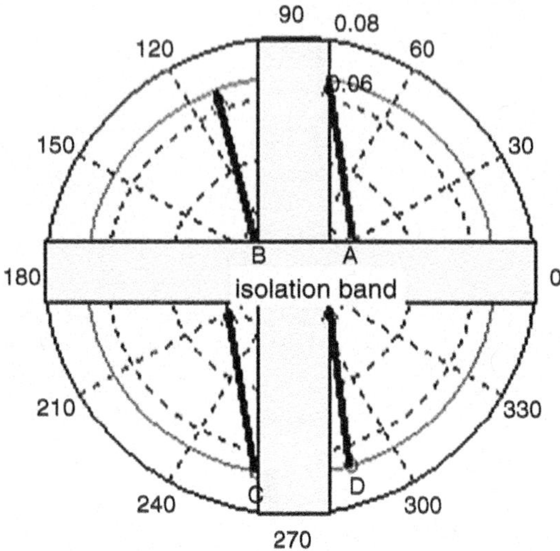

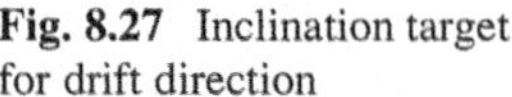
Fig. 8.27 Inclination target for drift direction

8.8 A Bi-Satellite E/I Combined Separation Method

For collocation control by different organizations, besides independent East-West control, independent North-South control is also expected. So, if it is acceptable to increase the frequency of North-South control, then split the inclination control circle into left and right half along i_y and satellite A and B are all controlled in their own half circle. The separation slot in the middle is determined by orbit determination and control precision.

Inclination Vector Setting Suppose the offset of inclination is δi, the inclination mean perturbation direction of the year is Ω_d, and the radius of the control circle is i_d. In order to maintain the longest free perturbation time in the control circle of the mean inclination of two satellites, the control target of the mean inclination of two satellites is shown in Fig. 8.28.

1. When the even perturbation direction of the mean inclination $\Omega_d \leq 90°$

   The control target of the inclination vector of satellite A is

$$\mathbf{i_f} : \left(i_f = i_d, \Omega_f = \frac{\pi}{2} + 2\Omega_d - \arcsin\left(\frac{\delta i}{2 i_d}\right)\right) \tag{8.70}$$

   The control target of the inclination vector of satellite B is

$$\mathbf{i_f} : \left(i_f = i_d, \Omega_f = \frac{3}{2}\pi + \arcsin\left(\frac{\delta i}{2 i_d}\right)\right) \tag{8.71}$$

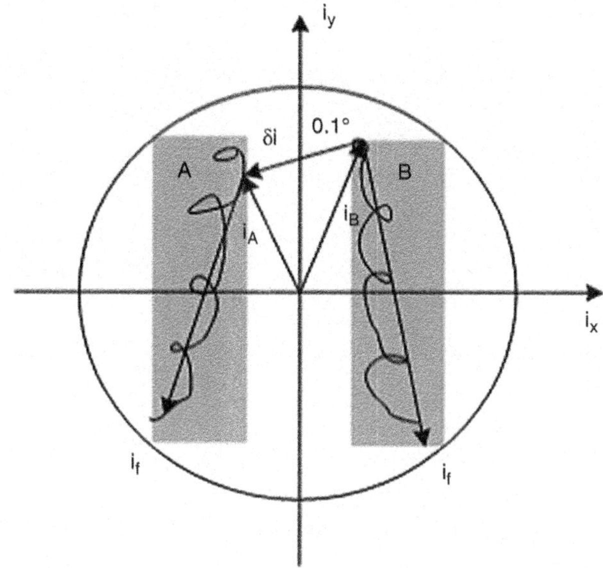

Fig. 8.28 The inclination separation strategy

Free perturbation time of the mean inclination in inclination control range is

$$T = \frac{2i_d}{\left(\frac{\mathrm{d}i}{\mathrm{d}t}\right)_D} \cdot \cos\left(\frac{\pi}{2} - \Omega_d + \arcsin\left(\frac{\delta i}{2i_d}\right)\right) \tag{8.72}$$

2. When the even perturbation direction of the mean inclination is $\Omega_d > 90°$

The control target of the inclination vector of satellite A is

$$\mathbf{i_f} : \left(i_f = i_d, \Omega_f = \frac{3\pi}{2} - \arcsin\left(\frac{\delta i}{2i_d}\right)\right) \tag{8.73}$$

The control target of the inclination vector of satellite B is

$$\mathbf{i_f} : \left(i_f = i_d, \Omega_f = \pi + \Omega_d + \arcsin\left(\frac{\delta i}{2i_d}\right)\right) \tag{8.74}$$

Free perturbation time of the mean inclination in inclination control range is

$$T = \frac{2i_d}{\left(\frac{\mathrm{d}i}{\mathrm{d}t}\right)_D} \cdot \cos\left(\Omega_d - \frac{\pi}{2} + \arcsin\left(\frac{\delta i}{2i_d}\right)\right) \tag{8.75}$$

For example, in order to satisfy the inclination separation requirement of two satellites, suppose the width of the inclination isolation band $\delta i = 0.02°$, and the radius of the mean inclination control circle $i_d = 0.07°$. If the perturbation speed of yearly mean inclination is $\left(\frac{\delta i}{\delta t}\right) = 0.89°$ and the perturbation direction of yearly mean inclination $\Omega_d = 89°$, then based on the above target inclination control strategy, the inclination control target of satellite A is

$$\mathbf{i_f} : \left(i_f = 0.07°, \quad \Omega_f = 278.1851\right)$$

And the inclination control target of satellite B is

$$\mathbf{i_f} : \left(i_f = 0.07°, \quad \Omega_f = 259.8149°\right),$$

The free perturbation string length of the mean inclination of two satellites is 0.1382°, and the period of inclination control $T = 56$ days; if yearly mean inclination perturbation direction is $\Omega_d = 95°$, then, according to the above target inclination control strategy, the inclination control target of satellite A is

$$\mathbf{i_f} : \left(i_f = 0.07°, \quad \Omega_f = 283.1851°\right)$$

And the inclination control target of satellite B is

$$\mathbf{i_f} : \left(i_f = 0.07°, \quad \Omega_f = 261.8149°\right)$$

The free perturbation string length of the mean inclination of two satellites is 0.1363°, and the period of inclination control $T = 55$ days.

Eccentricity Vector Setting Suppose that when the eccentricity vector is set, the mean ascension of the Sun is α_s, the eccentricity offset is δe, and the radii of the eccentricity perturbation circle of two satellites are e_A, e_B, as shown in Fig. 8.29.

The eccentricity of satellite A is set as

$$\mathbf{e_A} = \begin{pmatrix} e_x \\ e_y \end{pmatrix} = \begin{pmatrix} -\delta e/2 + e_A \cos \alpha_s \\ e_A \sin \alpha_s \end{pmatrix} \tag{8.76}$$

The eccentricity of satellite B is set as

$$\mathbf{e_B} = \begin{pmatrix} e_x \\ e_y \end{pmatrix} = \begin{pmatrix} \delta e/2 + e_B \cos \alpha_s \\ e_B \sin \alpha_s \end{pmatrix} \tag{8.77}$$

Case Study and Simulation The simulation results of independent control with combined E/I separation strategy are as follows: (1) The eccentricity separation strategy has no coordinated station-keeping maneuver, and (2) the inclination separation strategy has no coordinated station-keeping maneuver which are illustrated in Figs. 8.30 and 8.31, respectively.

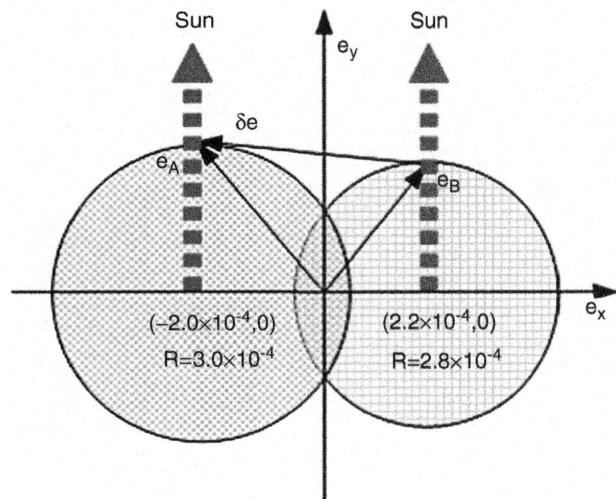

Fig. 8.29 The eccentricity separation method

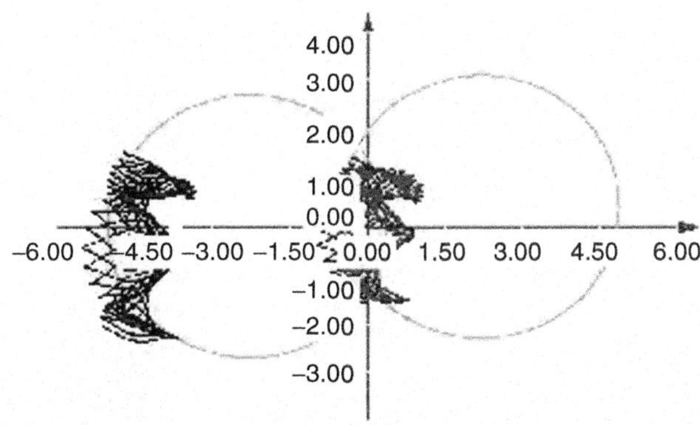

Fig. 8.30 Eccentricity separation strategy

The simulation of two geostationary satellites collocation with the above methods shows that those two satellites share overlapped dead band as shown in Fig. 8.32.

And there is a relative distance during one E/W station-keeping period as illustrated in Fig. 8.33.

The features of this method are as follows:

In principle, East/West or North-South maneuver of two satellites can be carried out independently.

The precision of East/West or North-South maneuver of two satellites can achieve about 0.1°.

Both the East/West and North-South control strategies of two satellites need to be adjusted. For East/West maneuver, the direction control of the eccentricity vector should be taken into account, and for North-South maneuver, the free perturbation direction of the next inclination period should be predicted.

The period of North-South maneuver of two satellites should be shortened.

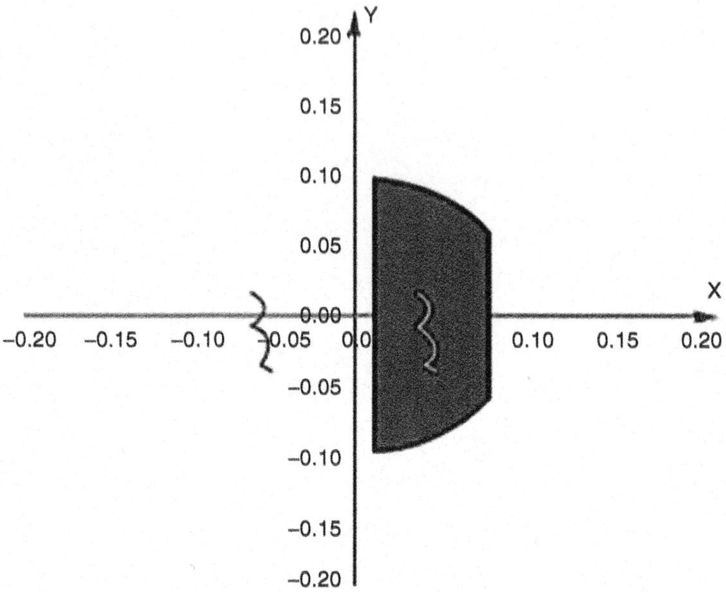

Fig. 8.31 Inclination separation strategy

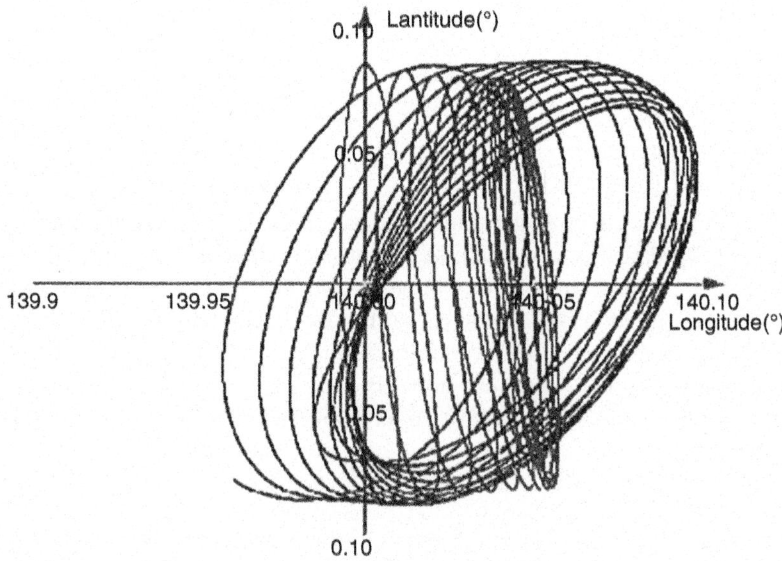

Fig. 8.32 Sharing overlapped dead band

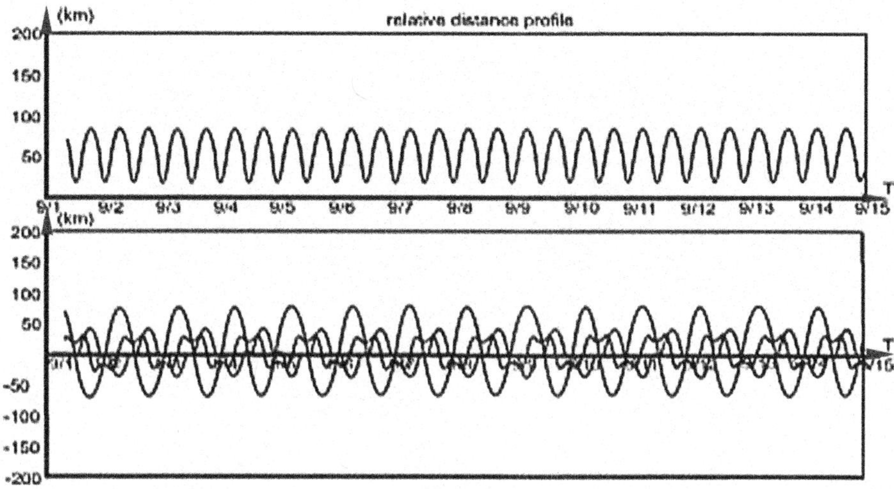

Fig. 8.33 Relative distance

8.9 A Coordinated E/I Combined Separation Method

Inclination Vector Setting For geostationary constellation controlled by one control center, combined separation strategy of coordinated maneuver of North-South and independent drift control of East/West can be applied. The perturbation direction of the mean inclination is basically a positive perturbation along y-axis of the coordinates of the mean vernal equinox and mean equator and the change rate of the perturbation is 0.75°/year–0.95°/year. As shown in Fig. 8.34 (a), in the inclination drift circle of 0.1°, the inclination vector of satellite A is set at the positive semiaxis of y and the inclination vector of satellite B is set at the negative semiaxis of y. And about 1 month after free drifting, the inclination vectors of two satellites will become the status shown in Fig. 8.34 (b). For Satellite A, North-South inclination maneuver is carried out and the direction is opposite to the mean inclination perturbation direction of that year. The inclination vector is illustrated in Fig. 8.34 (c). And about 1 month after free drifting, the inclination vector of two satellites will become the status shown in Fig. 8.34 (d), and at that time, North-South inclination maneuver is carried out for satellite B and the inclination vector of two satellites becomes the status shown in Fig. 8.34 (a). And after this repeated corporation control, the inclination vector of two satellites will loop in the four statuses of (a), (b), (c), (d) shown in Fig. 8.34.

(a) Top left: set point A for satellite A and point B for satellite B.
(b) Top right: leave the inclination of two satellites drifting freely within the inclination dead band.
(c) Bottom left: maneuver satellite A, targeting the inclination to point A.

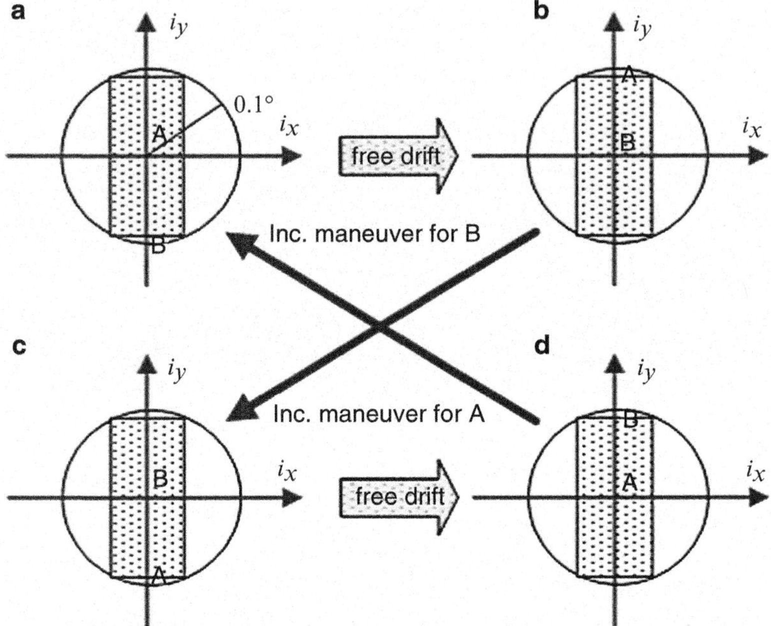

Fig. 8.34 The inclination allocation for two GEO satellites

(d) Bottom right: leave the inclination of two satellites drifting freely within the inclination dead band.

Considering the short period of perturbation, the osculation inclination stay in the gray area in the figure, and the offset attenuates and argument satisfies

$$\delta i > \frac{\sqrt{2}d_{\min}}{a_s} \cdot \frac{180}{\pi} |_{d_{\min}=14\text{km}} = 0.03°$$

$$\omega_i = \arctan\left(\frac{|\delta i_y|}{|\delta i_x|}\right) \in (70°, 110°)$$

Eccentricity Vector Setting To parallel the eccentricity offset and inclination offset, the eccentricity control circle of satellite A and B is shown in Fig. 8.35, which indicates the eccentricity allocation with the inclination separation strategy.

Suppose the solar mean right ascension of that day is α_s, and the solar lagging angle is β, and then the initial eccentricity is maneuvered to be

$$\begin{cases} e_x^A = e_{\text{A}} \cos(\alpha_s - \beta) \\ e_y^A = \delta e/2 + e_{\text{A}} \sin(\alpha_s - \beta) \end{cases} \tag{8.78}$$

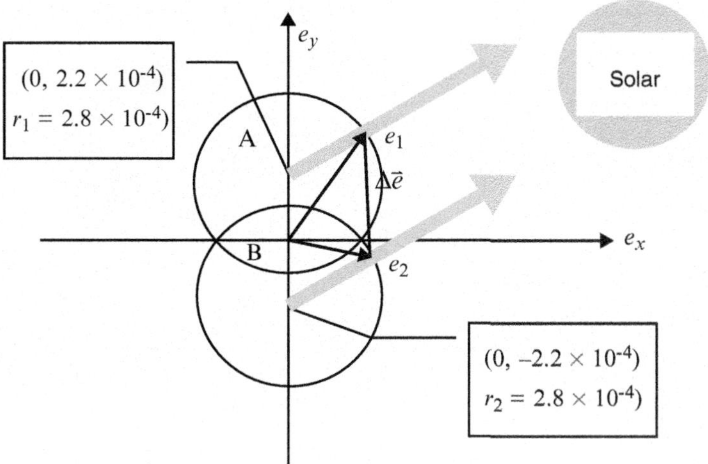

Fig. 8.35 The eccentricity allocation method

$$\begin{cases} e_x^{\mathrm{B}} = e_{\mathrm{B}} \cos\left(\alpha_s - \beta\right) \\ e_y^{\mathrm{B}} = -\delta e/2 + e_{\mathrm{B}} \sin\left(\alpha_s - \beta\right) \end{cases} \tag{8.79}$$

The eccentricity control follows the Sun pointing control mode, and the eccentricity offset satisfies

$e_{A-\max} = 5 \times 10^{-4}, e_{B-\max} = 5 \times 10^{-4}$ (daily period oscillation of longitude is less than 0.05°)

$$\delta e \approx 4.4 \times 10^{-4} > \frac{d_{\min}}{a_s}\Big|_{d_{\min}=14\mathrm{km}} = 3.4 \times 10^{-4}$$

$$\omega_e \approx 90^\circ$$

Case Study and Simulation A coordinated E/I combined separation strategy is planned to collocate two satellites, which belong to the same organization. Figure 8.36 shows the eccentricity setting by the coordinated separation strategy, and Fig. 8.37 illustrates the inclination setting by the coordinated separation strategy.

The two geostationary satellites by the coordinated strategy share overlapped dead band as shown in Fig. 8.38, and the relative distance during one E/W station-keeping period is the safety distance beyond collision as illustrated in Fig. 8.39.

The features of this strategy are as follows:

1. East/West maneuver of two satellites can be carried out independently but North-South control must be coordinated.
2. The precision of East/West and North-South control of two satellites can be 0.1°.

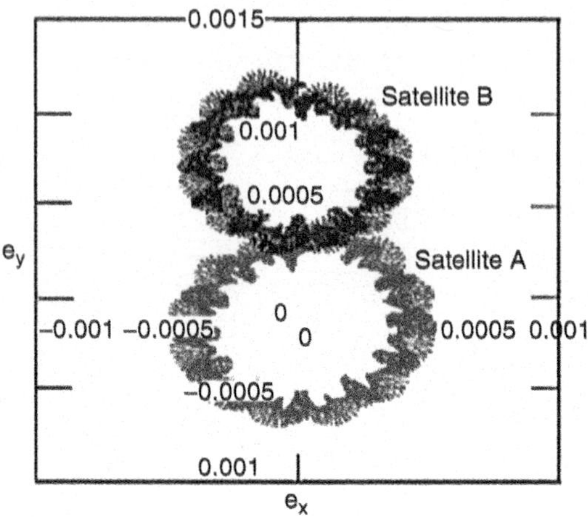

Fig. 8.36 Eccentricity profile

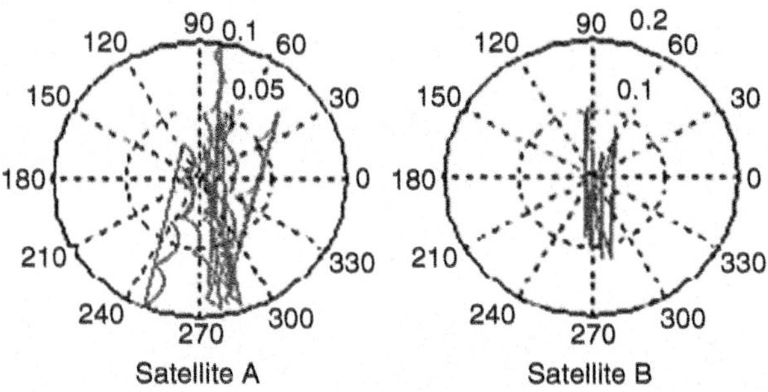

Fig. 8.37 Inclination profile

3. There are adjustments in the maneuver strategies of East/West and North-South control. For East/West control, the direction control of the eccentricity vector should be considered, and for North-South control, the free perturbation direction of inclination in the next period should be predicted.
4. The purpose of North-South corporation control is to make repeated corporation control and the inclination vector loops in four statuses as (a), (b), (c), (d), as shown in Fig. 8.34.

8.10 A Tri-Satellite Hybrid *e*-*i* Separation Method

Although many references have already discussed the design of multiple satellites (over 4) collocation strategy by using the combined offsetting strategies of inclination and eccentricity, if the separation distance is required to be larger, especially taking

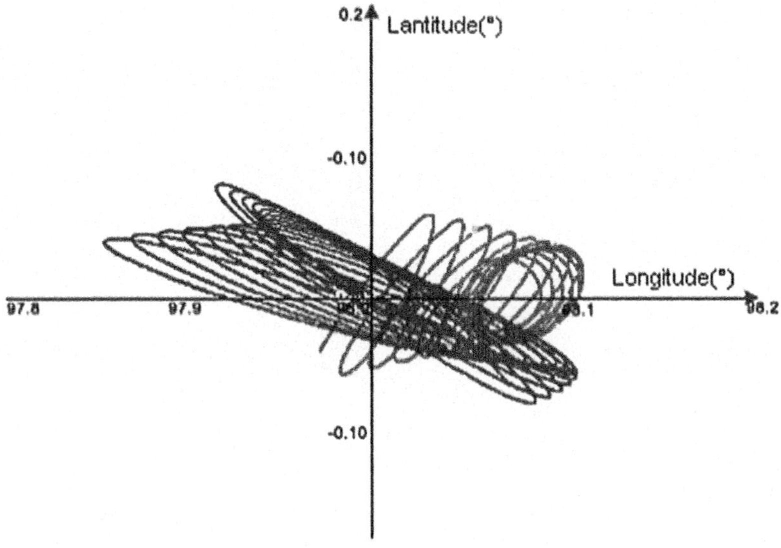

Fig. 8.38 The simulation of collocation

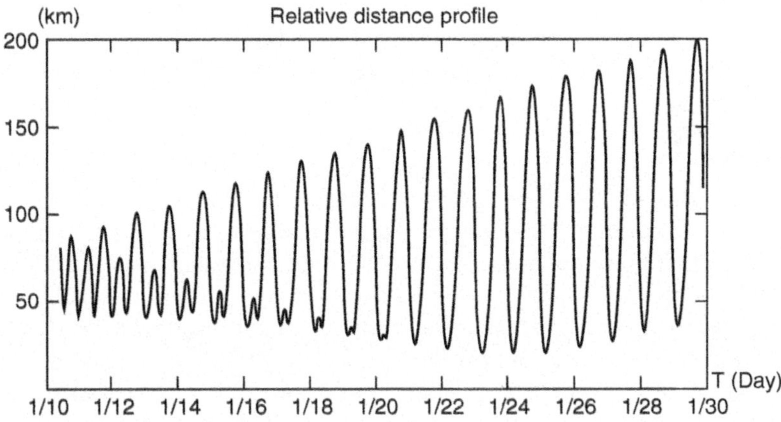

Fig. 8.39 The relative distance

into account of geostationary orbit perturbation movement and the control precision of collocated satellites, then to realize that the orbit offset of any two satellites among multiple collocated satellites satisfies the eccentricity and inclination offsets condition (8.46, 8.47, 8.48, and 8.49) is very difficult. Consequently, for reliable multiple satellites collocation strategy, besides the eccentricity and inclination offset, appropriate longitude (tangential) offset in East/West corporation station keeping should be used, which is called as the hybrid offsetting collocation strategy, and appropriate

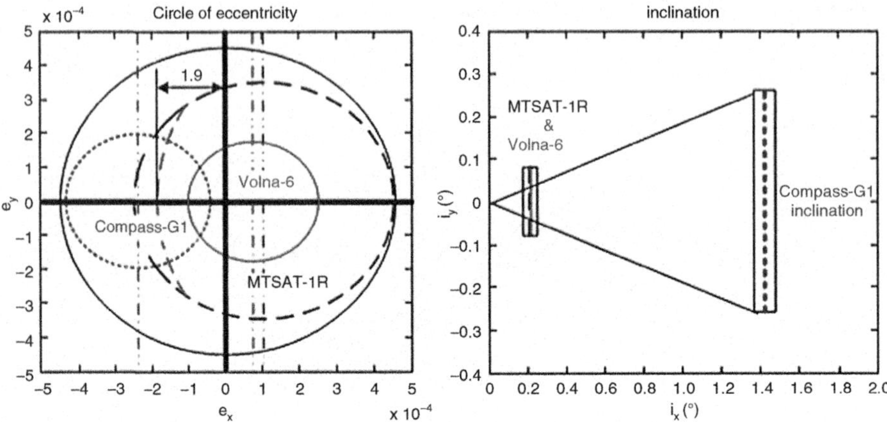

Fig. 8.40 A hybrid e-i separation strategy (*left*: eccentricity distribution; *right*: inclination distribution)

orbit phase difference of collocated satellites should be maintained in North-South corporation station keeping, which is called as the corporation synchronized control of collocated strategy.

Hybrid Distribution Offsetting An active separation strategy is demanded to safeguard three satellites belonging to different organizations collocated at longitude 140°E. Compass-G1 is one of geostationary satellites which is one satellite of Compass Regional Navigation Constellation, and since the operator expects relaxation slot to maximize the regular maneuver duration of E/W maneuver, the whole slot [139.9°, 140.1°] is expected; Volna-6 is a live-broadcast satellite which is operated by Russian Satellite Control Center (RSCC), and the operator expects relative small eccentricity to eliminate daily period longitude libration, as well as small inclination to minimum daily period latitude libration; and MTSAT-1R is a multifunction satellite which is operated by Japan Civil Aviation Bureau (JCAB), and since the operator expects relative relaxation slot to maximum the duration of E/W maneuver, the whole slot [139.9°, 140.1°] is expected, and regular inclination maneuvers are also expected to maintain zero-passing inclination strategy.

In consideration of operators' requirements, a simple and intuitionist longitude separation strategy with the drawback that the departed longitude makes the duration for E/W maneuver shorter than the ones all operators can accept is proposed. As a navigation satellite, the orbit plane of Compass-G1 is not coincident with the equatorial plane, so voluntary inclination offset by Compass-G1 can leave the cross-track distance with each other, making the eccentricity-inclination combined strategy work. In order to fully satisfy the requirements catering for three operators, a hybrid separation strategy is suggested as illustrated in Fig. 8.40. E-I distribution makes the three satellites with safety separation in spring, summer, and winter when the longitude distribution fully satisfies the requirements of three operators, except in autumn, when the longitude separation strategy should be adopted for Volna-6 and MTSAT.

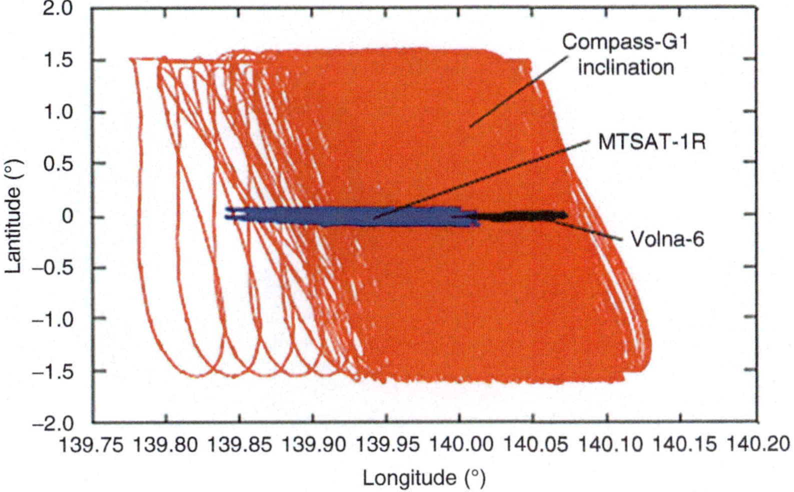

Fig. 8.41 Nominal position profile

In-Flight Evaluation In August 2011, Compass-G1 was swapped into 140°E slot, and hybrid offsets maneuver was performed for the three satellites by the collocation strategy that the three sides all agreed. In-flight evaluation was taken into real orbit parameters between Aug. 2011 and Oct. 2012 from Compass-G1 operator, MTSAT-1R operator, and Volna-6 operator, which are appreciated by the writer of this book. The nominal position history in 1-year interval is illustrated in Fig. 8.41. In-flight evaluation for MTSAT-1R took nominal slot with different seasons of 1 year. It is appreciated that three operators follow the longitude distribution as the must-be of the hybrid separation strategy constrained.

The osculating eccentricity in 1-year interval is illustrated in Fig. 8.42, which states that the eccentricity distribution as the must-be of the hybrid separation strategy constrained is followed strictly by three sides, and the eccentricity deviations between each other are maintained to ensure the minimal safety separation distance as strategy budgeted.

The inclination history in 1-year interval is illustrated in Fig. 8.43, which states that the inclination distribution as the must-be of the hybrid separation strategy constrained is followed strictly by three sides, and the inclination deviations between each other are maintained to ensure the minimal safety separation distance as strategy budgeted.

The relative distance in space between each other is presented in Fig. 8.44, which states the minimal distances the strategy budgeted achieved.

The prototypes for allowable relative distance with uncertainty of orbit determination (OD), as well as the orbit element offset for each pair of collocated satellites were established. A hybrid strategy to build such relationship to meet

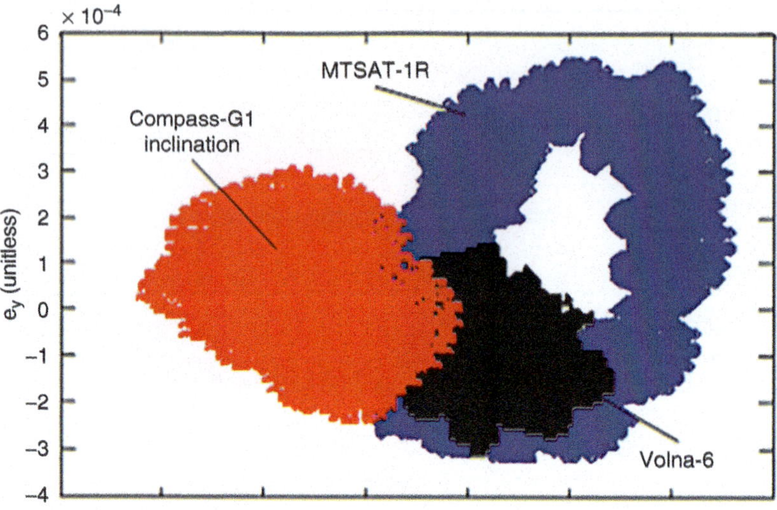

Fig. 8.42 Osculating eccentricity profile

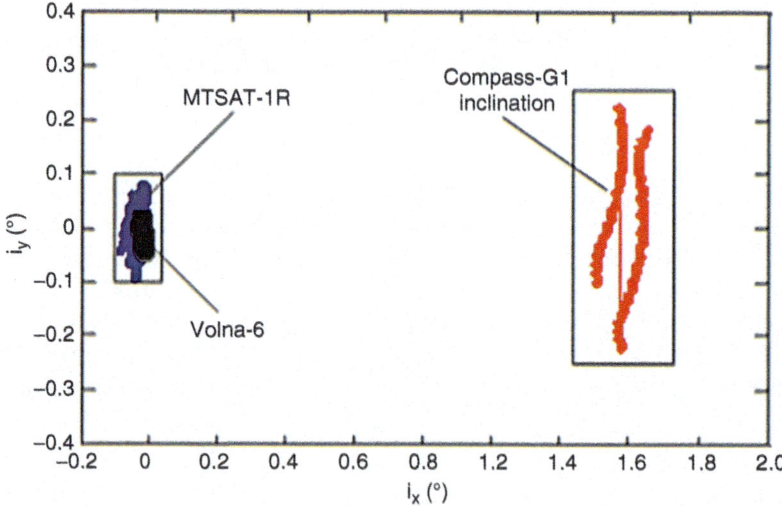

Fig. 8.43 Inclination profile

with the challenge of putting three satellites sharing the same position was put forward. The algorithms to allocate the longitude, eccentricity, and inclination for each satellite were developed to cater for the requirements. In-flight evaluation was used to ascertain that the mathematical prototypes presented are the guide specification to design collocation strategy for geostationary satellites.

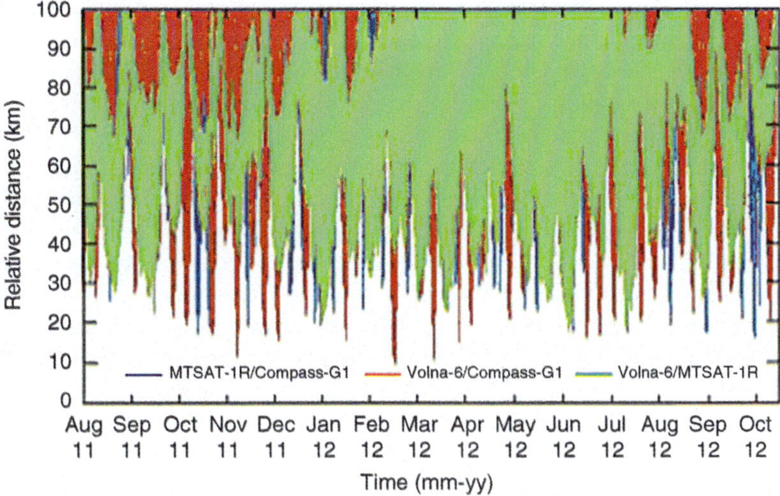

Fig. 8.44 Relative distance

8.11 Safety Analysis and Collision Warning

The collocation strategy design principles are as follows: The orbit constraint condition of two satellites is designed, leaving a relative separation distance between collocated satellites that are forced, satisfying the orbit constraint condition during the lifetime by controlling the satellites' East/West and North-South maneuver time, and then collocated satellites are maintained safe in collocated positions.

The safety of collocated satellites of different organizations is mainly as follows: Two sides should maintain the orbit constraint condition according to a consistent collocation plan and design the corresponding position keeping strategy to keep the satellite satisfying the orbit constraint condition during the whole lifetime.

The insecurity of collocated satellites of different organizations is mainly as follows: The collocation orbit constraint condition is damaged by any side, leaving a separation distance less than the safety distance, and the probability of disturbance and collision appears. So, necessary satellite parameters must be kept transparent, including satellite engineering parameters, orbit tracking error, and orbit control error. Furthermore, in long-period collocation, it is necessary to exchange necessary orbit information between two sides.

By adopting the mean longitude offset separation collocation strategy, the separation distance in the tangential direction for collocated satellites can be achieved by design overlapped or non-overlapped mean longitude drifting circle. But, many simulation results show that although the mean longitude separation plan is simple and intuitive, a random uncertainty element in the control (North-South, East/West) process, such as control delay, execution unit efficiency, etc., will cause zero tangential distance of collocated satellites and increase the chances of satellite collision or electronic disturbance.

By making use of the amount and phase offset of the mean eccentricity, a separation distance in the radial direction will be achieved between collocated satellites, which is a very appropriate method for non-cooperative collocation control for two or multiple satellites. According to the collocation plan, two satellites acquire the eccentricity vector and the choice of an appropriate control time. By East/West maneuver, the eccentricity vector offset can be maintained, satisfying the orbit constraint condition defined by the collocation plan. But, the eccentricity constraint condition may be damaged by North-South coupling control. Therefore, generally speaking, after North-South maneuver, the eccentricity vector will be reacquired and the eccentricity constraint condition will be reconstructed through East/West maneuver. Therefore, in terms of safety, necessary orbit information should be exchanged periodically between two sides, including orbit mean eccentricity magnitude and direction. Because both East/West and North-South maneuvers are carried out independently, the orbit elements and control plan exchanging are not necessary.

The combined mean inclination-mean eccentricity separation, shortened as e-i separation, is the commonly applied multiple satellites collocation strategy. The inclination offset and mean eccentricity offset of two satellites are parallel or non-parallel to each other. The mean eccentricity offset of two satellites points to the vernal equinox or the opposite direction and is maintained by East/West maneuver. The mean inclination offset of two satellites are paralleled with the vernal equinox, and therefore the mean inclination of two satellites must be coordinated, synchronized, and maneuvered. In terms of safety, necessary orbit information should be exchanged periodically between two sides, and detailed information should include

1. Kepler osculating orbit elements

   Coordinate reference: True Equator and True Time (TOD)
   Timing: Coordinated Universal Time (UTC)
   Format:

   YYYY MM DD HH mm SS.SSSS AAAAAAAA.AA E.EEEEEE I.IIIIII
   OOO.OOOO WWW.WWWW fff.ffff MMM.MMMM
   2012 10 07 12 25 00.0001 42165560.00 0.000123 0.564736
   315.5674 230.0230 340.0878 340.1540

YYYY	calendar year
MM	calendar month
DD	calendar date
HH	hours in 24 format
mm	minutes
SS.SSSS	seconds
AAAAAAAA.AA	semi major axis/m
E.EEEEEE	eccentricity
I.IIIIII	inclination/°
OOO.OOOO	R.A.A.N/°
WWW.WWWW	Argument of Perigee/°
fff.ffff	True Anomaly/°
MMM.MMMM	Mean Anomaly/°

2. Cartesian State parameters

Coordinate reference: True Equator and True Time (TOD)
Timing: Coordinated Universal Time (UTC)
Format:

YYYY MM DD HH mm SS.SSSS XXXXXXXX.XX YYYYYYYY.YY ZZZZZZZZ.ZZ XDDD.XXXX YDDD.YYYY ZDDD.ZZZZ
2012 10 07 12 25 00.0001 35077016.44 42976674.48 23340200.87 -1593.0834 1690.4147 2191.3174

YYYY	calendar year
MM	calendar month
DD	calendar date
HH	hours in 24 format
mm	minutes
SS.SSSS	seconds
XXXXXXXX.XX	x component/m
YYYYYYYY.YY	y component/m
ZZZZZZZZ.ZZ	z component/m
XDDD.XXXX	v_x (m/s)
YDDD.YYYY	v_y (m/s)
ZDDD.ZZZZ	v_z (m/s)

Two or multiple satellites collocation in the geostationary orbit is a crucial method for easing the tension of geostationary orbit resources. The collocation maneuver strategy is an inevitable demand for the safety of collocated satellites. In this chapter, based on the experience of China's geo-satellite collocation control practice, a comprehensive view of the design method of geostationary orbit collocation control strategy is provided; from the tangential, radial, and orthogonal direction separation control, respectively, the relation between collocated satellites orbit offset with orbit position precision and the minimum separation distance is given; the safety and effectiveness of typical geo-satellite collocation control strategies are analyzed. From the relation equations and strategy analysis for collocated satellites orbit offset with orbit position precision and the minimum separation distance, we can get the following: (1) To maintain at least three geo-satellites collocation, only by the longitude separation strategy, the precision of East/West maneuver decreases; (2) by the eccentricity separation strategy, the space separation distance among collocated satellites is maintained by offsetting the eccentricity; the absolute eccentricity separation strategy is suitable for collocating two satellites that have different East/West maneuver precision demands; (3) relative eccentricity separation has specific pointing requirements for eccentricity pointing, which is suitable for multiple satellites collocation control, but the control complexity and fuel requirements increase; (4) for the four satellites combined, eccentricity and inclination separation offset assignment algorithm discussed in this chapter, by increasing some inclination offset based on relative eccentricity offset, the complex problem of four-satellites collocation control under an appropriate East/West maneuver precision requirement can be solved.

References

1. Nascimento JM (2010) Hazard evaluation of the space debris in the geostationary orbital. In: Proceedings of AAS/AIAA astrodynamics specialist conference. Univelt Inc., Pittsburgh
2. Liu HT, Yang LP, Zhang QB et al (2012) An investigation on tether-tugging de-orbital of defunct geostationary satellites. Sci China Tech Sci 55:2019–2027. doi:10.1007/s11431-012-4878-6
3. Lee BS, Lee JS, Choi KH (1999) Analysis of a station keeping maneuver strategy for collocation of three geostationary satellites. Control Eng Pract 9:1152–1161
4. Luo GQ (1996) The strategies and selection for multi-GEO satellites collocation. Spacecr Eng 5(4):27–34 [In Chinese]
5. Luo GQ (1997) The Maneuver methods and orbital deviation for multi-GEO satellites collocation. Spacecr Eng 6(3):39–44 [In Chinese]
6. Li HN, Gao YJ, Yu PJ etc. (2009) The strategies and algorithms study for multi-GEO satellites collocation. J Astronautics 30(3):967–973. [In Chinese]
7. Pattinson L (1996) EUTELSAT satellite collocation. In: 16th AIAA international communications satellite systems conference, Washington, DC, 25–29 Feb 1996, pp 557–565
8. Collocation at 19°W, web site: www.DLR.GSOC.de. Accessed 20 Sept 2013
9. Soop EM (1987) Coordinated station keeping at longitude 19 degrees west, OAD paper No.342
10. Li HN (2010) Geostationary satellite orbital analysis and collocation strategies. National Defense Industry Press, Beijing, p 10 [In Chinese]
11. Li HN The separation methods and station keeping algorithms for Multi-GEOS collocation. In: The 60th international astronautical congress, Daejeon, Republic of Korea
12. Kelly T, White L, et al (2003) Stationkeeping of geostationary satellites with simultaneous eccentricity and longitude control. J Guid Control Dyn 17(4):1034–1039
13. Lee BS, Lee JS, Choi KH (1999) Analysis of a station keeping Maneuver strategy for collocation of three geostationary satellites. Control Eng Pract 9:1152–1161
14. Li HN, Gao YJ, etc. (2006) The strategies and algorithms study for multi-GEO satellites collocation. J Astronautics 30(3):967–973. [In Chinese]
15. Li HN, Li JS (2009) Analyzing perturbation motion and studying configuration maintenance strategy for compass-M navigation constellation. J Astronautics 31(7):1756–1761 [in Chinese]

The manufacturer's authorised representative in the EU is Springer Nature Customer Service Centre GmbH, Europaplatz 3, 69115 Heidelberg, Germany. If you have any concerns regarding our products, please contact ProductSafety@springernature.com

Printed and bound by CPI Group (UK) Ltd, Croydon, CR0 4YY

15/07/2026

02167627-0004